LOOK UP THERE!
STRAIGHT UNDER THE SOUTHERN CROSS.
IT'S THE RED MOON!
THE SPACE FLEET COULDN'T STOP IT! ATOM BOMBS COULDN'T STOP IT! NOTHING CAN STOP IT! THE RED MOON'S HERE!

THE SECOND DELUXE COLLECTOR'S EDITION OF

DAN DARE
PILOT OF THE FUTURE

FEATURING

THE RED MOON MYSTERY

AND

MAROONED ON MERCURY

FROM EAGLE VOL. 2, No. 26, OCTOBER 1951 TO VOL. 3, No. 46, FEBRUARY 1953. THE ARTWORK IS BY FRANK HAMPSON AND HAROLD JOHNS.

COMPILED BY MIKE HIGGS

HAWK
BOOKS

DAN DARE
Red Moon Mystery
Marooned on Mercury
FIRST EDITION

ISBN: 0 948248 80 7

Published by
HAWK BOOKS LIMITED
SUITE 411
76 SHOE LANE
LONDON EC4A 3JB

Concept & Design: Mike Higgs Graphics.
Colour Separation: Hockley Graphics Ltd.
Printed in Portugal.

DAN'S BACK!

This is the second volume of facsimile reproductions of Dan Dare and continues from where the first volume ends. Having saved Earth from the terrible Treens and the malevolent Mekon, our hero tries to relax a little but any thoughts of recreation are soon well and truly banished from his brain with the arrival of a very unwelcome heavenly body. If you thought The Mekon was a threat to Earth, then you haven't seen anything yet. The Red Moon is coming! Nothing it seems, is going to stop it. Although I don't think we should entirely dismiss the efforts of a certain Manchester-born Colonel in the Interplanet Space Fleet and his trusty batman, a proud son of Wigan.

Dan Dare and Digby are off on a new adventure amongst the stars with the fate of mankind in the balance and once again their adventures are reprinted here in exactly the same form as was originally presented in the 'Eagle' back in 1951-2.

Next comes 'Marooned on Mercury' the adventure that continues on from 'Red Moon'. This was drawn by Harold Johns, a member of Frank Hampson's studio team because Frank was ill at the time.

As a special bonus in this volume we also present a reprint of an 8-page Dan Dare adventure from the second Eagle annual just to show you our hero in a slightly different format from his weekly comic magazine appearances.

Talking about different formats, I wonder how many of you twiddled the tuning knob on your radio back in the early '50's and caught Radio Luxembourg's serial, 'Dan Dare, Pilot of the Future'? The programme was sponsored by Horlicks and ran from 1951 through to 1956. The actor who played Dan was none other than Noel Johnson, who had already achieved fame on the airwaves as 'Dick Barton, Special Agent.'

To continue our '50's feel we have reprinted overleaf a special feature to appeal to any of you who are keen on model making. All you need is some corrugated paper, a cardboard tube, paint, glue, a little patience, manual dexterity and one egg! Mix them together correctly and you could end up with a 'Dan Dare Spaceship' guaranteed to impress your friends and relatives.

To make the scenery you will need plasticine, garden weeds, sawdust and possibly a few well chosen clumps of asphalt preferably taken from the road **after** they've dug it up. I'm afraid toy shops don't sell Treens anymore, but maybe you can find someone who still has the odd rare figure lurking in an old forgotten attic toybox.

Now it's time to fasten your safety belts, grit your teeth, cross your fingers and take several deep breaths because it's time to go out there and face the dreaded Red Moon....

Mike Higgs

MAKE A DAN DARE SPACESHIP

REPRINTED FROM EAGLE 7th DECEMBER 1951

1.
To make a simple Space-ship, take an egg and blow it carefully. Paint the shell with Indian ink and stick thin strips of gold paper on to it. For the body of the Space-ship use a small cardboard tube and corrugated paper. Stick the cardboard round the tube so that the egg rests on top. Paint the corrugated card with gold paint and stick on windows with bits of black paper. The 'legs' are made of rolled paper, painted gold.

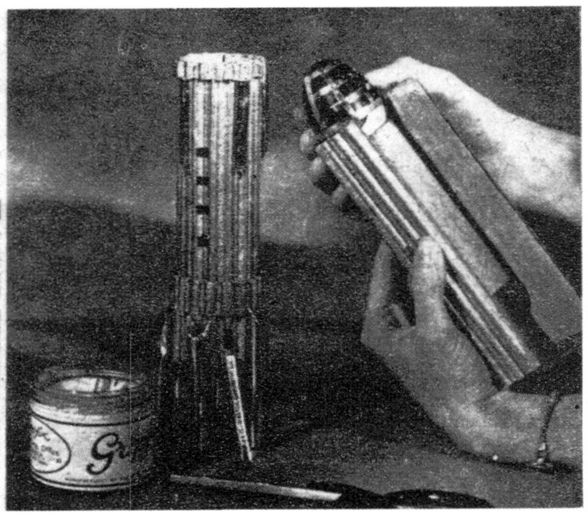

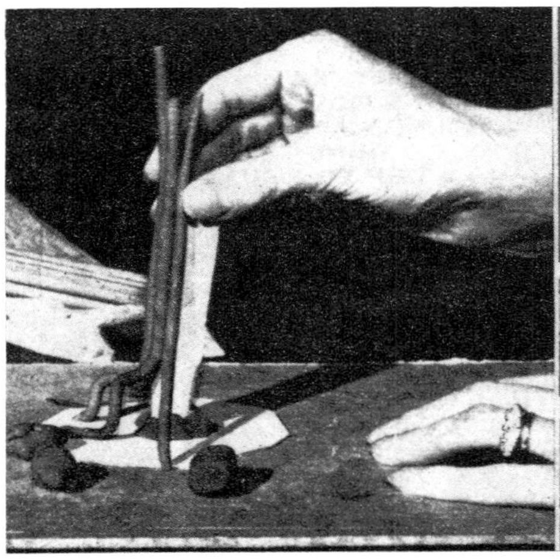

2.
To make the trees or any other "bits and pieces" from the Dan Dare stories – look back at your old numbers of EAGLE and, by using your imagination, you will find it simple to make very good copies of them. The tree tops may be a bit difficult, but you can use thistle weeds as in the picture at left. The peculiar tree trunks can easily be made in Plasticine.

3.
You can see from the two big pictures what the idea is this week. Hugh Gee thought you might like to use the Table Top idea and make some of the planet worlds for yourselves. To make these pictures all he used were some bits of asphalt that workmen had pick-axed out of the road during repairs – plus the sawdust that we always use.

4.
The trees he copied from the EAGLE drawings; the tree trunks he made from Plasticine, with thistle weeds on top. The "Treens" and other strange people can be bought from any toy shop.

EAGLE-GREAT NEW DAN DARE STORY STARTS TODAY

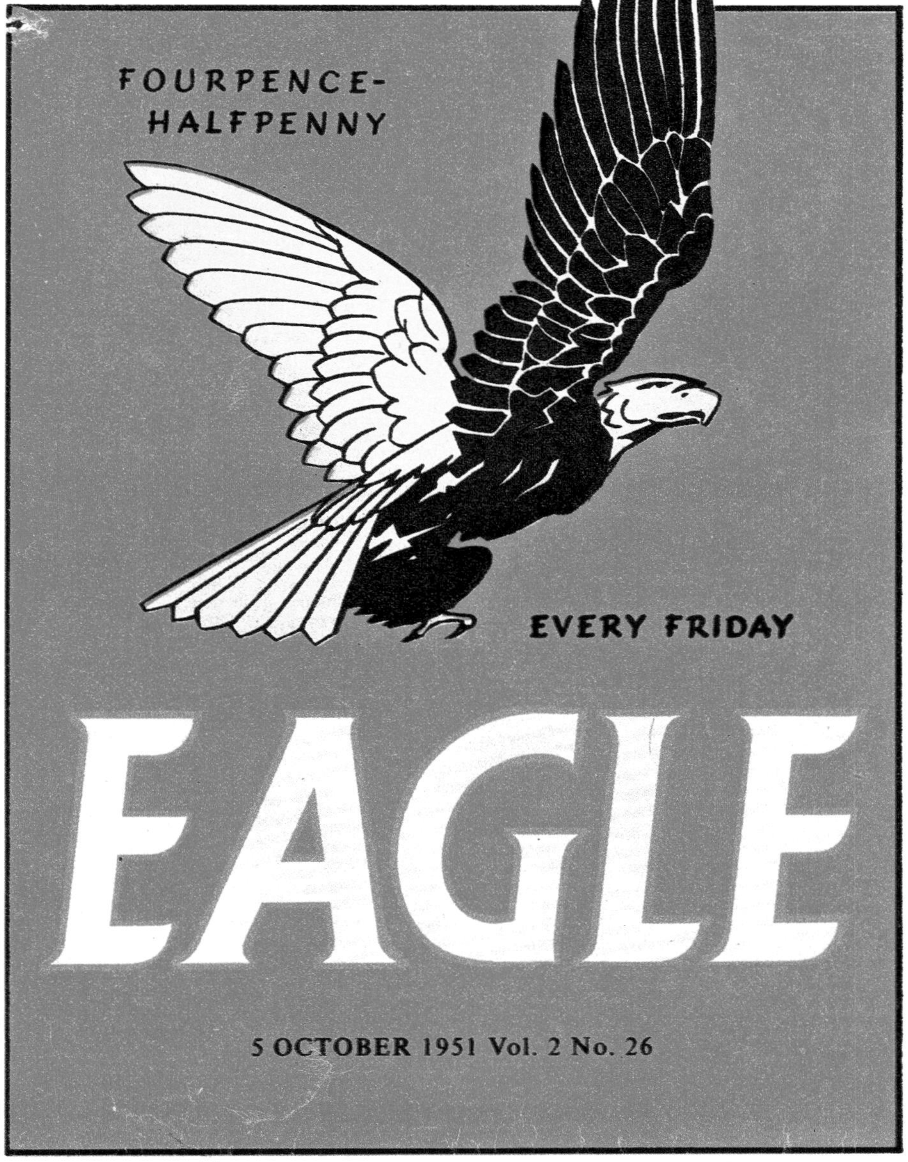

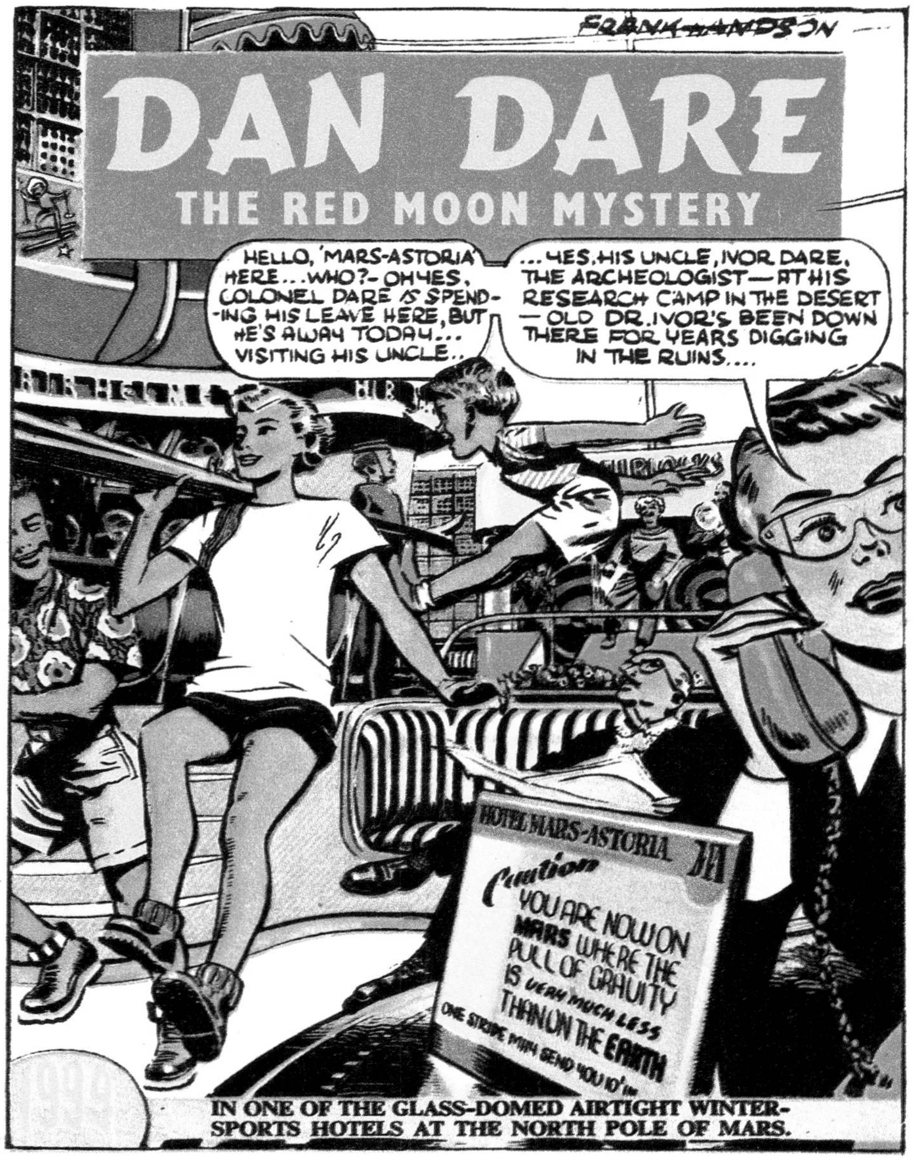

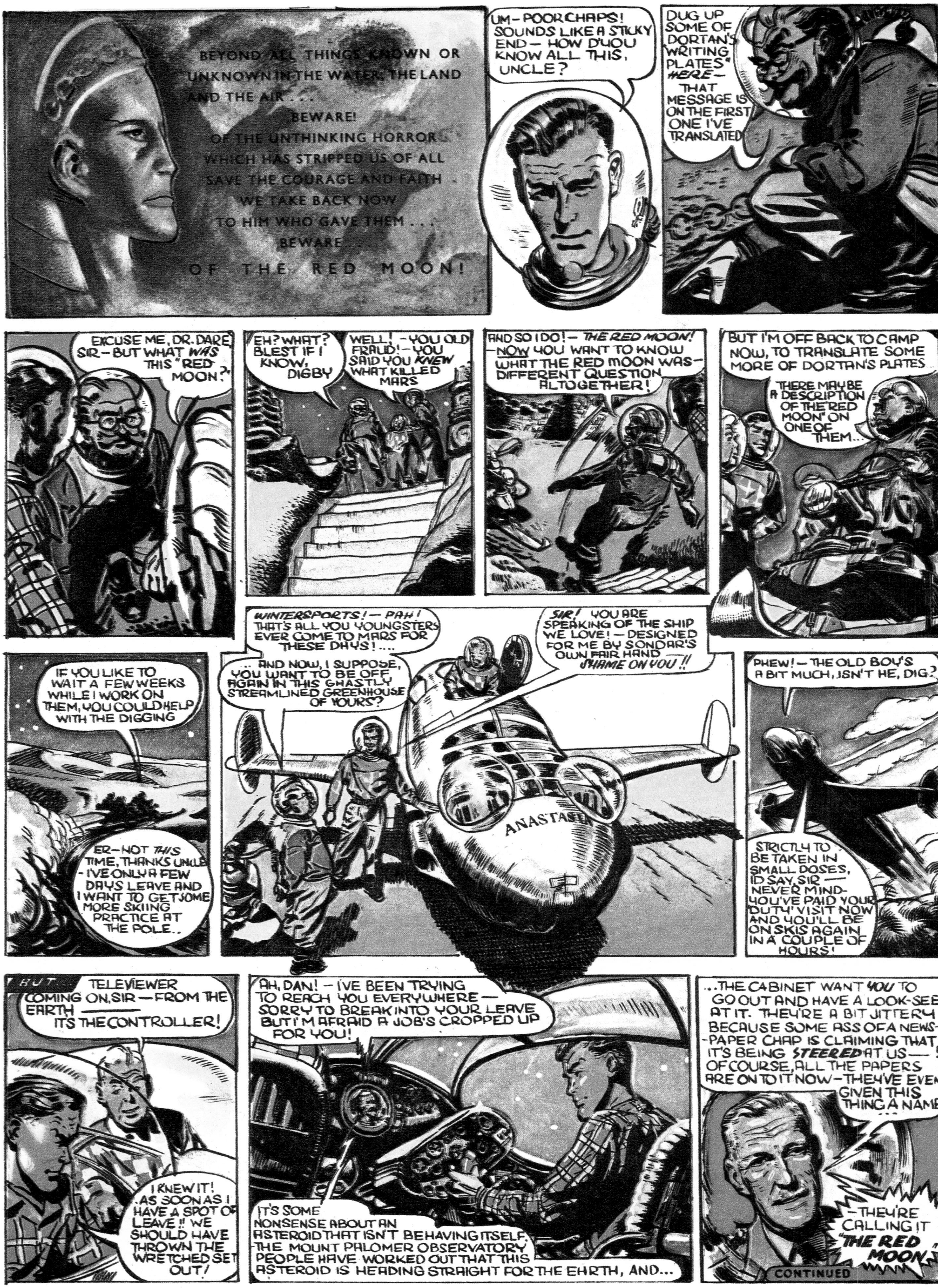
BEYOND ALL THINGS KNOWN OR UNKNOWN IN THE WATER, THE LAND AND THE AIR . . . BEWARE! OF THE UNTHINKING HORROR WHICH HAS STRIPPED US OF ALL SAVE THE COURAGE AND FAITH WE TAKE BACK NOW TO HIM WHO GAVE THEM . . . BEWARE . . . OF THE RED MOON!
UM – POOR CHAPS! SOUNDS LIKE A STICKY END – HOW D'YOU KNOW ALL THIS, UNCLE?
DUG UP SOME OF DORTAN'S WRITING PLATES" HERE – THAT MESSAGE IS ON THE FIRST ONE I'VE TRANSLATED
EXCUSE ME, DR. DARE, SIR – BUT WHAT WAS THIS "RED MOON"?
EH? WHAT? BLEST IF I KNOW, DIGBY
WELL! – YOU OLD FRAUD! – YOU SAID YOU KNEW WHAT KILLED MARS
AND SO I DO! – THE RED MOON! – NOW YOU WANT TO KNOW WHAT THE RED MOON WAS – DIFFERENT QUESTION ALTOGETHER!
BUT I'M OFF BACK TO CAMP NOW, TO TRANSLATE SOME MORE OF DORTAN'S PLATES . . .
THERE MAY BE A DESCRIPTION OF THE 'RED MOON' ON ONE OF THEM . . .
IF YOU LIKE TO WAIT A FEW WEEKS WHILE I WORK ON THEM, YOU COULD HELP WITH THE DIGGING
ER – NOT THIS TIME, THANKS UNCLE – I'VE ONLY A FEW DAYS LEAVE AND I WANT TO GET SOME MORE SKIING PRACTICE AT THE POLE . .
WINTERSPORTS! – PAH! THAT'S ALL YOU YOUNGSTERS EVER COME TO MARS FOR THESE DAYS! . . . .
. . . AND NOW, I SUPPOSE, YOU WANT TO BE OFF AGAIN IN THIS GHASTLY STREAMLINED GREENHOUSE OF YOURS?
SIR! YOU ARE SPEAKING OF THE SHIP WE LOVE! – DESIGNED FOR ME BY SONDAR'S OWN FAIR HAND SHAME ON YOU!!
ANASTASIA
PHEW! – THE OLD BOY'S A BIT MUCH, ISN'T HE, DIG?
STRICTLY TO BE TAKEN IN SMALL DOSES, I'D SAY, SIR – NEVER MIND – YOU'VE PAID YOUR 'DUTY' VISIT NOW AND YOU'LL BE ON SKIS AGAIN IN A COUPLE OF HOURS!
BUT . . .
TELEVIEWER COMING ON, SIR – FROM THE EARTH – IT'S THE CONTROLLER!
I KNEW IT! AS SOON AS I HAVE A SPOT OF LEAVE!! WE SHOULD HAVE THROWN THE WRETCHED SET OUT!
AH, DAN! – I'VE BEEN TRYING TO REACH YOU EVERYWHERE – SORRY TO BREAK INTO YOUR LEAVE BUT I'M AFRAID A JOB'S CROPPED UP FOR YOU!
IT'S SOME NONSENSE ABOUT AN ASTEROID THAT ISN'T BEHAVING ITSELF. THE MOUNT PALOMER OBSERVATORY PEOPLE HAVE WORKED OUT THAT THIS ASTEROID IS HEADING STRAIGHT FOR THE EARTH, AND . . .
. . . THE CABINET WANT YOU TO GO OUT AND HAVE A LOOK-SEE AT IT. THEY'RE A BIT JITTERY BECAUSE SOME ASS OF A NEWSPAPER CHAP IS CLAIMING THAT IT'S BEING STEERED AT US – ! OF COURSE, ALL THE PAPERS ARE ON TO IT NOW – THEY'VE EVEN GIVEN THIS THING A NAME . . .
– THEY'RE CALLING IT "THE RED MOON"
CONTINUED

FOURPENCE-HALFPENNY
EVERY FRIDAY
EAGLE
12 OCTOBER 1951 Vol. 2 No. 27
DAN DARE
THE RED MOON MYSTERY
DID YOU HEAR THAT, SIR?—THE RED MOON.
JUMPIN' JETS!! THE RED MOON!
"BEWARE OF THE RED MOON!"
DAN, HOLIDAYING ON MARS, IS BEING RECALLED TO DUTY BY SIR HUBERT, TO RECONNOITRE A MYSTERIOUS ASTEROID NICKNAMED "THE RED MOON" WHICH IS HEADING TOWARDS THE EARTH....
HEY! — JUST WHAT *ARE* YOU TWO JABBERING ABOUT?
OH, SORRY, SIR HUBERT — IT'S NOTHING — A QUOTATION — SOMETHING WE HEARD THAT'S ALL.
DOES THAT MEAN THAT YOU KNOW SOMETHING ABOUT THIS THING?...
HAVE YOU GOT SOME SORT OF LEAD?
I — I HARDLY THINK SO, SIR — IT'S JUST A WHACKING GREAT COINCIDENCE — IT *MUST* BE...
IT JUST HAPPENS THAT YOUR NEWSPAPERMEN HAVE CHANCED ON A NAME THAT WAS USED BY DORTAN-UTH-ALGER...
BUT *HE'S* BEEN DEAD FOR 200,000 YEARS.
HRMPH — I'M BLISTERED IF I KNOW WHAT YOU'RE TALKING ABOUT, DAN. AND I'VE ENOUGH WORRIES ANYWAY WITHOUT BOTHERING ABOUT SOMEBODY WHO DIED 200,000 YEARS AGO!
I'M LAYING EVERYTHING ON FOR YOU AT THE MARS SATELLITE SPACE STATION, SO GET THERE TOUT-DE-SUITE & THEN GIVE ME ANOTHER BUZZ...
THE SOONER EVERYONE KNOWS YOU'RE TAKING CARE OF THIS "RED MOON" NONSENSE, THE SOONER WE'LL HAVE SOME PEACE AND QUIET DOWN HERE.
PEACE AND QUIET DOWN THERE!
AYE!
BUT WHAT ABOUT US?
UP HERE!
FRANK HAMPSON

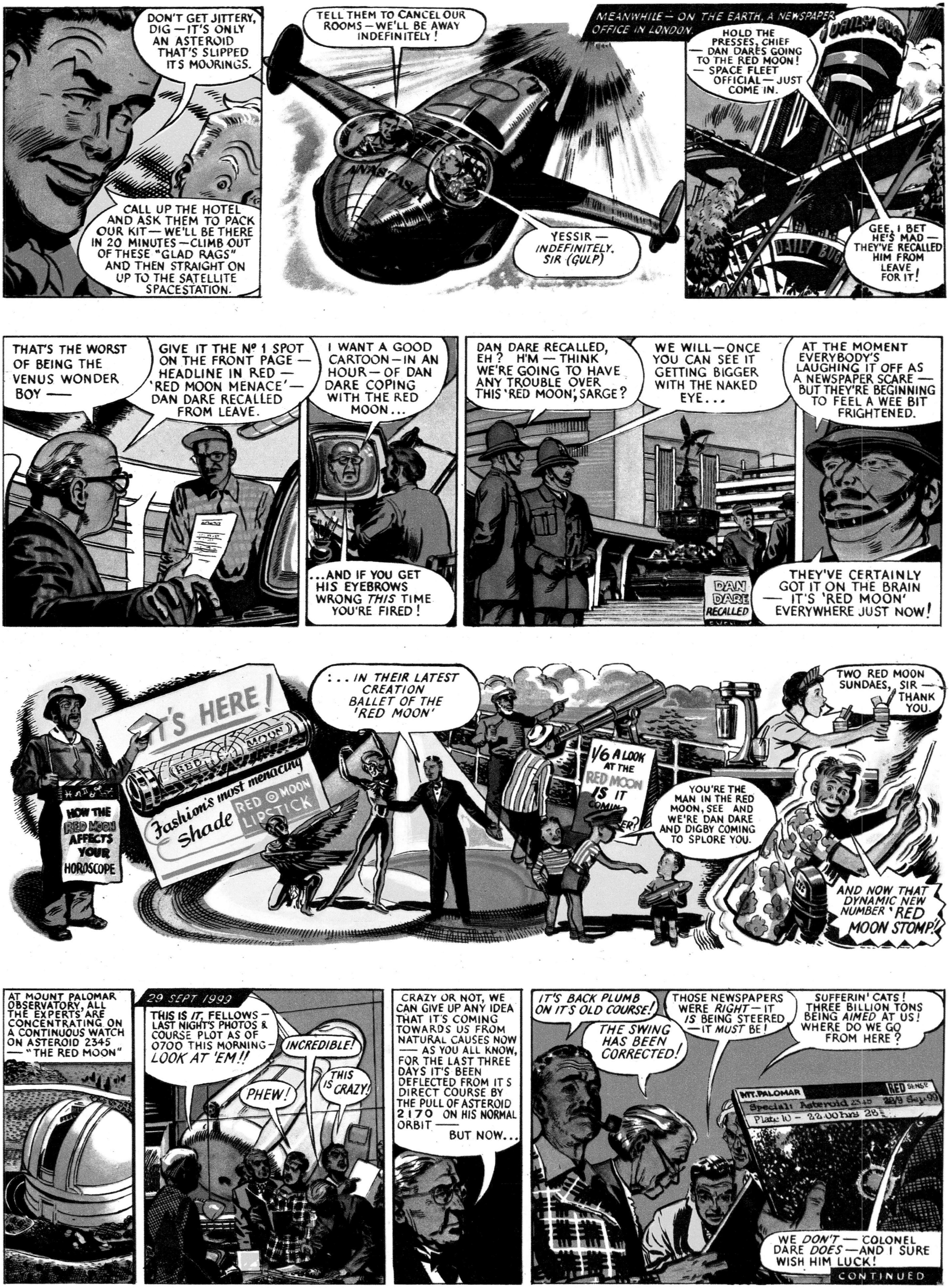
DON'T GET JITTERY, DIG — IT'S ONLY AN ASTEROID THAT'S SLIPPED ITS MOORINGS.
CALL UP THE HOTEL AND ASK THEM TO PACK OUR KIT — WE'LL BE THERE IN 20 MINUTES — CLIMB OUT OF THESE "GLAD RAGS" AND THEN STRAIGHT ON UP TO THE SATELLITE SPACESTATION.
TELL THEM TO CANCEL OUR ROOMS — WE'LL BE AWAY INDEFINITELY!
ANASTASIA
YESSIR — INDEFINITELY. SIR (GULP)
MEANWHILE — ON THE EARTH, A NEWSPAPER OFFICE IN LONDON.
HOLD THE PRESSES, CHIEF — DAN DARE'S GOING TO THE RED MOON! — SPACE FLEET OFFICIAL — JUST COME IN.
GEE, I BET HE'S MAD — THEY'VE RECALLED HIM FROM LEAVE FOR IT!
DAILY BUG
THAT'S THE WORST OF BEING THE VENUS WONDER BOY —
GIVE IT THE Nº 1 SPOT ON THE FRONT PAGE — HEADLINE IN RED — 'RED MOON MENACE' — DAN DARE RECALLED FROM LEAVE.
I WANT A GOOD CARTOON — IN AN HOUR — OF DAN DARE COPING WITH THE RED MOON...
...AND IF YOU GET HIS EYEBROWS WRONG THIS TIME YOU'RE FIRED!
DAN DARE RECALLED, EH? H'M — THINK WE'RE GOING TO HAVE ANY TROUBLE OVER THIS 'RED MOON', SARGE?
WE WILL — ONCE YOU CAN SEE IT GETTING BIGGER WITH THE NAKED EYE...
DAN DARE RECALLED
AT THE MOMENT EVERYBODY'S LAUGHING IT OFF AS A NEWSPAPER SCARE — BUT THEY'RE BEGINNING TO FEEL A WEE BIT FRIGHTENED.
THEY'VE CERTAINLY GOT IT ON THE BRAIN — IT'S 'RED MOON' EVERYWHERE JUST NOW!
HOW THE RED MOON AFFECTS YOUR HOROSCOPE
IT'S HERE!
RED MOON
Fashion's most menacing Shade
RED MOON LIPSTICK
:...IN THEIR LATEST CREATION BALLET OF THE 'RED MOON'
1/6 A LOOK AT THE RED MOON IS IT COMIN... ...ER?
YOU'RE THE MAN IN THE RED MOON, SEE AND WE'RE DAN DARE AND DIGBY COMING TO SPLORE YOU.
TWO RED MOON SUNDAES, SIR — THANK YOU.
AND NOW THAT DYNAMIC NEW NUMBER 'RED MOON STOMP'!
AT MOUNT PALOMAR OBSERVATORY, ALL THE EXPERTS ARE CONCENTRATING ON A CONTINUOUS WATCH ON ASTEROID 2345 — "THE RED MOON"
29 SEPT 1999
THIS IS IT, FELLOWS — LAST NIGHT'S PHOTOS & COURSE PLOT AS OF 0700 THIS MORNING — LOOK AT 'EM!!
INCREDIBLE!
THIS IS CRAZY!
PHEW!
CRAZY OR NOT, WE CAN GIVE UP ANY IDEA THAT IT'S COMING TOWARDS US FROM NATURAL CAUSES NOW — AS YOU ALL KNOW, FOR THE LAST THREE DAYS IT'S BEEN DEFLECTED FROM IT'S DIRECT COURSE BY THE PULL OF ASTEROID 2170 ON HIS NORMAL ORBIT — BUT NOW...
IT'S BACK PLUMB ON IT'S OLD COURSE!
THE SWING HAS BEEN CORRECTED!
THOSE NEWSPAPERS WERE RIGHT — IT IS BEING STEERED — IT MUST BE!
SUFFERIN' CATS! THREE BILLION TONS BEING AIMED AT US! WHERE DO WE GO FROM HERE?
MT. PALOMAR
Special: Asteroid 2345
Plate 10 — 22.00 hrs 28
WE DON'T — COLONEL DARE DOES — AND I SURE WISH HIM LUCK!

CONTINUED

EAGLE-BRITAIN'S NATIONAL STRIP CARTOON WEEKLY

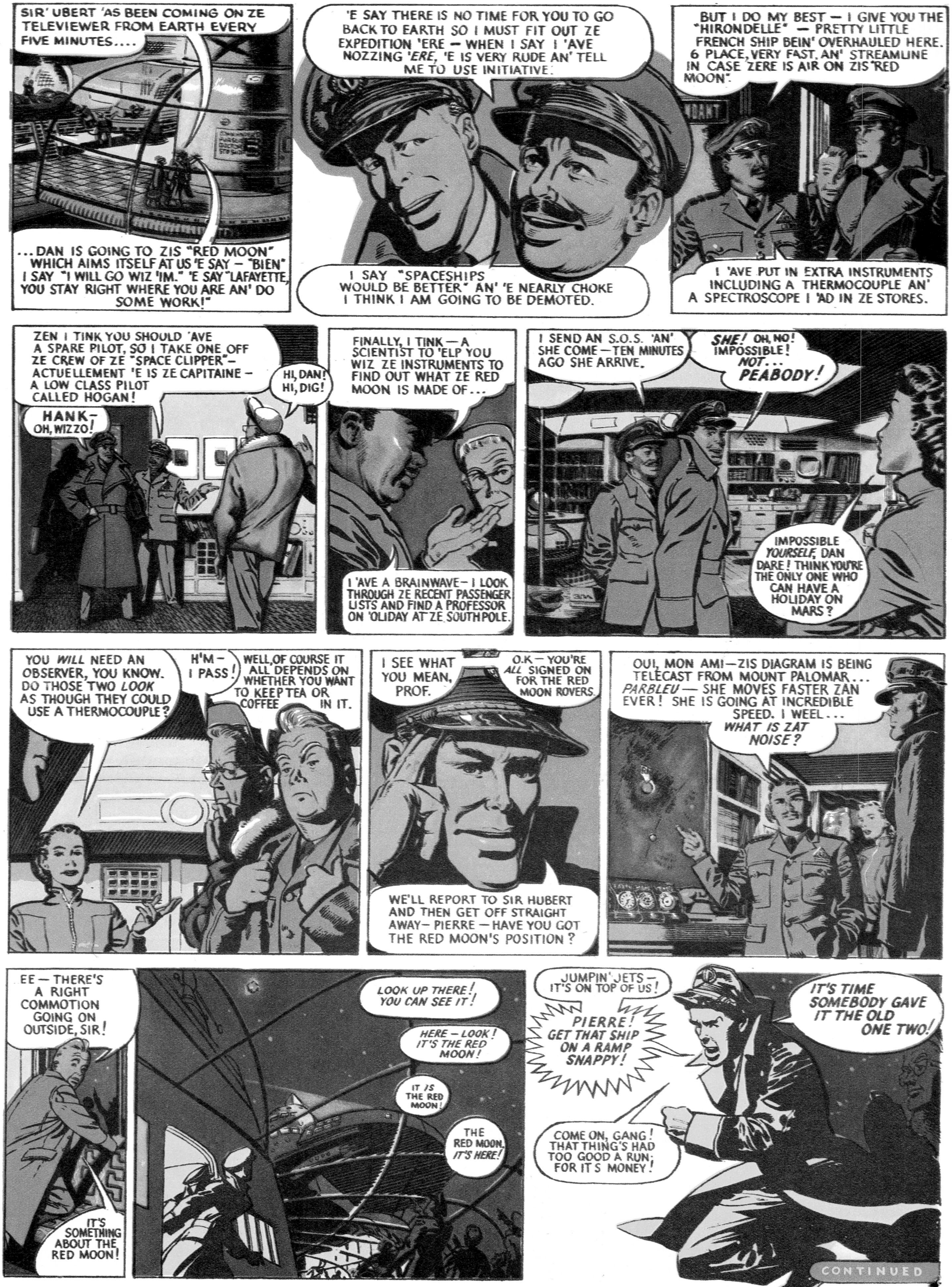
SIR' UBERT 'AS BEEN COMING ON ZE TELEVIEWER FROM EARTH EVERY FIVE MINUTES....
...DAN IS GOING TO ZIS "RED MOON" WHICH AIMS ITSELF AT US 'E SAY – "BIEN" I SAY "I WILL GO WIZ 'IM." 'E SAY "LAFAYETTE, YOU STAY RIGHT WHERE YOU ARE AN' DO SOME WORK!"
'E SAY THERE IS NO TIME FOR YOU TO GO BACK TO EARTH SO I MUST FIT OUT ZE EXPEDITION 'ERE – WHEN I SAY I 'AVE NOZZING 'ERE, 'E IS VERY RUDE AN' TELL ME TO USE INITIATIVE.
I SAY "SPACESHIPS WOULD BE BETTER" AN' 'E NEARLY CHOKE I THINK I AM GOING TO BE DEMOTED.
BUT I DO MY BEST – I GIVE YOU THE "HIRONDELLE" – PRETTY LITTLE FRENCH SHIP BEIN' OVERHAULED HERE. 6 PLACE, VERY FAST, AN' STREAMLINE IN CASE ZERE IS AIR ON ZIS "RED MOON".
I 'AVE PUT IN EXTRA INSTRUMENTS INCLUDING A THERMOCOUPLE AN' A SPECTROSCOPE I 'AD IN ZE STORES.
ZEN I TINK YOU SHOULD 'AVE A SPARE PILOT, SO I TAKE ONE OFF ZE CREW OF ZE "SPACE CLIPPER" – ACTUELLEMENT 'E IS ZE CAPITAINE – A LOW CLASS PILOT CALLED HOGAN!
HI, DAN! HI, DIG!
HANK – OH, WIZZO!
FINALLY, I TINK – A SCIENTIST TO 'ELP YOU WIZ ZE INSTRUMENTS TO FIND OUT WHAT ZE RED MOON IS MADE OF...
I 'AVE A BRAINWAVE – I LOOK THROUGH ZE RECENT PASSENGER LISTS AND FIND A PROFESSOR ON 'OLIDAY AT ZE SOUTH POLE.
I SEND AN S.O.S. 'AN' SHE COME – TEN MINUTES AGO SHE ARRIVE.
SHE! OH, NO! IMPOSSIBLE! NOT... PEABODY!
IMPOSSIBLE YOURSELF, DAN DARE! THINK YOU'RE THE ONLY ONE WHO CAN HAVE A HOLIDAY ON MARS?
YOU WILL NEED AN OBSERVER, YOU KNOW. DO THOSE TWO LOOK AS THOUGH THEY COULD USE A THERMOCOUPLE?
H'M – I PASS!
WELL, OF COURSE IT ALL DEPENDS ON WHETHER YOU WANT TO KEEP TEA OR COFFEE IN IT.
I SEE WHAT YOU MEAN, PROF.
O.K – YOU'RE ALL SIGNED ON FOR THE RED MOON ROVERS.
WE'LL REPORT TO SIR HUBERT AND THEN GET OFF STRAIGHT AWAY – PIERRE – HAVE YOU GOT THE RED MOON'S POSITION?
OUI, MON AMI – ZIS DIAGRAM IS BEING TELECAST FROM MOUNT PALOMAR... PARBLEU – SHE MOVES FASTER ZAN EVER! SHE IS GOING AT INCREDIBLE SPEED. I WEEL... WHAT IS ZAT NOISE?
EE – THERE'S A RIGHT COMMOTION GOING ON OUTSIDE, SIR!
IT'S SOMETHING ABOUT THE RED MOON!
LOOK UP THERE! YOU CAN SEE IT!
HERE – LOOK! IT'S THE RED MOON!
IT IS THE RED MOON!
THE RED MOON, IT'S HERE!
JUMPIN' JETS – IT'S ON TOP OF US!
PIERRE! GET THAT SHIP ON A RAMP SNAPPY!
IT'S TIME SOMEBODY GAVE IT THE OLD ONE TWO!
COME ON, GANG! THAT THING'S HAD TOO GOOD A RUN FOR IT'S MONEY!
CONTINUED

FOURPENCE-
HALFPENNY
EVERY FRIDAY
EAGLE
26 OCTOBER 1951 Vol. 2 No. 29

DAN DARE
THE RED MOON MYSTERY
THE RED MOON - HERE!!!
WHAT IS THE THING, ANYWAY? WHY DOESN'T THE GOVERNMENT OR SOMEBODY DO SOMETHING?
SOMEBODY IS! LOOK! - THAT SHIP TAKING OFF! - THAT'S NOT A FERRY!
NO SIR - IT'S COLONEL DARE GOING UP TO HAVE A PROPER LOOK AT THIS RED MOON!
DARE? DARE? - ISN'T HE THE FELLOW WHO DISCOVERED VENUS OR SOMETHING..
SPACE STATION S.F.J.2, MARS
PASSENGERS, SPACE CREWS AND STAFF ARE EXCITEDLY DISCUSSING THE "RED MOON" ASTEROID, WHICH HAS SUDDENLY BECOME VISIBLE IN THE SKY, WHEN THE WHIRR OF AN AIRLOCK IS HEARD AND THE SPACESHIP 'HIRONDELLE' GLIDES AWAY WITH DAN AND CO.

HE'S STOPPED AGAIN - HAS SOMETHING GONE WRONG, MISTER?
NO-O-O' I THINK WE'RE GOING TO SEE SOMETHING SPECIAL - YOU SEE, THE RAMPS HERE ARE FIXED TO AIM FERRIES AT MARS
TO GET TO THE RED MOON, COLONEL DARE WILL HAVE TO AIM UP AT RIGHT ANGLES
IN THE PASSENGERS' DINING SALOON OF THE SPACE STATION.....
THERE'S NO AIR HERE FOR HIS RUDDER FINS TO WORK IN.. AND THE GRAPHITE VANES IN THE EXHAUST ONLY GIVE A SLIGHT DEGREE OF TURN....
IT TAKES HALF AN HOUR TO TURN A RIGHT ANGLE, USING THEM...
SO HE'S TRYING TO KICK HER UP AND ROUND BY "PLAYING" THE ROCKETS - THE MAIN ONES ON ONE SIDE AGAINST THE REACTOR BRAKES ON THE OTHER
IT'S LIKE PULLING ONE OAR OF A BOAT AND BACKING WITH THE OTHER, BUT THE POWER HAS TO BE SO DELICATELY EQUALISED....
THAT THERE ARE ONLY ONE OR TWO MEN ALIVE WHO CAN DO IT WITHOUT STARTING THE SHIP SPINNING - AND A SPIN IN SPACE TAKES HOURS TO GET OUT OF...
OH, DAN! BE CAREFUL, MON AMI
HE'LL NEVER MAKE IT. SHE'S TWISTING..
WE'RE STARTING TO SPIN!
HOLD IT, SIR HOLD IT!

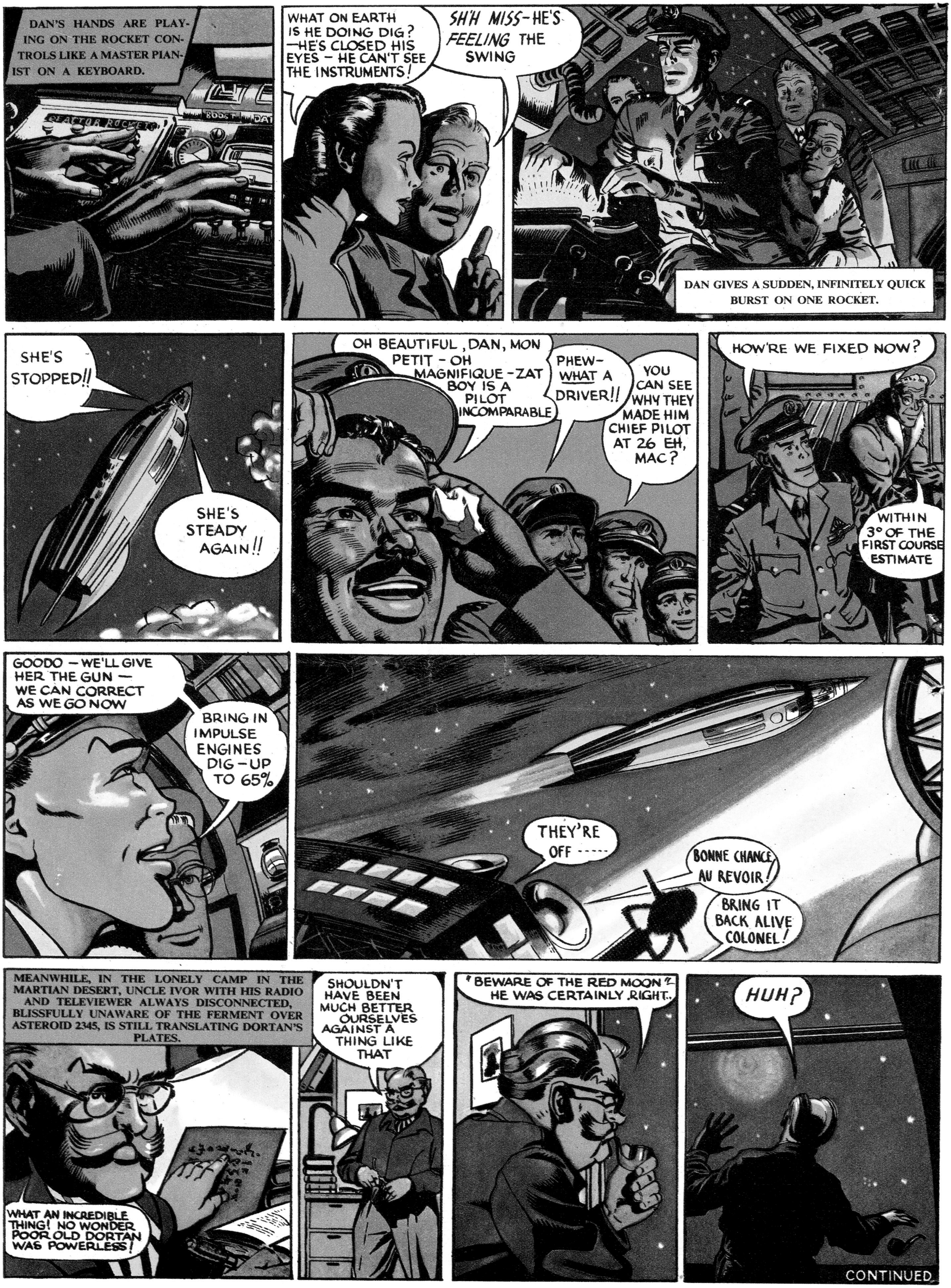

DAN'S HANDS ARE PLAYING ON THE ROCKET CONTROLS LIKE A MASTER PIANIST ON A KEYBOARD.
WHAT ON EARTH IS HE DOING DIG? —HE'S CLOSED HIS EYES — HE CAN'T SEE THE INSTRUMENTS!
SH'H MISS-HE'S FEELING THE SWING
DAN GIVES A SUDDEN, INFINITELY QUICK BURST ON ONE ROCKET.
SHE'S STOPPED!!
SHE'S STEADY AGAIN!!
OH BEAUTIFUL, DAN, MON PETIT - OH MAGNIFIQUE - ZAT BOY IS A PILOT INCOMPARABLE
PHEW- WHAT A DRIVER!!
YOU CAN SEE WHY THEY MADE HIM CHIEF PILOT AT 26 EH, MAC?
HOW'RE WE FIXED NOW?
WITHIN 3° OF THE FIRST COURSE ESTIMATE
GOODO — WE'LL GIVE HER THE GUN — WE CAN CORRECT AS WE GO NOW
BRING IN IMPULSE ENGINES DIG - UP TO 65%
THEY'RE OFF -----
BONNE CHANCE AU REVOIR!
BRING IT BACK ALIVE COLONEL!
MEANWHILE, IN THE LONELY CAMP IN THE MARTIAN DESERT, UNCLE IVOR WITH HIS RADIO AND TELEVIEWER ALWAYS DISCONNECTED, BLISSFULLY UNAWARE OF THE FERMENT OVER ASTEROID 2345, IS STILL TRANSLATING DORTAN'S PLATES.
WHAT AN INCREDIBLE THING! NO WONDER POOR OLD DORTAN WAS POWERLESS!
SHOULDN'T HAVE BEEN MUCH BETTER OURSELVES AGAINST A THING LIKE THAT
"BEWARE OF THE RED MOON"? HE WAS CERTAINLY RIGHT.
HUH?
CONTINUED

EAGLE-BRITAIN'S NATIONAL STRIP CARTOON WEEKLY

FOURPENCE-HALFPENNY
EVERY FRIDAY
EAGLE
2 NOVEMBER 1951 Vol. 2 No. 30
DAN DARE
THE RED MOON MYSTERY
COURSE CHECKED WITH MOUNT PALOMAR, DAN – MARS ZTB7 – A1/44 – I'VE SET THE ASTRANAVIGATOR.
RIGHT – I'VE GOT HER ON... NOW! LOCK CONTROLS!
SPACE FLEET H.Q. ARE GOING TO GIVE US A COURSE CHECK EVERY 5 MINUTES.
GOOD – NOW I'D BETTER TALK TO SIR HUBERT.
HELLO, SIR – SORRY I DIDN'T CHECK IN FROM THE SATELLITE, BUT WHEN THIS THING APPEARED I THOUGHT I'D BETTER GET SPACEBORNE FIRST AND TALK AFTERWARDS!
GOOD WORK, DAN – NOW LISTEN. THE SITUATION BEGINS TO LOOK REALLY SERIOUS. PALOMAR SAYS THE WRETCHED MOON IS BEING STEERED – AND WHAT'S MORE, IT'S BEGINNING TO VARY ITS SPEED NOW AS WELL...
SOMEBODY OR SOMETHIN' IS GUIDIN' THAT THING AND ITS COURSE STILL SEEMS TO BE TO PASS CLOSE BY MARS AN' HIT US.
WHAT WE MUST HAVE NOW IS INFORMATION – ALL YOU CAN GET AS QUICKLY AS YOU CAN...
...WHAT IT'S MADE OF – ITS EXACT SIZE – SIGNS OF LIFE – ATMOSPHERE – EVERYTHING!
ROGER, SIR – DON'T WORRY – WE'LL WRAP A RIBBON ROUND IT AND BRING IT HOME ON A PLATTER...
YOU LOOK PRETTY WORN, SIR – ARE THINGS BAD DOWN THERE?
OH – THE USUAL CHAOS – NOBODY COULD DECIDE WHICH DEPARTMENT A RED MOON CAME UNDER – SO THEY'VE MADE A NEW ONE CALLED 'RED MOON COMMISSION' AND STUCK ME IN CHARGE...
... AND NOW EVERY CRACKPOT IN THE WORLD IS TRYING TO RING ME UP AND TELL ME HOW TO DEAL WITH IT.
SOMEONE ON MARS AS WELL – PERSISTENT OLD LUNATIC – SAYS HE'S YOUR UNCLE
URGENT
DOLTS! IMBECILES! JACKS-IN-OFFICE!
THEY DESERVE TO PERISH!

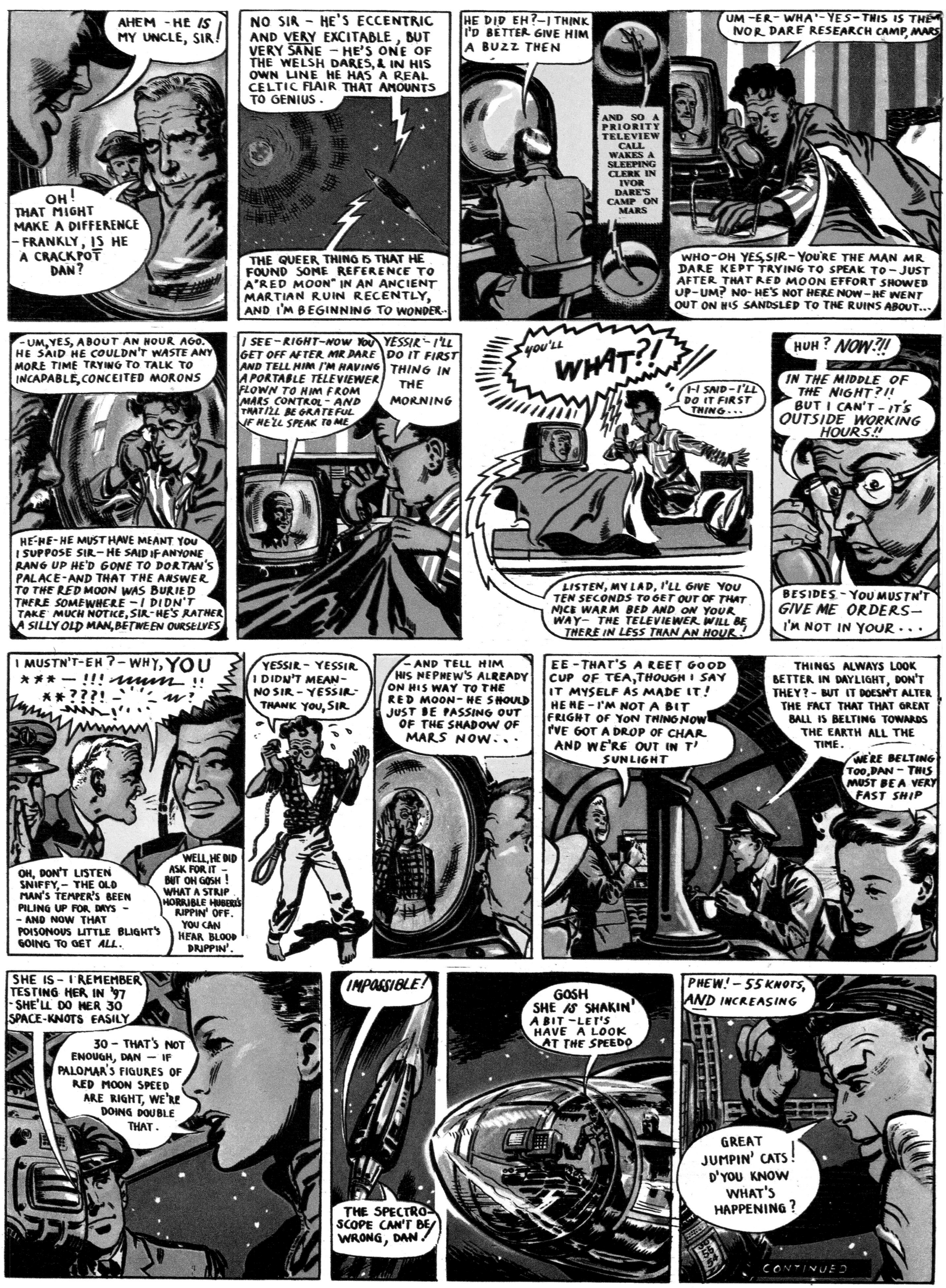
AHEM - HE IS MY UNCLE, SIR!
OH! THAT MIGHT MAKE A DIFFERENCE - FRANKLY, IS HE A CRACKPOT DAN?
NO SIR - HE'S ECCENTRIC AND VERY EXCITABLE, BUT VERY SANE - HE'S ONE OF THE WELSH DARES, & IN HIS OWN LINE HE HAS A REAL CELTIC FLAIR THAT AMOUNTS TO GENIUS.
THE QUEER THING IS THAT HE FOUND SOME REFERENCE TO A "RED MOON" IN AN ANCIENT MARTIAN RUIN RECENTLY, AND I'M BEGINNING TO WONDER..
HE DID EH? - I THINK I'D BETTER GIVE HIM A BUZZ THEN
AND SO A PRIORITY TELEVIEW CALL WAKES A SLEEPING CLERK IN IVOR DARE'S CAMP ON MARS
UM - ER - WHA' - YES - THIS IS THE NOR DARE RESEARCH CAMP, MARS
WHO - OH YES, SIR - YOU'RE THE MAN MR DARE KEPT TRYING TO SPEAK TO - JUST AFTER THAT RED MOON EFFORT SHOWED UP - UM? NO - HE'S NOT HERE NOW - HE WENT OUT ON HIS SANDSLED TO THE RUINS ABOUT...
- UM, YES, ABOUT AN HOUR AGO. HE SAID HE COULDN'T WASTE ANY MORE TIME TRYING TO TALK TO INCAPABLE, CONCEITED MORONS
HE-HE-HE MUST HAVE MEANT YOU I SUPPOSE SIR - HE SAID IF ANYONE RANG UP HE'D GONE TO DORTAN'S PALACE - AND THAT THE ANSWER TO THE RED MOON WAS BURIED THERE SOMEWHERE - I DIDN'T TAKE MUCH NOTICE, SIR - HE'S RATHER A SILLY OLD MAN, BETWEEN OURSELVES
I SEE - RIGHT - NOW YOU GET OFF AFTER MR DARE AND TELL HIM I'M HAVING A PORTABLE TELEVIEWER FLOWN TO HIM FROM MARS CONTROL - AND THAT I'LL BE GRATEFUL IF HE'LL SPEAK TO ME
YESSIR - I'LL DO IT FIRST THING IN THE MORNING
YOU'LL WHAT?!
I-I SAID - I'LL DO IT FIRST THING...
LISTEN, MY LAD, I'LL GIVE YOU TEN SECONDS TO GET OUT OF THAT NICE WARM BED AND ON YOUR WAY - THE TELEVIEWER WILL BE THERE IN LESS THAN AN HOUR!
HUH? NOW?!!
IN THE MIDDLE OF THE NIGHT?!! BUT I CAN'T - IT'S OUTSIDE WORKING HOURS!!
BESIDES - YOU MUSTN'T GIVE ME ORDERS - I'M NOT IN YOUR...
I MUSTN'T - EH? - WHY, YOU ***—!!! **???!
OH, DON'T LISTEN SNIFFY, - THE OLD MAN'S TEMPER'S BEEN PILING UP FOR DAYS - - AND NOW THAT POISONOUS LITTLE BLIGHT'S GOING TO GET ALL.
WELL, HE DID ASK FOR IT - BUT OH GOSH! WHAT A STRIP HORRIBLE HUBERT'S RIPPIN' OFF. YOU CAN HEAR BLOOD DRIPPIN'.
YESSIR - YESSIR I DIDN'T MEAN - NO SIR - YESSIR - THANK YOU, SIR
- AND TELL HIM HIS NEPHEW'S ALREADY ON HIS WAY TO THE RED MOON - HE SHOULD JUST BE PASSING OUT OF THE SHADOW OF MARS NOW...
EE - THAT'S A REET GOOD CUP OF TEA, THOUGH I SAY IT MYSELF AS MADE IT! HE HE - I'M NOT A BIT FRIGHT OF YON THING NOW I'VE GOT A DROP OF CHAR AND WE'RE OUT IN T' SUNLIGHT
THINGS ALWAYS LOOK BETTER IN DAYLIGHT, DON'T THEY? - BUT IT DOESN'T ALTER THE FACT THAT THAT GREAT BALL IS BELTING TOWARDS THE EARTH ALL THE TIME.
WE'RE BELTING TOO, DAN - THIS MUST BE A VERY FAST SHIP
SHE IS - I REMEMBER TESTING HER IN '97 - SHE'LL DO HER 30 SPACE-KNOTS EASILY
30 - THAT'S NOT ENOUGH, DAN - IF PALOMAR'S FIGURES OF RED MOON SPEED ARE RIGHT, WE'RE DOING DOUBLE THAT.
IMPOSSIBLE!
THE SPECTRO-SCOPE CAN'T BE WRONG, DAN!
GOSH SHE IS SHAKIN' A BIT - LET'S HAVE A LOOK AT THE SPEEDO
PHEW! - 55 KNOTS, AND INCREASING
GREAT JUMPIN' CATS! D'YOU KNOW WHAT'S HAPPENING?
CONTINUED

EAGLE-BRITAIN'S NATIONAL STRIP CARTOON WEEKLY

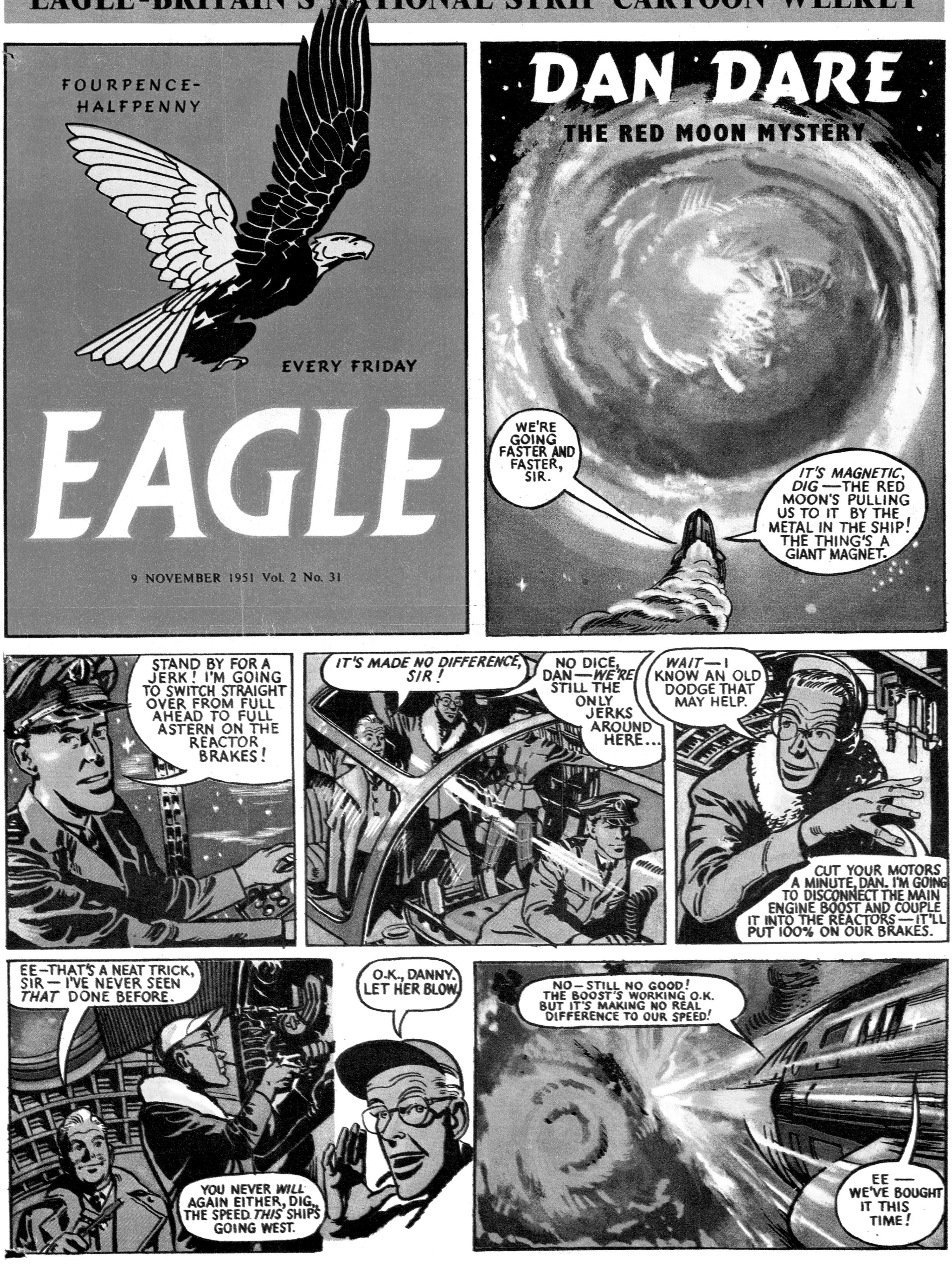
FOURPENCE-HALFPENNY
EVERY FRIDAY
EAGLE
9 NOVEMBER 1951 Vol. 2 No. 31
DAN DARE
THE RED MOON MYSTERY
WE'RE GOING FASTER AND FASTER, SIR.
IT'S MAGNETIC, DIG—THE RED MOON'S PULLING US TO IT BY THE METAL IN THE SHIP! THE THING'S A GIANT MAGNET.
STAND BY FOR A JERK! I'M GOING TO SWITCH STRAIGHT OVER FROM FULL AHEAD TO FULL ASTERN ON THE REACTOR BRAKES!
IT'S MADE NO DIFFERENCE, SIR!
NO DICE, DAN—WE'RE STILL THE ONLY JERKS AROUND HERE...
WAIT—I KNOW AN OLD DODGE THAT MAY HELP.
CUT YOUR MOTORS A MINUTE, DAN. I'M GOING TO DISCONNECT THE MAIN ENGINE BOOST AND COUPLE IT INTO THE REACTORS—IT'LL PUT 100% ON OUR BRAKES.
EE—THAT'S A NEAT TRICK, SIR—I'VE NEVER SEEN THAT DONE BEFORE.
O.K., DANNY. LET HER BLOW.
YOU NEVER WILL AGAIN EITHER, DIG, THE SPEED THIS SHIP'S GOING WEST.
NO—STILL NO GOOD! THE BOOST'S WORKING O.K. BUT IT'S MAKING NO REAL DIFFERENCE TO OUR SPEED!
EE—WE'VE BOUGHT IT THIS TIME!

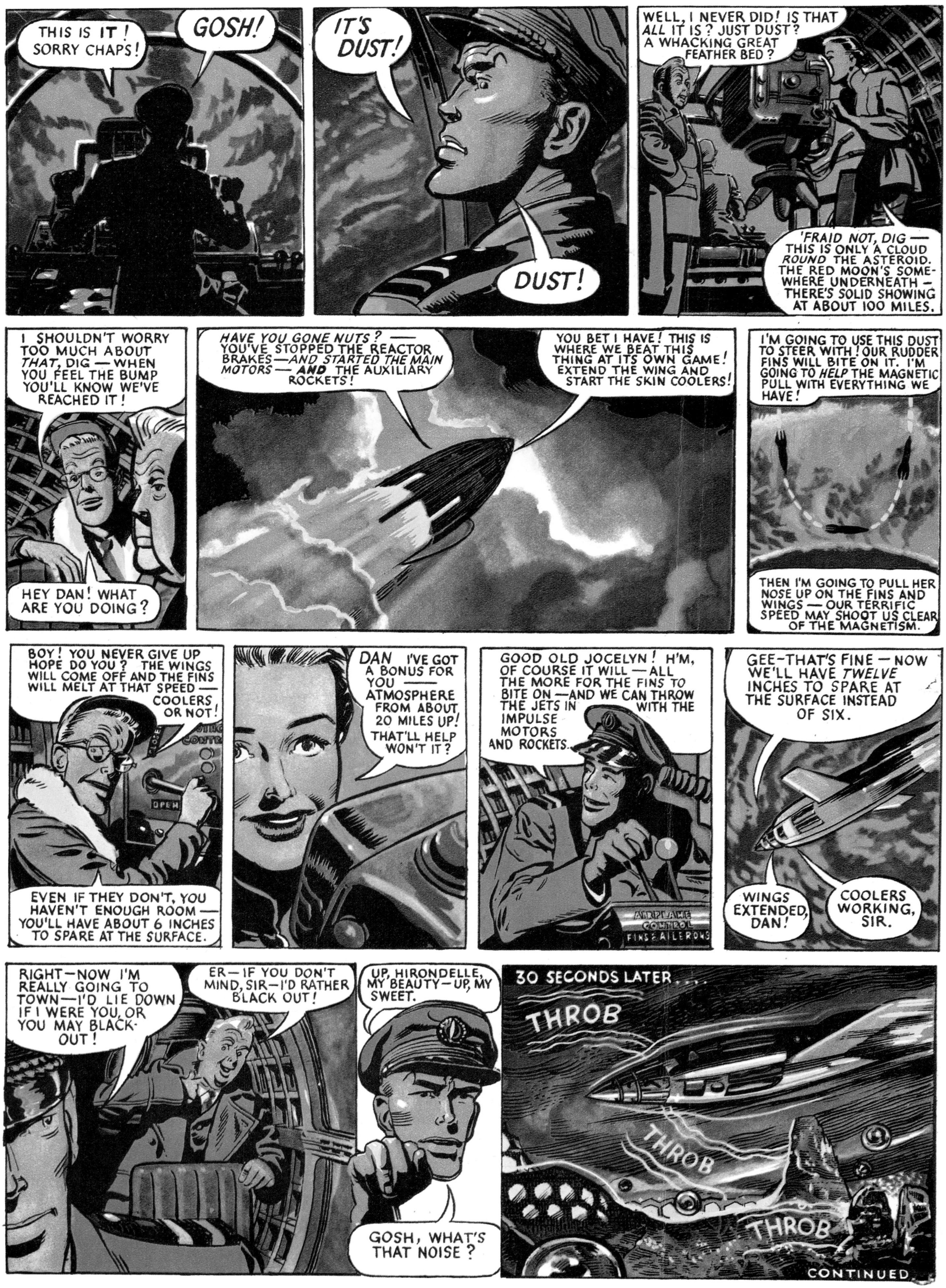
THIS IS IT! SORRY CHAPS!
GOSH!
IT'S DUST!
DUST!
WELL, I NEVER DID! IS THAT ALL IT IS? JUST DUST? A WHACKING GREAT FEATHER BED?
'FRAID NOT, DIG — THIS IS ONLY A CLOUD ROUND THE ASTEROID. THE RED MOON'S SOMEWHERE UNDERNEATH — THERE'S SOLID SHOWING AT ABOUT 100 MILES.
I SHOULDN'T WORRY TOO MUCH ABOUT THAT, DIG — WHEN YOU FEEL THE BUMP YOU'LL KNOW WE'VE REACHED IT!
HEY DAN! WHAT ARE YOU DOING?
HAVE YOU GONE NUTS? — YOU'VE STOPPED THE REACTOR BRAKES — AND STARTED THE MAIN MOTORS — AND THE AUXILIARY ROCKETS!
YOU BET I HAVE! THIS IS WHERE WE BEAT THIS THING AT ITS OWN GAME! EXTEND THE WING AND START THE SKIN COOLERS!
I'M GOING TO USE THIS DUST TO STEER WITH! OUR RUDDER FINS WILL BITE ON IT. I'M GOING TO HELP THE MAGNETIC PULL WITH EVERYTHING WE HAVE!
THEN I'M GOING TO PULL HER NOSE UP ON THE FINS AND WINGS — OUR TERRIFIC SPEED MAY SHOOT US CLEAR OF THE MAGNETISM.
BOY! YOU NEVER GIVE UP HOPE DO YOU? THE WINGS WILL COME OFF AND THE FINS WILL MELT AT THAT SPEED — COOLERS OR NOT!
OPEN
EVEN IF THEY DON'T, YOU HAVEN'T ENOUGH ROOM — YOU'LL HAVE ABOUT 6 INCHES TO SPARE AT THE SURFACE.
DAN I'VE GOT A BONUS FOR YOU — ATMOSPHERE FROM ABOUT 20 MILES UP! THAT'LL HELP WON'T IT?
GOOD OLD JOCELYN! H'M, OF COURSE IT WILL — ALL THE MORE FOR THE FINS TO BITE ON — AND WE CAN THROW THE JETS IN WITH THE IMPULSE MOTORS AND ROCKETS.
AIRPLANE CONTROL
FINS & AILERONS
GEE — THAT'S FINE — NOW WE'LL HAVE TWELVE INCHES TO SPARE AT THE SURFACE INSTEAD OF SIX.
WINGS EXTENDED, DAN!
COOLERS WORKING, SIR.
RIGHT — NOW I'M REALLY GOING TO TOWN — I'D LIE DOWN IF I WERE YOU, OR YOU MAY BLACK-OUT!
ER — IF YOU DON'T MIND, SIR — I'D RATHER BLACK OUT!
UP, HIRONDELLE, MY BEAUTY — UP, MY SWEET.
GOSH, WHAT'S THAT NOISE?
30 SECONDS LATER...
THROB
THROB
THROB
CONTINUED

EAGLE-BRITAIN'S NATIONAL STRIP CARTOON WEEKLY

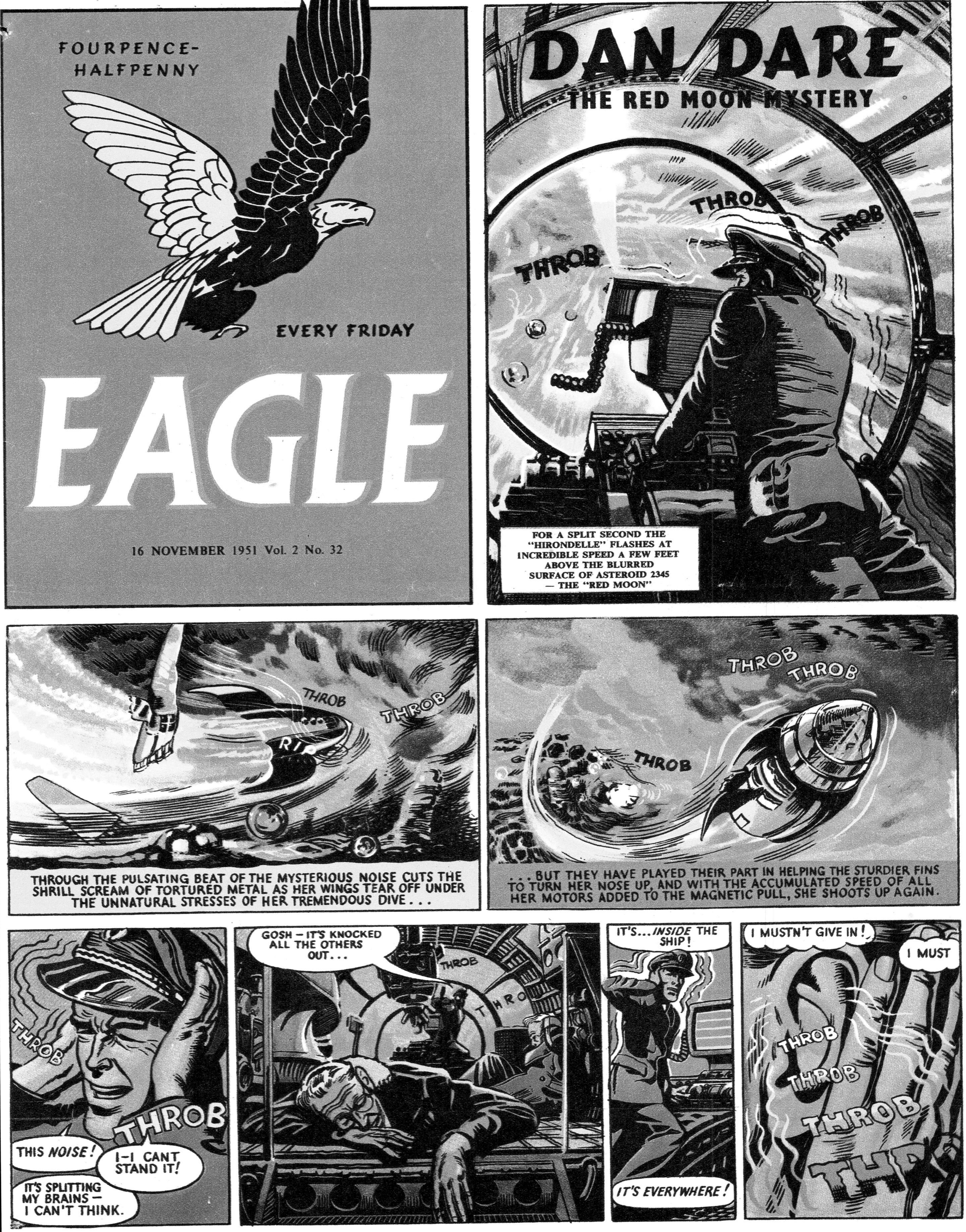
FOURPENCE-
HALFPENNY
EVERY FRIDAY
EAGLE
16 NOVEMBER 1951 Vol. 2 No. 32
DAN DARE
THE RED MOON MYSTERY
THROB
THROB
THROB
FOR A SPLIT SECOND THE "HIRONDELLE" FLASHES AT INCREDIBLE SPEED A FEW FEET ABOVE THE BLURRED SURFACE OF ASTEROID 2345 — THE "RED MOON"
THROB
THROB
RIP
THROUGH THE PULSATING BEAT OF THE MYSTERIOUS NOISE CUTS THE SHRILL SCREAM OF TORTURED METAL AS HER WINGS TEAR OFF UNDER THE UNNATURAL STRESSES OF HER TREMENDOUS DIVE . . .
THROB
THROB
THROB
. . . BUT THEY HAVE PLAYED THEIR PART IN HELPING THE STURDIER FINS TO TURN HER NOSE UP, AND WITH THE ACCUMULATED SPEED OF ALL HER MOTORS ADDED TO THE MAGNETIC PULL, SHE SHOOTS UP AGAIN.
THROB
THROB
THIS NOISE!
I-I CANT STAND IT!
IT'S SPLITTING MY BRAINS — I CAN'T THINK.
GOSH — IT'S KNOCKED ALL THE OTHERS OUT...
THROB
THRO
IT'S... INSIDE THE SHIP!
IT'S EVERYWHERE!
I MUSTN'T GIVE IN!
I MUST
THROB
THROB
THROB
THR

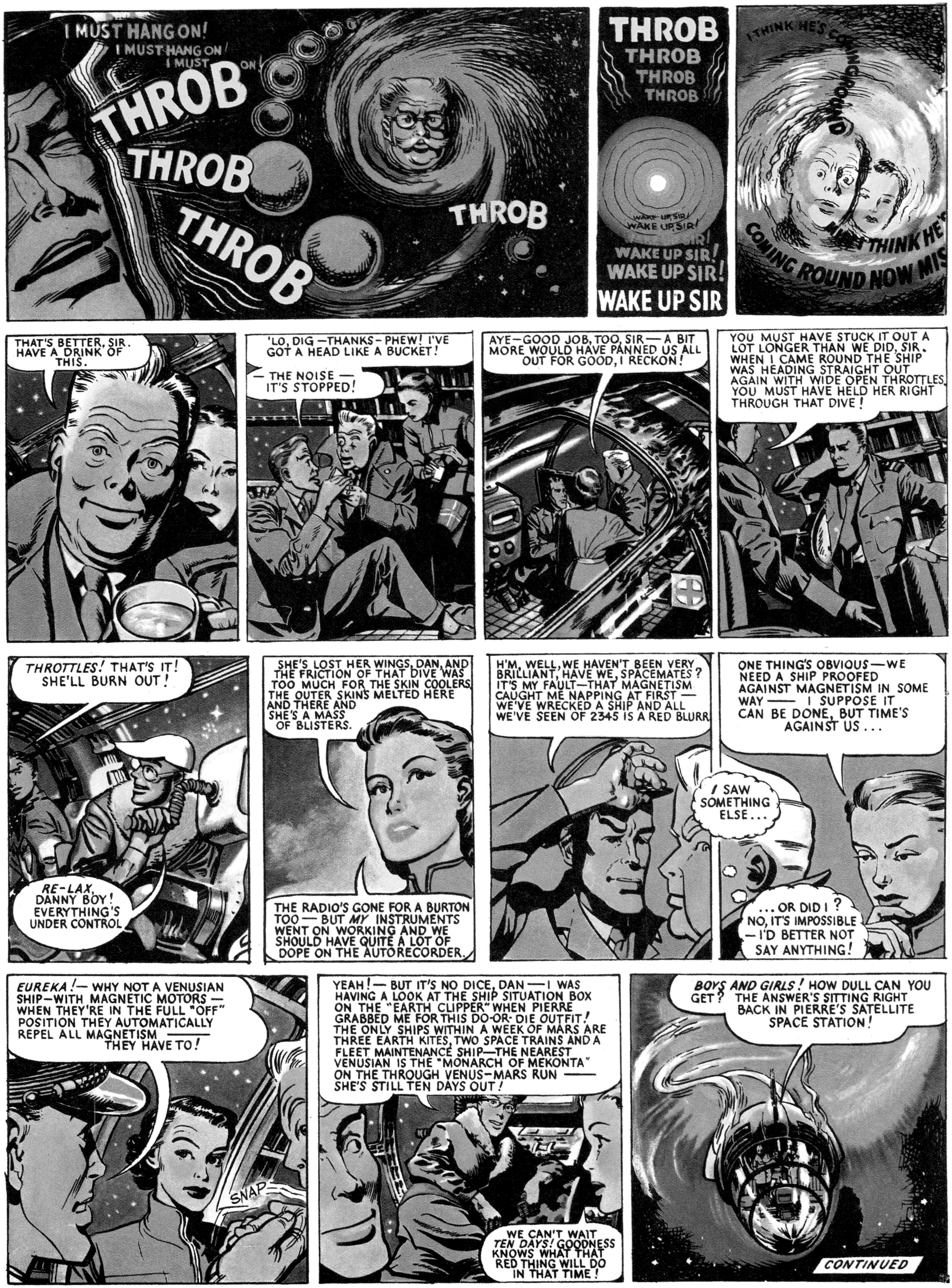

I MUST HANG ON!
I MUST HANG ON!
I MUST ON!
THROB
THROB
THROB
THROB
THROB
THROB
THROB
THROB
WAKE UP SIR!
WAKE UP SIR!
WAKE UP SIR!
WAKE UP SIR!
WAKE UP SIR
I THINK HE'S COMING ROUND
I THINK HE'S COMING ROUND NOW MIS
THAT'S BETTER, SIR. HAVE A DRINK OF THIS.
'LO, DIG —THANKS— PHEW! I'VE GOT A HEAD LIKE A BUCKET!
— THE NOISE — IT'S STOPPED!
AYE—GOOD JOB, TOO, SIR — A BIT MORE WOULD HAVE PANNED US ALL OUT FOR GOOD, I RECKON!
YOU MUST HAVE STUCK IT OUT A LOT LONGER THAN WE DID, SIR. WHEN I CAME ROUND THE SHIP WAS HEADING STRAIGHT OUT AGAIN WITH WIDE OPEN THROTTLES. YOU MUST HAVE HELD HER RIGHT THROUGH THAT DIVE!
THROTTLES! THAT'S IT! SHE'LL BURN OUT!
RE-LAX, DANNY BOY! EVERYTHING'S UNDER CONTROL
SHE'S LOST HER WINGS, DAN, AND THE FRICTION OF THAT DIVE WAS TOO MUCH FOR THE SKIN COOLERS. THE OUTER SKIN'S MELTED HERE AND THERE AND SHE'S A MASS OF BLISTERS.
THE RADIO'S GONE FOR A BURTON TOO — BUT MY INSTRUMENTS WENT ON WORKING AND WE SHOULD HAVE QUITE A LOT OF DOPE ON THE AUTORECORDER.
H'M, WELL, WE HAVEN'T BEEN VERY BRILLIANT, HAVE WE, SPACEMATES? IT'S MY FAULT—THAT MAGNETISM CAUGHT ME NAPPING AT FIRST — WE'VE WRECKED A SHIP AND ALL WE'VE SEEN OF 2345 IS A RED BLURR.
I SAW SOMETHING ELSE...
ONE THING'S OBVIOUS — WE NEED A SHIP PROOFED AGAINST MAGNETISM IN SOME WAY — I SUPPOSE IT CAN BE DONE, BUT TIME'S AGAINST US...
...OR DID I? NO, IT'S IMPOSSIBLE — I'D BETTER NOT SAY ANYTHING!
EUREKA! — WHY NOT A VENUSIAN SHIP—WITH MAGNETIC MOTORS — WHEN THEY'RE IN THE FULL "OFF" POSITION THEY AUTOMATICALLY REPEL ALL MAGNETISM — THEY HAVE TO!
SNAP
YEAH! — BUT IT'S NO DICE, DAN — I WAS HAVING A LOOK AT THE SHIP SITUATION BOX ON THE "EARTH CLIPPER" WHEN PIERRE GRABBED ME FOR THIS DO-OR-DIE OUTFIT! THE ONLY SHIPS WITHIN A WEEK OF MARS ARE THREE EARTH KITES, TWO SPACE TRAINS AND A FLEET MAINTENANCE SHIP—THE NEAREST VENUSIAN IS THE "MONARCH OF MEKONTA" ON THE THROUGH VENUS-MARS RUN — SHE'S STILL TEN DAYS OUT!
WE CAN'T WAIT TEN DAYS! GOODNESS KNOWS WHAT THAT RED THING WILL DO IN THAT TIME!
BOYS AND GIRLS! HOW DULL CAN YOU GET? THE ANSWER'S SITTING RIGHT BACK IN PIERRE'S SATELLITE SPACE STATION!
CONTINUED

EAGLE-BRITAIN'S NATIONAL STRIP CARTOON WEEKLY

FOURPENCE-HALFPENNY
EVERY FRIDAY
EAGLE
23 NOVEMBER 1951 Vol. 2 No. 33

DAN DARE
THE RED MOON MYSTERY
THE OMINOUS RED SHAPE OF ASTEROID 2345, THE 'RED MOON', LOOMS EVER LARGER IN THE SKY OF MARS, AS, GUIDED BY SOME MYSTERIOUS FORCE, IT HURTLES THROUGH SPACE . . . IN THE VISTA-DOME OF THE MARS-ASTORIA HOTEL AN EXCITED CROWD HAS GATHERED.
LADIES AND GENTLEMEN—PLEEZ TO GO TO BED!
IT IS TREE O'CLOCK, A.M., IN ZE MORNING!
FRANK HAMPSON & HAROLD JOHNS

ASTORIA
ZE MANAGEMENT WILL MAKE ANNOUNCEMENT AS SOON AS ZERE IS NEWS OF COLONEL DARE.

CARAMBA! WHAT A NIGHT! WHY DID I EVER LEAVE MY GOOD JOB AT ZE SAVOY? MISS, PLISS YOU RING ZE SATELLITE SPACE STATION AGAIN.
YES, SIR!

NO, MISS, NO NEWS YET, BUT THERE IS NO CAUSE FOR ALARM. WE EXPECTED COLONEL DARE'S RADIO TO BE BLANKED OUT AS HE APPROACHED THE ASTEROID. PLEASE DO NOT WORRY. THE ASTEROID 2345 IS MERELY PASSING MARS AND—WAIT A MINUTE! . . .
...THERE'S AN UNSIGNALLED SHIP COMING IN FAST!

IT'S—YES, IT'S THE "HIRONDELLE"
COLONEL DARE'S BACK!
—AND IS HE IN A HURRY!

A COLLAPSIBLE AIRTIGHT GANGWAY IS RUSHED TO THE HIRONDELLE.

HI, PIERRE—'FRAID I'VE MADE RATHER A MESS OF YOUR SHIP—CAN YOU GET SIR HUBERT FOR ME?—I MUST REPORT STRAIGHT AWAY!
'E WAITS FOR YOU, MON AMI—ON ZE TELE-VIEWER ON ZE BRIDGE.

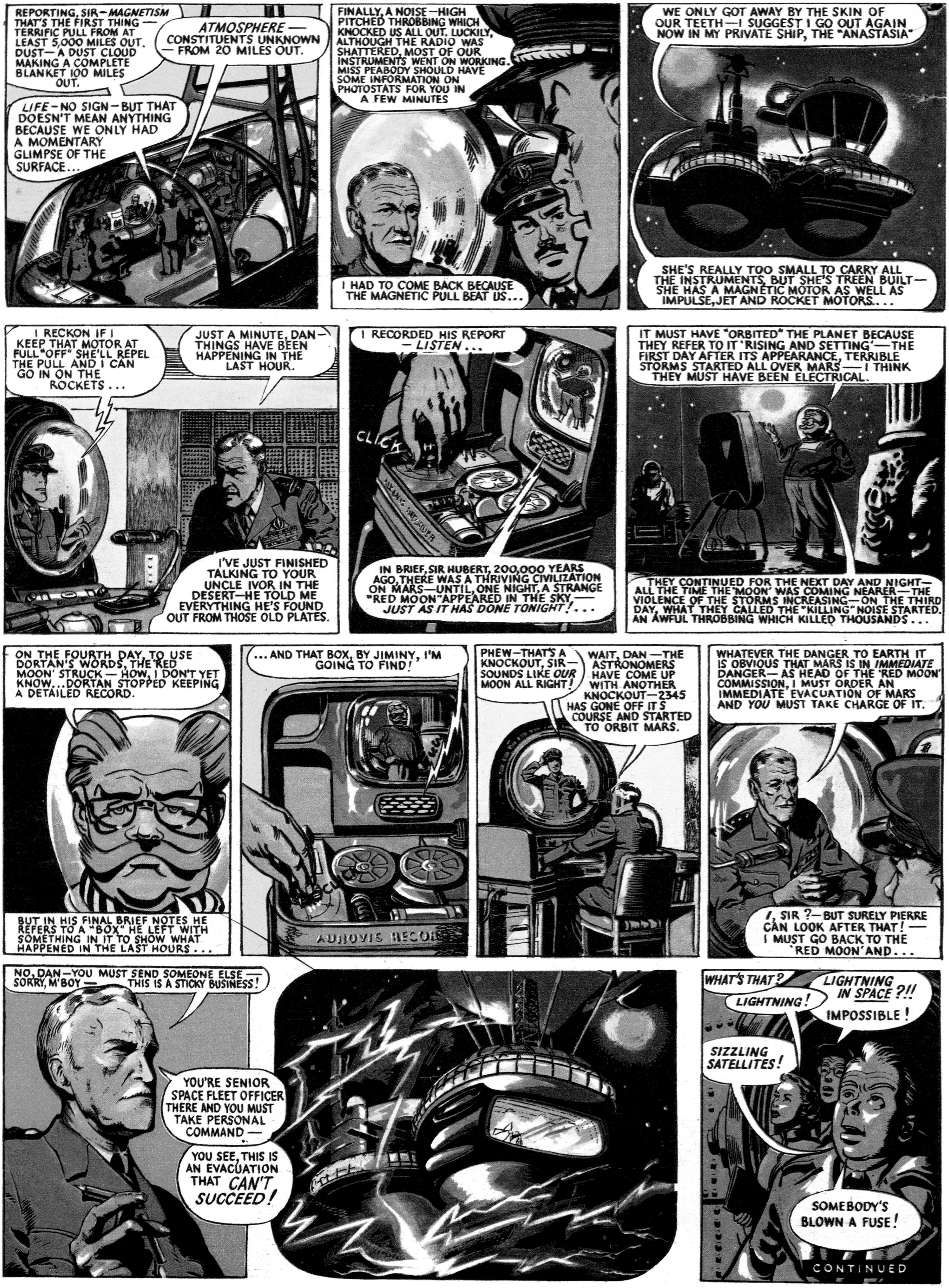

REPORTING, SIR—MAGNETISM THAT'S THE FIRST THING — TERRIFIC PULL FROM AT LEAST 5,000 MILES OUT. DUST—A DUST CLOUD MAKING A COMPLETE BLANKET 100 MILES OUT.
ATMOSPHERE — CONSTITUENTS UNKNOWN — FROM 20 MILES OUT.
LIFE—NO SIGN—BUT THAT DOESN'T MEAN ANYTHING BECAUSE WE ONLY HAD A MOMENTARY GLIMPSE OF THE SURFACE...
FINALLY, A NOISE—HIGH PITCHED THROBBING WHICH KNOCKED US ALL OUT. LUCKILY, ALTHOUGH THE RADIO WAS SHATTERED, MOST OF OUR INSTRUMENTS WENT ON WORKING. MISS PEABODY SHOULD HAVE SOME INFORMATION ON PHOTOSTATS FOR YOU IN A FEW MINUTES
I HAD TO COME BACK BECAUSE THE MAGNETIC PULL BEAT US...
WE ONLY GOT AWAY BY THE SKIN OF OUR TEETH—I SUGGEST I GO OUT AGAIN NOW IN MY PRIVATE SHIP, THE "ANASTASIA"
SHE'S REALLY TOO SMALL TO CARRY ALL THE INSTRUMENTS, BUT SHE'S TREEN BUILT— SHE HAS A MAGNETIC MOTOR AS WELL AS IMPULSE, JET AND ROCKET MOTORS...
I RECKON IF I KEEP THAT MOTOR AT FULL "OFF" SHE'LL REPEL THE PULL AND I CAN GO IN ON THE ROCKETS...
JUST A MINUTE, DAN— THINGS HAVE BEEN HAPPENING IN THE LAST HOUR.
I'VE JUST FINISHED TALKING TO YOUR UNCLE IVOR IN THE DESERT—HE TOLD ME EVERYTHING HE'S FOUND OUT FROM THOSE OLD PLATES.
I RECORDED HIS REPORT — LISTEN...
CLICK
IN BRIEF, SIR HUBERT, 200,000 YEARS AGO, THERE WAS A THRIVING CIVILIZATION ON MARS—UNTIL, ONE NIGHT, A STRANGE "RED MOON" APPEARED IN THE SKY,— JUST AS IT HAS DONE TONIGHT!...
IT MUST HAVE "ORBITED" THE PLANET BECAUSE THEY REFER TO IT 'RISING AND SETTING'—THE FIRST DAY AFTER ITS APPEARANCE, TERRIBLE STORMS STARTED ALL OVER MARS — I THINK THEY MUST HAVE BEEN ELECTRICAL.
THEY CONTINUED FOR THE NEXT DAY AND NIGHT— ALL THE TIME THE 'MOON' WAS COMING NEARER—THE VIOLENCE OF THE STORMS INCREASING—ON THE THIRD DAY, WHAT THEY CALLED THE "KILLING" NOISE STARTED. AN AWFUL THROBBING WHICH KILLED THOUSANDS...
ON THE FOURTH DAY, TO USE DORTAN'S WORDS, THE 'RED MOON' STRUCK — HOW, I DON'T YET KNOW...DORTAN STOPPED KEEPING A DETAILED RECORD.
BUT IN HIS FINAL BRIEF NOTES HE REFERS TO A "BOX" HE LEFT WITH SOMETHING IN IT TO SHOW WHAT HAPPENED IN THE LAST HOURS...
...AND THAT BOX, BY JIMINY, I'M GOING TO FIND!
AUDOVIS RECOR
PHEW—THAT'S A KNOCKOUT, SIR— SOUNDS LIKE OUR MOON ALL RIGHT!
WAIT, DAN—THE ASTRONOMERS HAVE COME UP WITH ANOTHER KNOCKOUT—2345 HAS GONE OFF ITS COURSE AND STARTED TO ORBIT MARS.
WHATEVER THE DANGER TO EARTH IT IS OBVIOUS THAT MARS IS IN IMMEDIATE DANGER—AS HEAD OF THE 'RED MOON' COMMISSION, I MUST ORDER AN IMMEDIATE EVACUATION OF MARS AND YOU MUST TAKE CHARGE OF IT.
I, SIR?—BUT SURELY PIERRE CAN LOOK AFTER THAT!— I MUST GO BACK TO THE 'RED MOON' AND...
NO, DAN—YOU MUST SEND SOMEONE ELSE— SORRY, M'BOY— THIS IS A STICKY BUSINESS!
YOU'RE SENIOR SPACE FLEET OFFICER THERE AND YOU MUST TAKE PERSONAL COMMAND—
YOU SEE, THIS IS AN EVACUATION THAT CAN'T SUCCEED!
WHAT'S THAT?
LIGHTNING!
LIGHTNING IN SPACE?!!
IMPOSSIBLE!
SIZZLING SATELLITES!
SOMEBODY'S BLOWN A FUSE!
CONTINUED

EAGLE-BRITAIN'S NATIONAL STRIP CARTOON WEEKLY

FOURPENCE-HALFPENNY
EVERY FRIDAY
EAGLE
30 NOVEMBER 1951 Vol. 2 No. 34
DAN DARE
THE RED MOON MYSTERY
SIZZLING SATELLITES! SOMEBODY'S BLOWN A FUSE.
AS DAN AND CO. RETURN TO THE SATELLITE AFTER AN UNSUCCESSFUL ATTEMPT TO REACH THE RED MOON A TERRIFIC FLASH OF LIGHTNING ENCIRCLES THE SPACE STATION.
FRANK HAMPSON AND HAROLD JOHNS
IT'S CRAZY — YOU CAN'T HAVE LIGHTNING IN A VACUUM!
NO — BUT ALL SPACE ISN'T A VACUUM, HANK — THIS SATELLITE'S BEEN ANCHORED OUT HERE FOR A YEAR...
THERE'S BEEN AIR LEAKING OUT OF IT ALL THE TIME — BOUND TO HAVE BEEN — AND GASES BEING DRIVEN OUT OF THE EXHAUST VALVE OF THE AIR CONDITIONING PLANT.
SHE'S SURROUNDED BY A 'CLOUD' OF AIR NOW! ENOUGH TO ALLOW A LOCAL DISPLAY OF LIGHTNING.
BUT WHAT'S CAUSED IT, MISS? — IT'S NEVER HAPPENED BEFORE!
NO, DIG, AND THAT THING HASN'T BEEN OUT THERE BEFORE — TEN TO ONE THE RED MOON'S AT THE BOTTOM OF IT.
THIS IS GETTING HOT — COME ON, FELLOWS — LET'S SEE WHAT DAN'S FOUND OUT ON THE BRIDGE!
ELEVA
MEANWHILE, ON EARTH, URGENT ORDERS ARE BEING FLASHED OUT FROM SPACE FLEET H.Q.
...TO THE SPACE TRAIN "MARYLAND" TWO DAYS OUT FROM MARS, BOUND FOR THE EARTH.
RIGHT, SIR — MESSAGE UNDERSTOOD. MARYLAND SIGNING OFF.
HEY, RED — TURN THE CRATE AROUND.
WHAT? RIGHT ROUND?

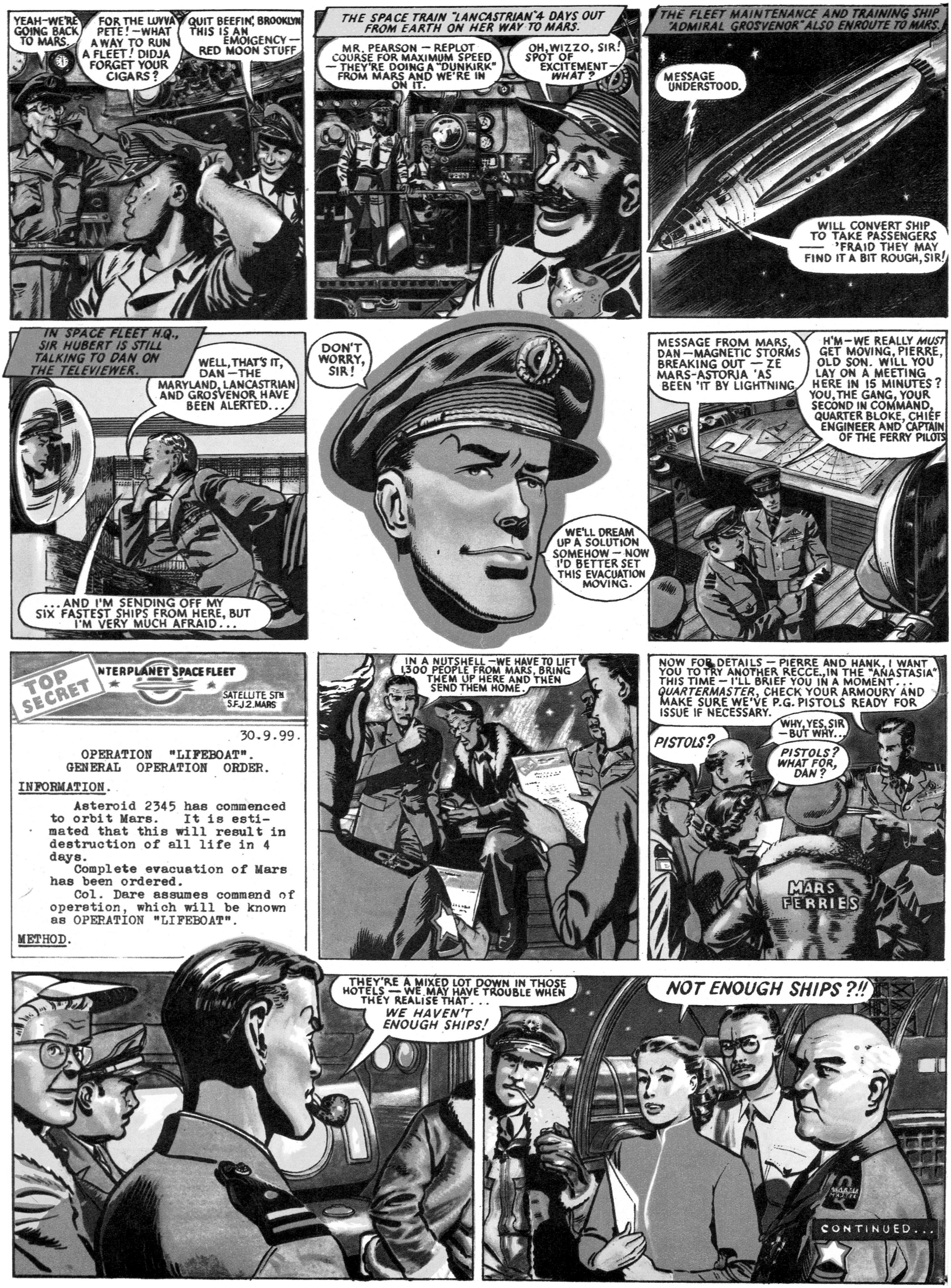

YEAH-WE'RE GOING BACK TO MARS.
FOR THE LUVVA PETE! —WHAT A WAY TO RUN A FLEET! DIDJA FORGET YOUR CIGARS?
QUIT BEEFIN', BROOKLYN THIS IS AN EMOIGENCY — RED MOON STUFF
THE SPACE TRAIN "LANCASTRIAN" 4 DAYS OUT FROM EARTH ON HER WAY TO MARS.
MR. PEARSON — REPLOT COURSE FOR MAXIMUM SPEED — THEY'RE DOING A "DUNKIRK" FROM MARS AND WE'RE IN ON IT.
OH, WIZZO, SIR! SPOT OF EXCITEMENT — WHAT?
THE FLEET MAINTENANCE AND TRAINING SHIP "ADMIRAL GROSVENOR" ALSO ENROUTE TO MARS.
MESSAGE UNDERSTOOD.
WILL CONVERT SHIP TO TAKE PASSENGERS — 'FRAID THEY MAY FIND IT A BIT ROUGH, SIR!
IN SPACE FLEET H.Q., SIR HUBERT IS STILL TALKING TO DAN ON THE TELEVIEWER.
WELL, THAT'S IT, DAN — THE MARYLAND, LANCASTRIAN AND GROSVENOR HAVE BEEN ALERTED...
...AND I'M SENDING OFF MY SIX FASTEST SHIPS FROM HERE, BUT I'M VERY MUCH AFRAID...
DON'T WORRY, SIR!
WE'LL DREAM UP A SOLUTION SOMEHOW — NOW I'D BETTER SET THIS EVACUATION MOVING.
MESSAGE FROM MARS, DAN — MAGNETIC STORMS BREAKING OUT — ZE MARS-ASTORIA 'AS BEEN 'IT BY LIGHTNING.
H'M — WE REALLY MUST GET MOVING, PIERRE, OLD SON. WILL YOU LAY ON A MEETING HERE IN 15 MINUTES? YOU, THE GANG, YOUR SECOND IN COMMAND, QUARTER BLOKE, CHIEF ENGINEER AND CAPTAIN OF THE FERRY PILOTS
TOP SECRET
NTERPLANET SPACE FLEET
SATELLITE STN S.F.J.2. MARS
30.9.99.
OPERATION "LIFEBOAT".
GENERAL OPERATION ORDER.
INFORMATION.
Asteroid 2345 has commenced to orbit Mars. It is estimated that this will result in destruction of all life in 4 days.
Complete evacuation of Mars has been ordered.
Col. Dare assumes command of operation, which will be known as OPERATION "LIFEBOAT".
METHOD.
IN A NUTSHELL — WE HAVE TO LIFT 1300 PEOPLE FROM MARS, BRING THEM UP HERE AND THEN SEND THEM HOME.
NOW FOR DETAILS — PIERRE AND HANK, I WANT YOU TO TRY ANOTHER RECCE. IN THE "ANASTASIA" THIS TIME — I'LL BRIEF YOU IN A MOMENT... QUARTERMASTER, CHECK YOUR ARMOURY AND MAKE SURE WE'VE P.G. PISTOLS READY FOR ISSUE IF NECESSARY.
PISTOLS?
WHY, YES, SIR — BUT WHY...
PISTOLS? WHAT FOR, DAN?
MARS FERRIES
THEY'RE A MIXED LOT DOWN IN THOSE HOTELS — WE MAY HAVE TROUBLE WHEN THEY REALISE THAT... WE HAVEN'T ENOUGH SHIPS!
NOT ENOUGH SHIPS?!!
CONTINUED...

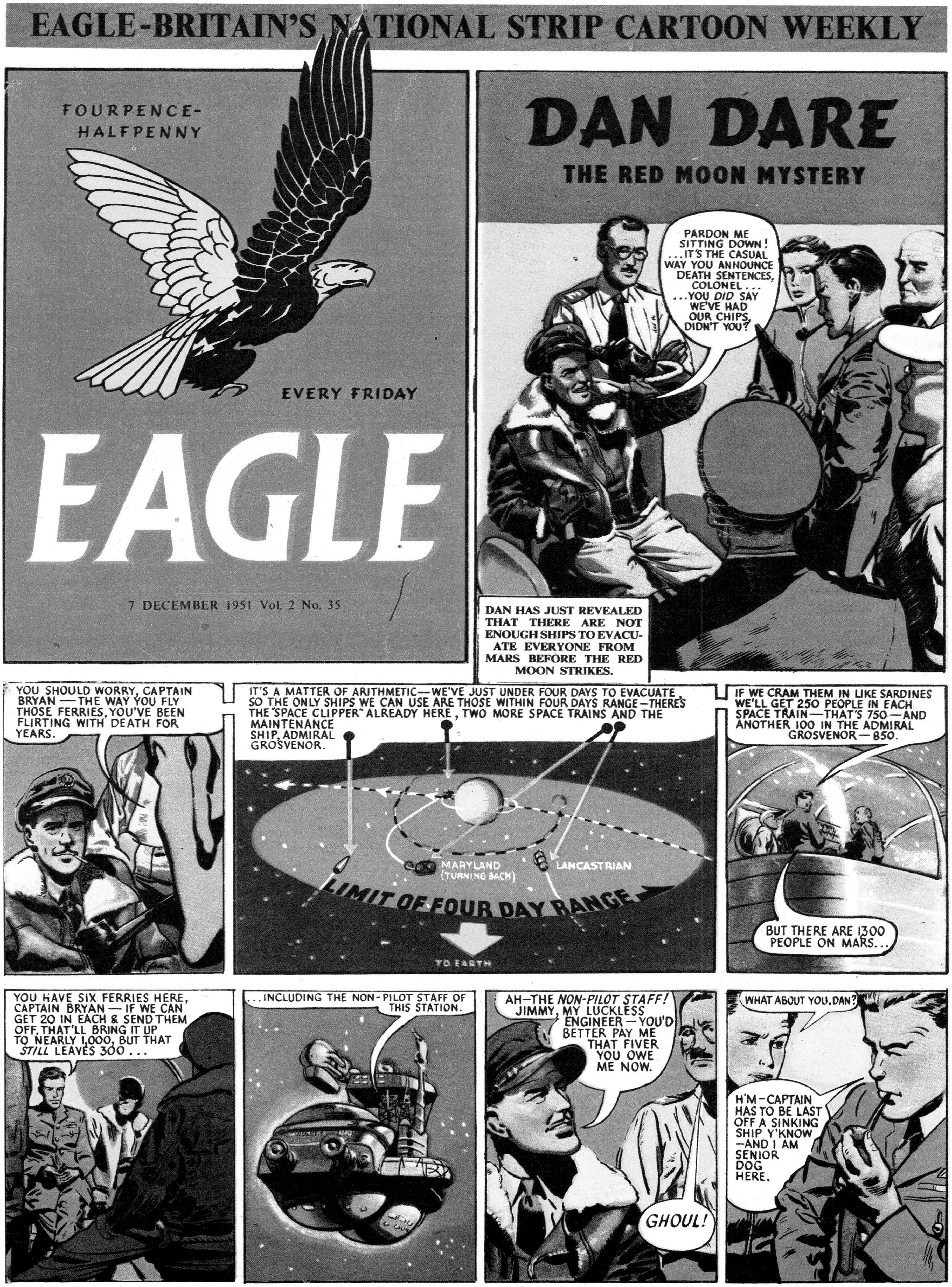
EAGLE-BRITAIN'S NATIONAL STRIP CARTOON WEEKLY
FOURPENCE-HALFPENNY
EVERY FRIDAY
EAGLE
7 DECEMBER 1951 Vol. 2 No. 35
DAN DARE
THE RED MOON MYSTERY
PARDON ME SITTING DOWN! ...IT'S THE CASUAL WAY YOU ANNOUNCE DEATH SENTENCES, COLONEL... ...YOU DID SAY WE'VE HAD OUR CHIPS, DIDN'T YOU?
DAN HAS JUST REVEALED THAT THERE ARE NOT ENOUGH SHIPS TO EVACUATE EVERYONE FROM MARS BEFORE THE RED MOON STRIKES.
YOU SHOULD WORRY, CAPTAIN BRYAN — THE WAY YOU FLY THOSE FERRIES, YOU'VE BEEN FLIRTING WITH DEATH FOR YEARS.
IT'S A MATTER OF ARITHMETIC — WE'VE JUST UNDER FOUR DAYS TO EVACUATE, SO THE ONLY SHIPS WE CAN USE ARE THOSE WITHIN FOUR DAYS RANGE — THERE'S THE "SPACE CLIPPER" ALREADY HERE, TWO MORE SPACE TRAINS AND THE MAINTENANCE SHIP, ADMIRAL GROSVENOR.
MARYLAND (TURNING BACK)
LANCASTRIAN
LIMIT OF FOUR DAY RANGE
TO EARTH
IF WE CRAM THEM IN LIKE SARDINES WE'LL GET 250 PEOPLE IN EACH SPACE TRAIN — THAT'S 750 — AND ANOTHER 100 IN THE ADMIRAL GROSVENOR — 850.
BUT THERE ARE 1300 PEOPLE ON MARS...
YOU HAVE SIX FERRIES HERE, CAPTAIN BRYAN — IF WE CAN GET 20 IN EACH & SEND THEM OFF, THAT'LL BRING IT UP TO NEARLY 1,000, BUT THAT STILL LEAVES 300...
...INCLUDING THE NON-PILOT STAFF OF THIS STATION.
AH — THE NON-PILOT STAFF! JIMMY, MY LUCKLESS ENGINEER — YOU'D BETTER PAY ME THAT FIVER YOU OWE ME NOW.
GHOUL!
WHAT ABOUT YOU, DAN?
H'M — CAPTAIN HAS TO BE LAST OFF A SINKING SHIP Y'KNOW — AND I AM SENIOR DOG HERE.

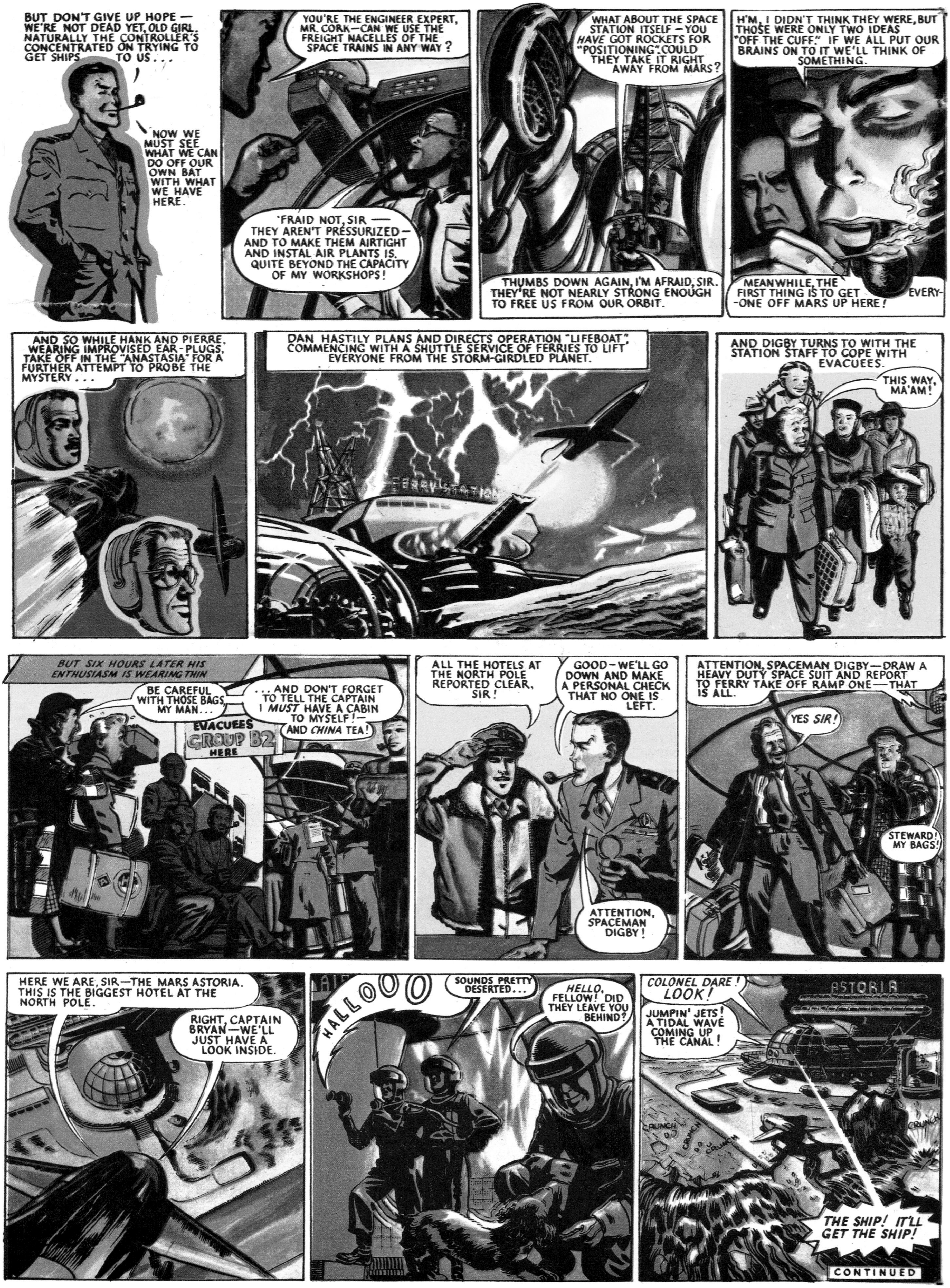

BUT DON'T GIVE UP HOPE — WE'RE NOT DEAD YET, OLD GIRL. NATURALLY THE CONTROLLER'S CONCENTRATED ON TRYING TO GET SHIPS TO US . . .
NOW WE MUST SEE WHAT WE CAN DO OFF OUR OWN BAT WITH WHAT WE HAVE HERE.
YOU'RE THE ENGINEER EXPERT, MR. CORK — CAN WE USE THE FREIGHT NACELLES OF THE SPACE TRAINS IN ANY WAY ?
'FRAID NOT, SIR — THEY AREN'T PRESSURIZED — AND TO MAKE THEM AIRTIGHT AND INSTAL AIR PLANTS IS, QUITE BEYOND THE CAPACITY OF MY WORKSHOPS!
WHAT ABOUT THE SPACE STATION ITSELF — YOU *HAVE* GOT ROCKETS FOR "POSITIONING". COULD THEY TAKE IT RIGHT AWAY FROM MARS?
THUMBS DOWN AGAIN, I'M AFRAID, SIR. THEY'RE NOT NEARLY STRONG ENOUGH TO FREE US FROM OUR ORBIT.
H'M, I DIDN'T THINK THEY WERE, BUT THOSE WERE ONLY TWO IDEAS "OFF THE CUFF." IF WE ALL PUT OUR BRAINS ON TO IT WE'LL THINK OF SOMETHING.
MEANWHILE, THE FIRST THING IS TO GET EVERY-ONE OFF MARS UP HERE!
AND SO WHILE HANK AND PIERRE, WEARING IMPROVISED EAR-PLUGS, TAKE OFF IN THE "ANASTASIA" FOR A FURTHER ATTEMPT TO PROBE THE MYSTERY . . .
DAN HASTILY PLANS AND DIRECTS OPERATION "LIFEBOAT", COMMENCING WITH A SHUTTLE SERVICE OF FERRIES TO LIFT EVERYONE FROM THE STORM-GIRDLED PLANET.
FERRY STATION
AND DIGBY TURNS TO WITH THE STATION STAFF TO COPE WITH EVACUEES.
THIS WAY, MA'AM!
BUT SIX HOURS LATER HIS ENTHUSIASM IS WEARING THIN
BE CAREFUL WITH THOSE BAGS, MY MAN . . .
. . . AND DON'T FORGET TO TELL THE CAPTAIN I *MUST* HAVE A CABIN TO MYSELF! — AND *CHINA* TEA!
EVACUEES GROUP B2 HERE
ALL THE HOTELS AT THE NORTH POLE REPORTED CLEAR, SIR!
GOOD — WE'LL GO DOWN AND MAKE A PERSONAL CHECK THAT NO ONE IS LEFT.
ATTENTION, SPACEMAN DIGBY!
ATTENTION, SPACEMAN DIGBY — DRAW A HEAVY DUTY SPACE SUIT AND REPORT TO FERRY TAKE OFF RAMP ONE — THAT IS ALL.
YES *SIR*!
STEWARD! MY BAGS!
HERE WE ARE, SIR — THE MARS ASTORIA. THIS IS THE BIGGEST HOTEL AT THE NORTH POLE.
RIGHT, CAPTAIN BRYAN — WE'LL JUST HAVE A LOOK INSIDE.
HALLOOOO
SOUNDS PRETTY DESERTED . . .
HELLO, FELLOW! DID THEY LEAVE YOU BEHIND?
COLONEL DARE! *LOOK!*
JUMPIN' JETS! A TIDAL WAVE COMING UP THE CANAL!
ASTORIA
CRUNCH
CRUNCH
CRUNCH
CRUNCH
THE SHIP! IT'LL GET THE SHIP!
CONTINUED

EAGLE-BRITAIN'S NATIONAL STRIP CARTOON WEEKLY

FOURPENCE-
HALFPENNY
EVERY FRIDAY
EAGLE
14 DECEMBER 1951 Vol. 2 No. 36
DAN DARE
THE RED MOON MYSTERY
QUICK! GET TO THE SHIP!
DAN, DIG AND CAPTAIN BRYAN ARE IN THE DESERTED MARS-ASTORIA HOTEL WHEN A TIDAL WAVE ROARS DOWN ON THEIR WAITING SPACEFERRY OUTSIDE
WE CAN'T, SIR — WE'LL NEVER GET THROUGH THE AIR LOCK IN TIME!
BLOW THE AIRLOCK! WE DON'T NEED IT NOW! STAND CLEAR, CHAPS!
HERE'S WHERE WE MAKE OUR OWN EXIT.
DAN USES THE FLAME PROJECTOR WHICH IS IN EVERY HEAVY DUTY SPACE KIT
BUT AS THE FLAME BLASTS A HOLE, THE PRESSURIZED AIR ESCAPES INTO THE RARER MARS ATMOSPHERE AND THE HOTEL BURSTS LIKE A BALLOON.
BOOM

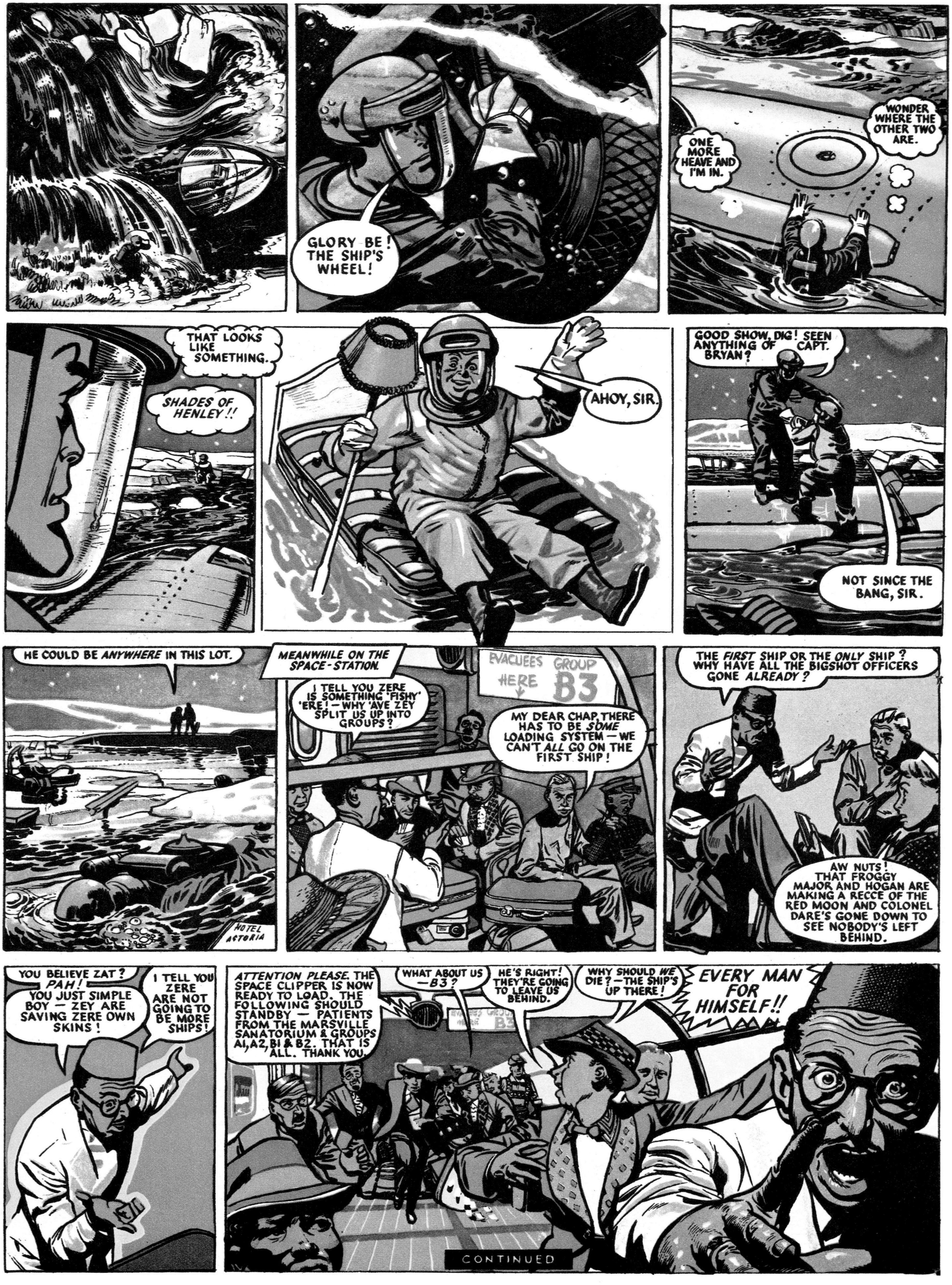
GLORY BE! THE SHIP'S WHEEL!
ONE MORE HEAVE AND I'M IN.
WONDER WHERE THE OTHER TWO ARE.
THAT LOOKS LIKE SOMETHING.
SHADES OF HENLEY!!
AHOY, SIR.
GOOD SHOW, DIG! SEEN ANYTHING OF CAPT. BRYAN?
NOT SINCE THE BANG, SIR.
HE COULD BE ANYWHERE IN THIS LOT.
HOTEL ASTORIA
MEANWHILE ON THE SPACE-STATION.
EVACUEES GROUP HERE B3
I TELL YOU ZERE IS SOMETHING 'FISHY' 'ERE! — WHY 'AVE ZEY SPLIT US UP INTO GROUPS?
MY DEAR CHAP, THERE HAS TO BE SOME LOADING SYSTEM — WE CAN'T ALL GO ON THE FIRST SHIP!
THE FIRST SHIP OR THE ONLY SHIP? WHY HAVE ALL THE BIGSHOT OFFICERS GONE ALREADY?
AW NUTS! THAT FROGGY MAJOR AND HOGAN ARE MAKING A RECCE OF THE RED MOON AND COLONEL DARE'S GONE DOWN TO SEE NOBODY'S LEFT BEHIND.
YOU BELIEVE ZAT? PAH! YOU JUST SIMPLE BOY — ZEY ARE SAVING ZERE OWN SKINS!
I TELL YOU ZERE ARE NOT GOING TO BE MORE SHIPS!
ATTENTION PLEASE. THE SPACE CLIPPER IS NOW READY TO LOAD. THE FOLLOWING SHOULD STANDBY — PATIENTS FROM THE MARSVILLE SANATORIUM & GROUPS A1, A2, B1 & B2. THAT IS ALL. THANK YOU.
WHAT ABOUT US —B3?
HE'S RIGHT! THEY'RE GOING TO LEAVE US BEHIND.
WHY SHOULD WE DIE? — THE SHIP'S UP THERE!
EVERY MAN FOR HIMSELF!!
CONTINUED

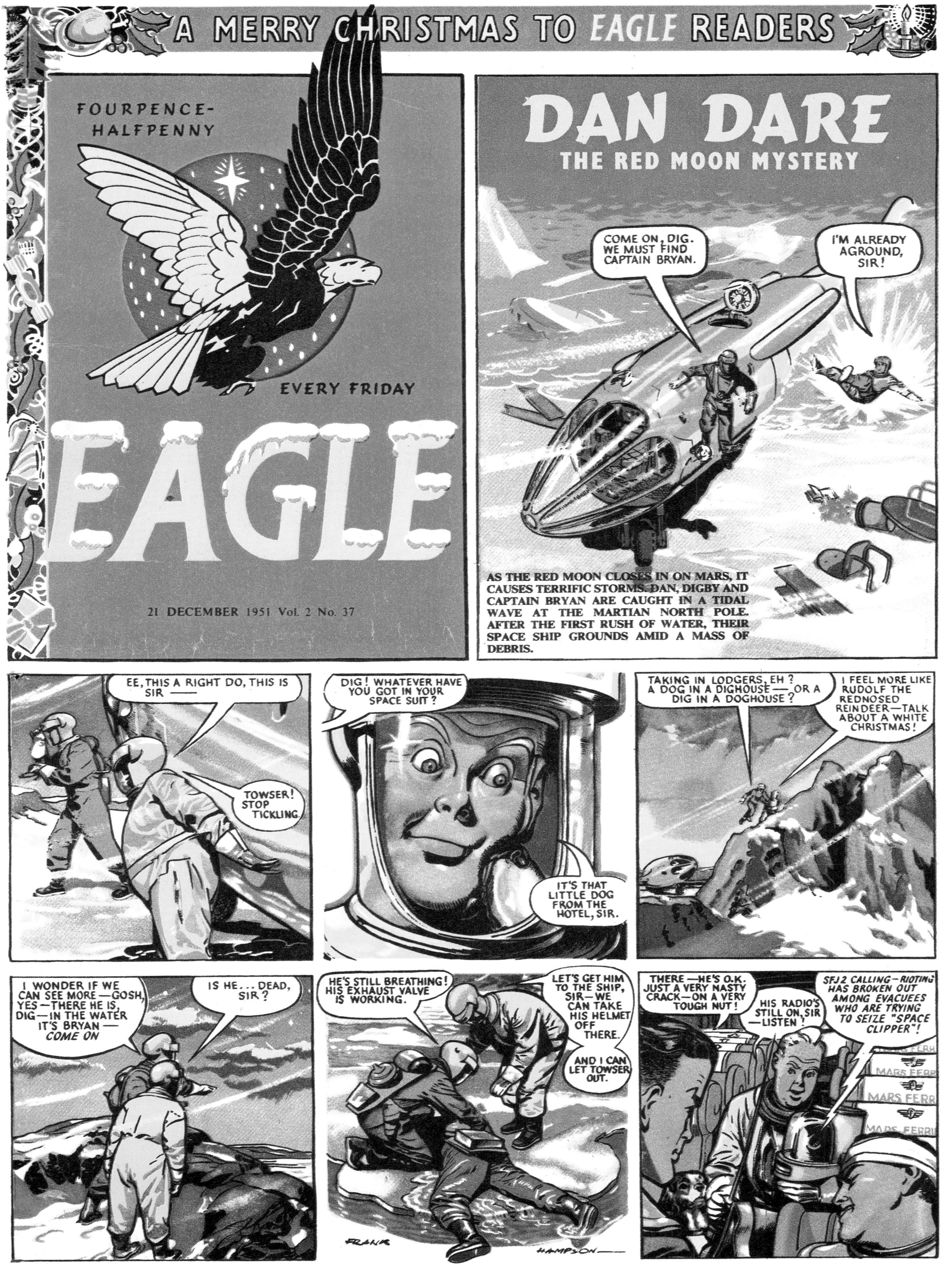

A MERRY CHRISTMAS TO EAGLE READERS
FOURPENCE-HALFPENNY
EVERY FRIDAY
EAGLE
21 DECEMBER 1951 Vol. 2 No. 37
DAN DARE
THE RED MOON MYSTERY
COME ON, DIG. WE MUST FIND CAPTAIN BRYAN.
I'M ALREADY AGROUND, SIR!
AS THE RED MOON CLOSES IN ON MARS, IT CAUSES TERRIFIC STORMS. DAN, DIGBY AND CAPTAIN BRYAN ARE CAUGHT IN A TIDAL WAVE AT THE MARTIAN NORTH POLE. AFTER THE FIRST RUSH OF WATER, THEIR SPACE SHIP GROUNDS AMID A MASS OF DEBRIS.
EE, THIS A RIGHT DO, THIS IS SIR ——
TOWSER! STOP TICKLING.
DIG! WHATEVER HAVE YOU GOT IN YOUR SPACE SUIT?
IT'S THAT LITTLE DOG FROM THE HOTEL, SIR.
TAKING IN LODGERS, EH? A DOG IN A DIGHOUSE — OR A DIG IN A DOGHOUSE?
I FEEL MORE LIKE RUDOLF THE REDNOSED REINDEER—TALK ABOUT A WHITE CHRISTMAS!
I WONDER IF WE CAN SEE MORE —GOSH, YES—THERE HE IS, DIG—IN THE WATER IT'S BRYAN — COME ON
IS HE... DEAD, SIR?
HE'S STILL BREATHING! HIS EXHAUST VALVE IS WORKING.
LET'S GET HIM TO THE SHIP, SIR—WE CAN TAKE HIS HELMET OFF THERE.
AND I CAN LET TOWSER OUT.
FRANK HAMPSON
THERE —HE'S O.K. JUST A VERY NASTY CRACK—ON A VERY TOUGH NUT!
HIS RADIO'S STILL ON, SIR —LISTEN!
SFJ2 CALLING—RIOTING HAS BROKEN OUT AMONG EVACUEES WHO ARE TRYING TO SEIZE "SPACE CLIPPER"!
MARS FERR
MARS FERR
MARS FERRI

RIOTS! COME ON, DIG — UP AND OUT.
WE'VE GOT TO GET THIS CRATE FLYING AGAIN.
AIR LOCK EMERGENCY ONLY
I WASN'T EXPECTING TROUBLE YET.
THAT THING'S BEATING US ALL ENDS UP SO FAR...
WE MUST GET ON TOP OF IT SOMEHOW.
AT SPACE STATION SFJ 2
WHAT'S HAPPENING?
THE SPACE FLEET OFFICERS HAVE RUN OUT.
THERE AREN'T GOING TO BE ANY MORE RESCUE SHIPS.
IT'S EVERY MAN FOR HIMSELF.
THE RATS!
WE'RE GOING TO SEIZE THE "SPACE-CLIPPER!"
LIFT TO DEEP SPACE TRAINS
OH, ARE YOU?
CHIEF ENGINEER
STOP, YOU IDIOTS — THERE ARE THREE MORE SHIPS COMING FOR YOU! — STOP — OR I'LL SHOOT
HE'S GOT A GUN!
IT'S A PARALYSING PISTOL!
RUSH HIM!!
RUSH HIM! HE CAN'T GET MORE THAN TWO OF US.
LIFT TO DEEP SPACE TRAINS
DOWN UP
ZAT'S ENOUGH! ZE LIFT IS FULL. WE SEND 'ER BACK FOR ZE OZZERS. NOW WE GO UP — AN' NO FUNNY SPACE FLEET TRICKS!
LIFTMAN
LISTEN, EVERY-BODY — WHEN WE GET TO ZE TOP MAKE ONE RUSH FOR ZE "SPACE CLIPPER!"...
...AN' CAPTURE ZE CONTROL BRIDGE — ZEN WE WILL GIVE ZE ORDERS!
YEAH — WE'LL SHOW THESE SPACE FLEET RATS!
DRESSED UP OFFICERS — PAH!
SAVING THEIR OWN DIRTY SKINS
AN' PITY 'ELP ANYONE WHO GETS IN MY WAY!
WE ARE ZERE — OPEN ZE DOORS AND...
MARS
LOADING GANGWAY No 1 SPACE CLIPPER FOR EARTH
HELP!
HELP!
HELP! PUT ME DOWN!
CONTINUED

EAGLE-BRITAIN'S NATIONAL STRIP CARTOON WEEKLY

FOURPENCE-HALFPENNY

EVERY FRIDAY

EAGLE

28 DECEMBER 1951 Vol. 2 No. 38

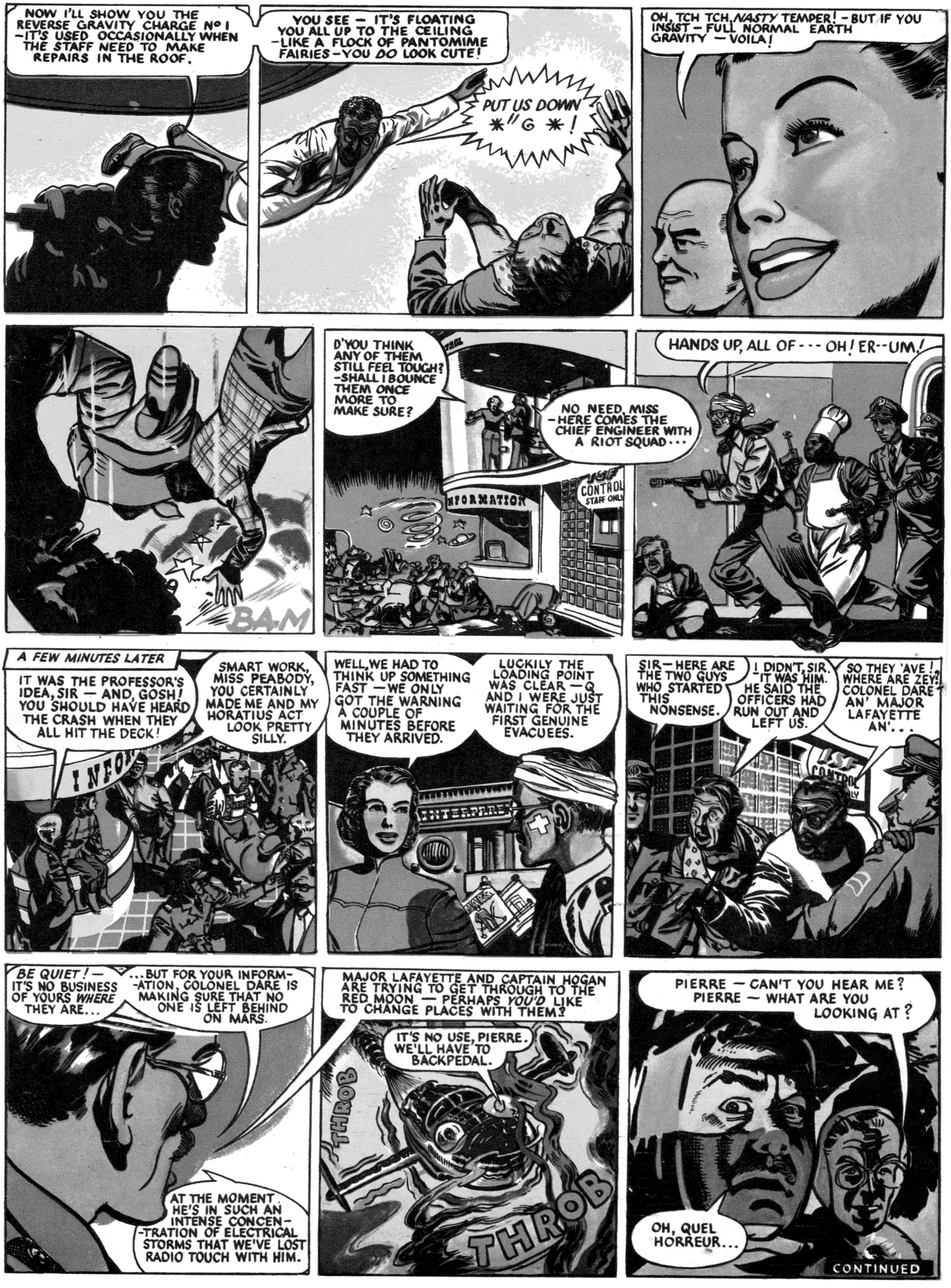
NOW I'LL SHOW YOU THE REVERSE GRAVITY CHARGE Nº 1 –IT'S USED OCCASIONALLY WHEN THE STAFF NEED TO MAKE REPAIRS IN THE ROOF.
YOU SEE — IT'S FLOATING YOU ALL UP TO THE CEILING –LIKE A FLOCK OF PANTOMIME FAIRIES—YOU *DO* LOOK CUTE!
PUT US DOWN *"G*!
OH, TCH TCH, *NASTY* TEMPER! – BUT IF YOU INSIST – FULL NORMAL EARTH GRAVITY — VOILA!
BAM
D'YOU THINK ANY OF THEM STILL FEEL TOUGH? –SHALL I BOUNCE THEM ONCE MORE TO MAKE SURE?
NO NEED, MISS –HERE COMES THE CHIEF ENGINEER WITH A RIOT SQUAD...
INFORMATION
CONTROL STAFF ONLY
HANDS UP, ALL OF --- OH! ER--UM!
A FEW MINUTES LATER
IT WAS THE PROFESSOR'S IDEA, SIR — AND, GOSH! YOU SHOULD HAVE HEARD THE CRASH WHEN THEY ALL HIT THE DECK!
SMART WORK, MISS PEABODY, YOU CERTAINLY MADE ME AND MY HORATIUS ACT LOOK PRETTY SILLY.
WELL, WE HAD TO THINK UP SOMETHING FAST — WE ONLY GOT THE WARNING A COUPLE OF MINUTES BEFORE THEY ARRIVED.
LUCKILY THE LOADING POINT WAS CLEAR — Q AND I WERE JUST WAITING FOR THE FIRST GENUINE EVACUEES.
SIR — HERE ARE THE TWO GUYS WHO STARTED THIS NONSENSE.
I DIDN'T, SIR. –IT WAS HIM. HE SAID THE OFFICERS HAD RUN OUT AND LEFT US.
SO THEY 'AVE! WHERE ARE ZEY? COLONEL DARE AN' MAJOR LAFAYETTE AN'...
BE QUIET! — IT'S NO BUSINESS OF YOURS *WHERE* THEY ARE...
...BUT FOR YOUR INFORM- -ATION, COLONEL DARE IS MAKING SURE THAT NO ONE IS LEFT BEHIND ON MARS.
AT THE MOMENT HE'S IN SUCH AN INTENSE CONCEN- -TRATION OF ELECTRICAL STORMS THAT WE'VE LOST RADIO TOUCH WITH HIM.
MAJOR LAFAYETTE AND CAPTAIN HOGAN ARE TRYING TO GET THROUGH TO THE RED MOON — PERHAPS *YOU'D* LIKE TO CHANGE PLACES WITH THEM?
IT'S NO USE, PIERRE. WE'LL HAVE TO BACKPEDAL.
THROB
THROB
THROB
PIERRE — CAN'T YOU HEAR ME? PIERRE — WHAT ARE YOU LOOKING AT?
OH, QUEL HORREUR...
CONTINUED

EAGLE-BRITAIN'S NATIONAL STRIP CARTOON WEEKLY

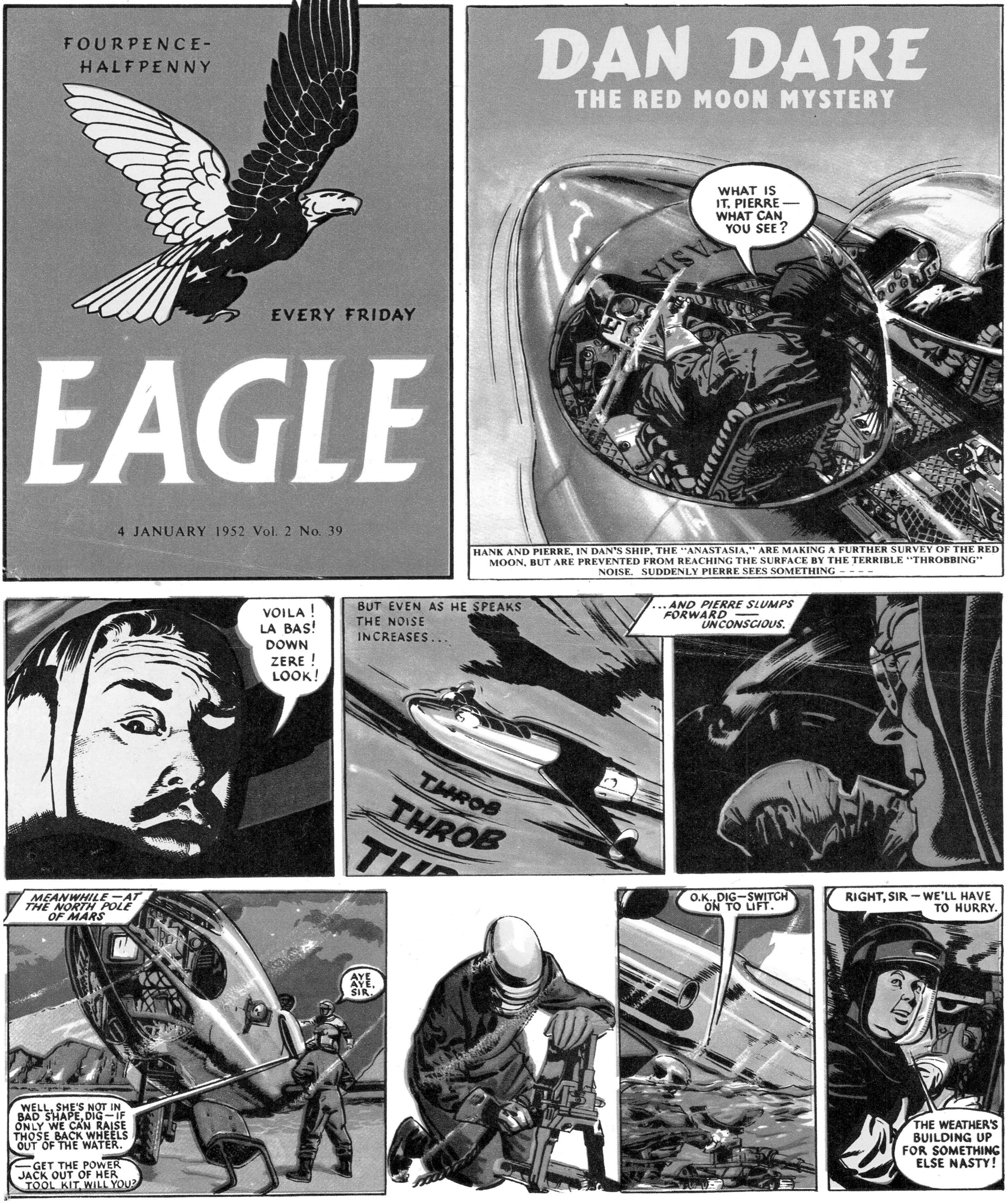
FOURPENCE-HALFPENNY
EVERY FRIDAY
EAGLE
4 JANUARY 1952 Vol. 2 No. 39
DAN DARE
THE RED MOON MYSTERY
WHAT IS IT, PIERRE — WHAT CAN YOU SEE?
HANK AND PIERRE, IN DAN'S SHIP, THE "ANASTASIA," ARE MAKING A FURTHER SURVEY OF THE RED MOON, BUT ARE PREVENTED FROM REACHING THE SURFACE BY THE TERRIBLE "THROBBING" NOISE. SUDDENLY PIERRE SEES SOMETHING - - - -
VOILA! LA BAS! DOWN ZERE! LOOK!
BUT EVEN AS HE SPEAKS THE NOISE INCREASES...
THROB
THROB
...AND PIERRE SLUMPS FORWARD — UNCONSCIOUS.
MEANWHILE — AT THE NORTH POLE OF MARS
AYE AYE, SIR.
WELL, SHE'S NOT IN BAD SHAPE, DIG — IF ONLY WE CAN RAISE THOSE BACK WHEELS OUT OF THE WATER.
— GET THE POWER JACK OUT OF HER TOOL KIT, WILL YOU?
O.K., DIG — SWITCH ON TO LIFT.
RIGHT, SIR — WE'LL HAVE TO HURRY.
THE WEATHER'S BUILDING UP FOR SOMETHING ELSE NASTY!

AS IF TIDAL WAVES AREN'T ENOUGH!
TIDAL WAVES ARE ONLY THE FIRST SHOT IN THE RED MOON'S LOCKER, DIG.
THERE'S A LOT WORSE IN STORE FOR US — IF UNCLE IVOR'S RIGHT...
... AND THE OLD BOY NEARLY ALWAYS IS RIGHT.
SHE'S HIGH ENOUGH NOW — STAND BY TO ROLL!
THE JACK IS OPERATED BY BY-PASSING THE FERRY'S AUXILIARY POWER UNIT. BALANCE IS KEPT BY GYRO POINTS IN EACH LEG.
WE SHOULD BE ABLE TO RISK A TAKE OFF NOW, DIG.
WAIT A MINUTE, SIR — LISTEN!
THE SHIP—IT'S VERY FAINT BUT YOU CAN JUST HEAR IT —
IT'S THROBBING
THROBBING — THE "KILLING NOISE"! — COME ON, DIG — WE'VE GOT TO BURN SPACE BACK TO THE SATELLITE...
SEE IF YOU CAN GET SFJ2 ON THE RADIO, DIG.
SIR! — I CAN'T GET THE SPACE STATION, BUT I'M RECEIVING MR. HANK CALLING ON THE EMERGENCY WAVEBAND.
HELLO, HANK — CAN YOU HEAR ME? — WHAT'S HAPPENED? — HAVE YOU MANAGED TO LAND ON THE RED MOON?
DAN?—OH SWELL—I CAN'T GET THE SATELLITE
YOUR HUNCH ABOUT "ANASTASIA" WAS RIGHT. SHE'S NOT AFFECTED BY THE MAGNETIC PULL — BUT I STILL CAN'T DO MUCH BECAUSE OF THIS NOISE — IT'S BUILDING UP TERRIFICALLY NOW...
WE GOT WITHIN 10 MILES OF THE SURFACE, BUT THE RACKET WAS UNBEARABLE. PIERRE'S OUT COLD AND I NEARLY PASSED OUT. I HAD TO TURN BACK
... I DIDN'T SEE MUCH FOR THE DUST — BUT, DAN — THERE'S SOMETHING MOVING DOWN THERE NOW...
...THERE ARE LIGHTS FLASHING THROUGH THE DUST AND ON THE RADAR SCANNER. THE WHOLE SURFACE OF THE 'RED MOON' IS CRAWLING WITH LIFE...
THE POT'S A-BOILING, DAN.
CONTINUED

EAGLE-BRITAIN'S NATIONAL STRIP CARTOON WEEKLY

FOURPENCE-HALFPENNY
EVERY FRIDAY
EAGLE
11 JANUARY 1952 Vol. 2 No. 40
DAN DARE
THE RED MOON MYSTERY
LANCASTRIAN
GOSH, SIR —IT'S LIKE CLAPHAM JUNCTION.
AS DAN AND DIGBY RETURN TO SPACE STATION SFJ2 FROM THE NORTH POLE OF MARS, THEY FIND THAT "OPERATION LIFEBOAT" - THE EVACUATION OF MARS, IN FACE OF A THREATENED ATTACK BY THE RED MOON - IS IN FULL SWING.
YES — WE'RE BEGINNING TO GET SOME ACTION — THE LANCASTRIAN'S HERE SO THE MARYLAND CAN'T BE FAR BEHIND — THAT LINE OF FERRIES MUST BE THE LAST EVACUEES FROM THE SOUTH POLE...
AND...OH, GOODO — THERE'S HANK STREAK-ING IN WITH THE 'ANASTASIA'
TAKE OVER, DIG — AND JOIN THE QUEUE FOR THE FERRY AIRLOCK — I'M GOING STRAIGHT IN TO SEE WHAT HAPPENED TO THAT RIOT THEY REPORTED — AND CONTACT HANK...
HELLO, JIMMY — WHERE'S YOUR RIOT ?
DAN! — RIOT ? — OH MISS PEABODY TOOK CARE OF THAT — AFTER IT HAD TRAMPLED OVER ME !!
MISS PEABODY? — HOW...? NEVER MIND — IT CAN WAIT — I SEE THE 'ANASTASIA'S' THROUGH THE AIRLOCK — IS PIERRE ALL RIGHT ?
TWO MINUTES AGO — WE'RE TRYING TO GET PIERRE OUT OF HER NOW — HE'S IN A PRETTY BAD WAY — UNCONSCIOUS AND BLEEDING FROM BOTH EARS
ANASTASIA
HAS HE SAID ANYTHING, HANK?
'LO, DAN — NOPE, HE'S BEEN OUT COLD ALL THE WAY HOME — BUT HE SURE SAW SOMETHING — YOU SHOULD HAVE SEEN HIS FACE!

PUT HIM STRAIGHT IN THE SICK BAY ON THE "SPACE CLIPPER" — AND DETAIL SOMEONE TO TRY AND FIND OUT WHAT HE SAW THE MINUTE HE COMES ROUND...
HANK! GO AND REPORT OVER THE VIEWER TO SIR HUBERT.
JIMMY—HOW'S THE EVACUATION GOING?
WE'VE GOT EVERYBODY FROM MARS UP HERE NOW...
...EXCEPT A VOLUNTEER CREW WORKING THE IMPULSE RELAY STATION — AND YOUR STUBBORN OLD UNCLE IVOR — THAT EMINENT ARCHÆOLOGIST IS STILL DOWN AT THE RUINS OF EMPEROR DORTAN'S PALACE...
...LOOKING FOR THE BOX THAT HE SWEARS WILL GIVE US THE ANSWER TO THE RED MOON...
I MUSTN'T FAIL — I CAN'T FAIL — IVOR DARE NEVER FAILS! —
AND I AM THE ONLY MAN WHO CAN SAVE THE EARTH FROM THE RED MOON
IN THE 200,000 YEAR OLD RUINS
BUT TIME, TIME, TIME IS RACING AWAY — AND THE NEXT TIME THE RED MOON PASSES OVERHEAD WILL BE THE END OF IVOR DARE.
D'YOU HEAR, DORTAN? THE RED MOON IS HERE AGAIN.
YOU KNOW, DORTAN — YOU KNOW WHAT IT IS THAT COMES OUT OF THE RED MOON.
WHAT COMES AFTER THE STORMS AND THE NOISE — AND SWEEPS WHOLE WORLDS AWAY?
TELL ME — SHOW ME IN TIME — WHERE IS YOUR BOX?
OH, WHAT'S THE USE OF TALKING TO THE STATUE OF A DEAD EMPEROR! — PULL YOURSELF TOGETHER, IVOR DARE — DRAMATIC REVELATIONS ONLY HAPPEN IN BOOKS AND FILMS.
AS IVOR RESUMES HIS SEARCH, THE RED MOON, ON ITS THIRD ORBIT OF MARS LOOMS LARGER IN THE SKY...
AND SOON...
IT'S NO USE!
IT'S NO USE — THIS IS THE END — THE NOISE! THE NOISE IS STARTING AND...
THROB THROB
AS THE THROBBING COMMENCES, THERE IS A VIOLENT TUG ON IVOR'S MECHANICAL SPADE...
MY TOOLS — THEY'RE... IT'S MAGNETISM — THE RED MOON IS DRAWING THEM UP TO IT! MY STARS! — WHAT MAGNETISM!
ALL RIGHT! ALL RIGHT! YOU'VE WON, YOU MURDERING, RED...
WHAT'S THAT?
KNOCK! KNOCK! KNOCK!
CONTINUED

EAGLE-BRITAIN'S NATIONAL STRIP CARTOON WEEKLY

FOURPENCE-HALFPENNY

EVERY FRIDAY

EAGLE

18 JANUARY 1952 Vol. 2 No. 41

DAN DARE
THE RED MOON MYSTERY
I'M GOING CRAZY!
KNOCK KNOCK! KNOCK
IT'S SOMEONE KNOCKING!
FOR NEW READERS –
ALTHOUGH EVERYONE ELSE ON MARS HAS BEEN EVACUATED TO THE SATELLITE SPACE STATION BECAUSE OF AN IMPENDING ATTACK BY THE MYSTERIOUS RED MOON, IVOR DARE, DAN'S UNCLE, HAS STAYED IN THE RUINS OF DORTAN'S PALACE SEARCHING FOR A BOX WHICH WILL REVEAL THE RED MOON'S SECRETS . . . AS HE DIGS, THE TERRIFIC MAGNETISM OF THE RED MOON DRAWS UP ALL THE METALLIC OBJECTS TO IT – AND THEN . .
BUT IT CAN'T BE—THERE'S ONLY ME HERE!
NO – I'VE GOT IT...
...THERE'S A METAL OBJECT BURIED UNDER THE THRONE — AND THE MAGNETISM IS PULLING IT UP AND MAKING IT KNOCK ON THE STONES
THE BOX — IT MUST BE — IT HAS TO BE — DORTAN'S BOX — HA, HA WE'LL BEAT YOU YET.
DORTAN AND IVOR DARE WILL BEAT YOU YET, MY RED FRIEND.
THERE MUST BE A SECRET MECHANISM H'M ... PERHAPS THIS CARVING...
YES, BY THE STARS! — IT'S ... BEGINNING TO MOVE — IT'S SWIVELLING...
CLICK
THERE'S THE HOLE ALL RIGHT.
NOW THE BOX SHOULD COME UP...
AH! THERE YOU ARE, MY BEAUTY. OH, NO, YOU DON'T . . .
I WAS A CARDIFF THREEQUARTER IN '59.

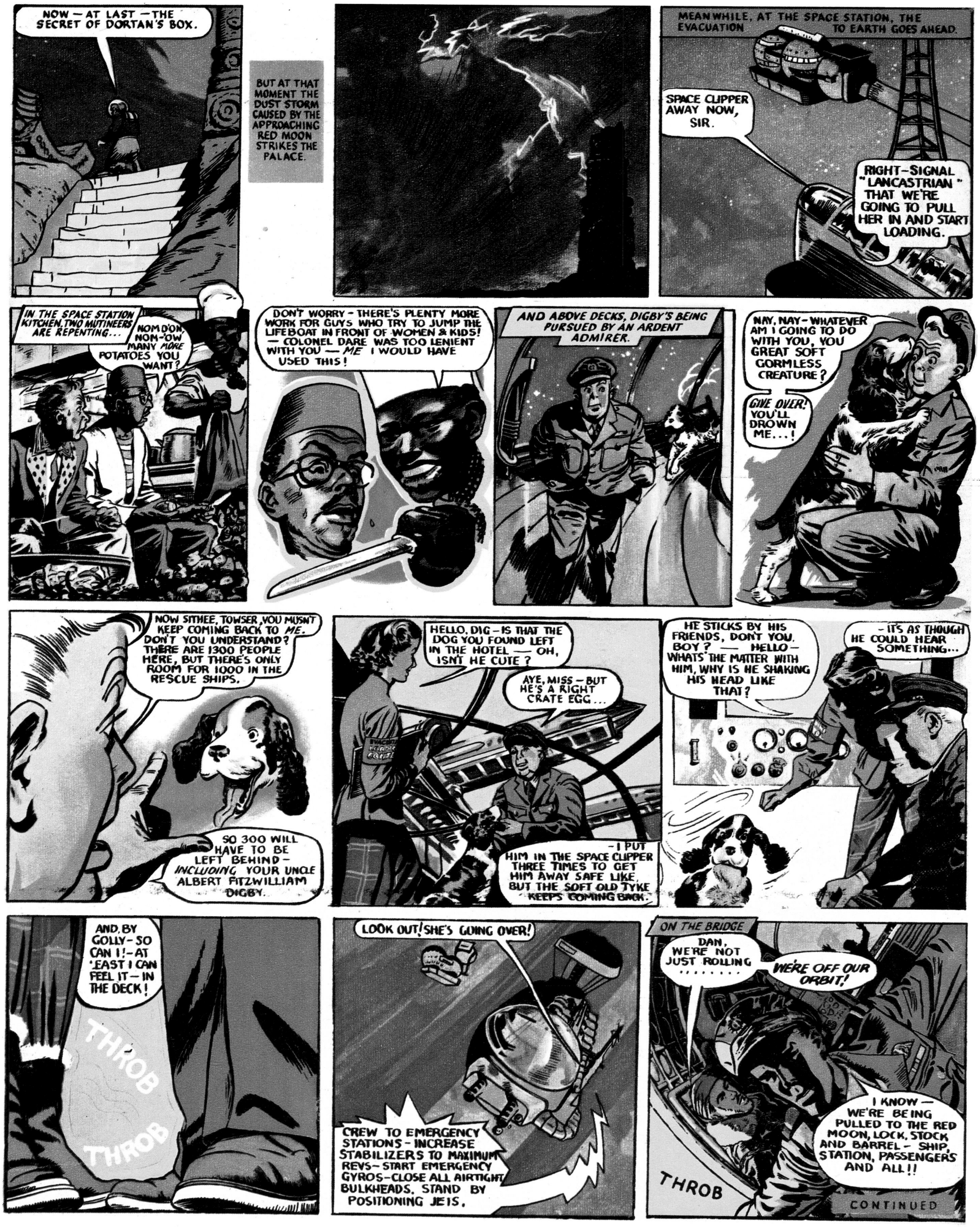
NOW — AT LAST — THE SECRET OF DORTAN'S BOX.
BUT AT THAT MOMENT THE DUST STORM CAUSED BY THE APPROACHING RED MOON STRIKES THE PALACE.
MEANWHILE, AT THE SPACE STATION, THE EVACUATION TO EARTH GOES AHEAD.
SPACE CLIPPER AWAY NOW, SIR.
RIGHT — SIGNAL "LANCASTRIAN" THAT WE'RE GOING TO PULL HER IN AND START LOADING.
IN THE SPACE STATION KITCHEN, TWO MUTINEERS ARE REPENTING...
NOM D'ON, NOM-OW MANY MORE POTATOES YOU WANT?
DON'T WORRY - THERE'S PLENTY MORE WORK FOR GUYS WHO TRY TO JUMP THE LIFEBOAT IN FRONT OF WOMEN & KIDS! — COLONEL DARE WAS TOO LENIENT WITH YOU — ME I WOULD HAVE USED THIS!
AND ABOVE DECKS, DIGBY'S BEING PURSUED BY AN ARDENT ADMIRER.
NAY, NAY - WHATEVER AM I GOING TO DO WITH YOU, YOU GREAT SOFT GORMLESS CREATURE?
GIVE OVER! YOU'LL DROWN ME...!
NOW SITHEE, TOWSER, YOU MUSN'T KEEP COMING BACK TO ME. DON'T YOU UNDERSTAND? THERE ARE 1300 PEOPLE HERE, BUT THERE'S ONLY ROOM FOR 1000 IN THE RESCUE SHIPS.
SO 300 WILL HAVE TO BE LEFT BEHIND — INCLUDING YOUR UNCLE ALBERT FITZWILLIAM DIGBY.
HELLO, DIG - IS THAT THE DOG YOU FOUND LEFT IN THE HOTEL — OH, ISN'T HE CUTE?
AYE, MISS — BUT HE'S A RIGHT CRATE EGG...
— I PUT HIM IN THE SPACE CLIPPER THREE TIMES TO GET HIM AWAY SAFE LIKE, BUT THE SOFT OLD TYKE KEEPS COMING BACK.
HE STICKS BY HIS FRIENDS, DON'T YOU, BOY? — HELLO — WHAT'S THE MATTER WITH HIM, WHY IS HE SHAKING HIS HEAD LIKE THAT?
— IT'S AS THOUGH HE COULD HEAR SOMETHING...
AND, BY GOLLY — SO CAN I! — AT 'EAST I CAN FEEL IT — IN THE DECK!
THROB
THROB
LOOK OUT! SHE'S GOING OVER!
CREW TO EMERGENCY STATIONS — INCREASE STABILIZERS TO MAXIMUM REVS — START EMERGENCY GYROS — CLOSE ALL AIRTIGHT BULKHEADS. STAND BY POSITIONING JETS.
ON THE BRIDGE
DAN, WE'RE NOT JUST ROLLING ....
WE'RE OFF OUR ORBIT!
I KNOW — WE'RE BEING PULLED TO THE RED MOON, LOCK, STOCK AND BARREL — SHIP, STATION, PASSENGERS AND ALL!!
THROB
CONTINUED

EAGLE-BRITAIN'S NATIONAL STRIP CARTOON WEEKLY

FOURPENCE-HALFPENNY
EVERY FRIDAY
EAGLE
25 JANUARY 1952 Vol. 2 No. 42
DAN DARE
THE RED MOON MYSTERY
GENERAL ALARM! ALL CREW TO EMERGENCY STATIONS...
...EVACUEES STAY WHERE YOU ARE — PLEASE DON'T HINDER THE CREW — WE MUST ACT SWIFTLY.
ALARM
CLOSE AIRTIGHT BULKHEADS!
ON THE BRIDGE OF SPACE STATION SFJ2, DAN DARE FACES ONE OF THE GREATEST CRISES OF HIS CAREER, THE SPACE STATION IS IN THE GRIP OF THE TERRIFIC MAGNETISM OF THE MYSTERIOUS RED MOON - AND DAN, AS COMMANDER OF THE EVACUATION OF MARS, HAS THE LIVES OF OVER 1,000 EVACUEES IN HIS HANDS.
DANGER DOOR AIRLOCKED
FERRY PILOTS — MAN YOUR SHIPS AND TAKE OFF IMMEDIATELY TO TAKE THE STATION IN TOW.
ENGINE ROOM — START UP POSITIONING IMPULSE AND ROCKET MOTORS — MAXIMUM POWER TO OPPOSE MAGNETIC PULL!
"LANCASTRIAN" COME IN TO MOORINGS ON LOADING PLATFORM AND USE YOUR ENGINES AS BRAKES ON THE STATION.
IMPULSE 7
LANCASTRIAN

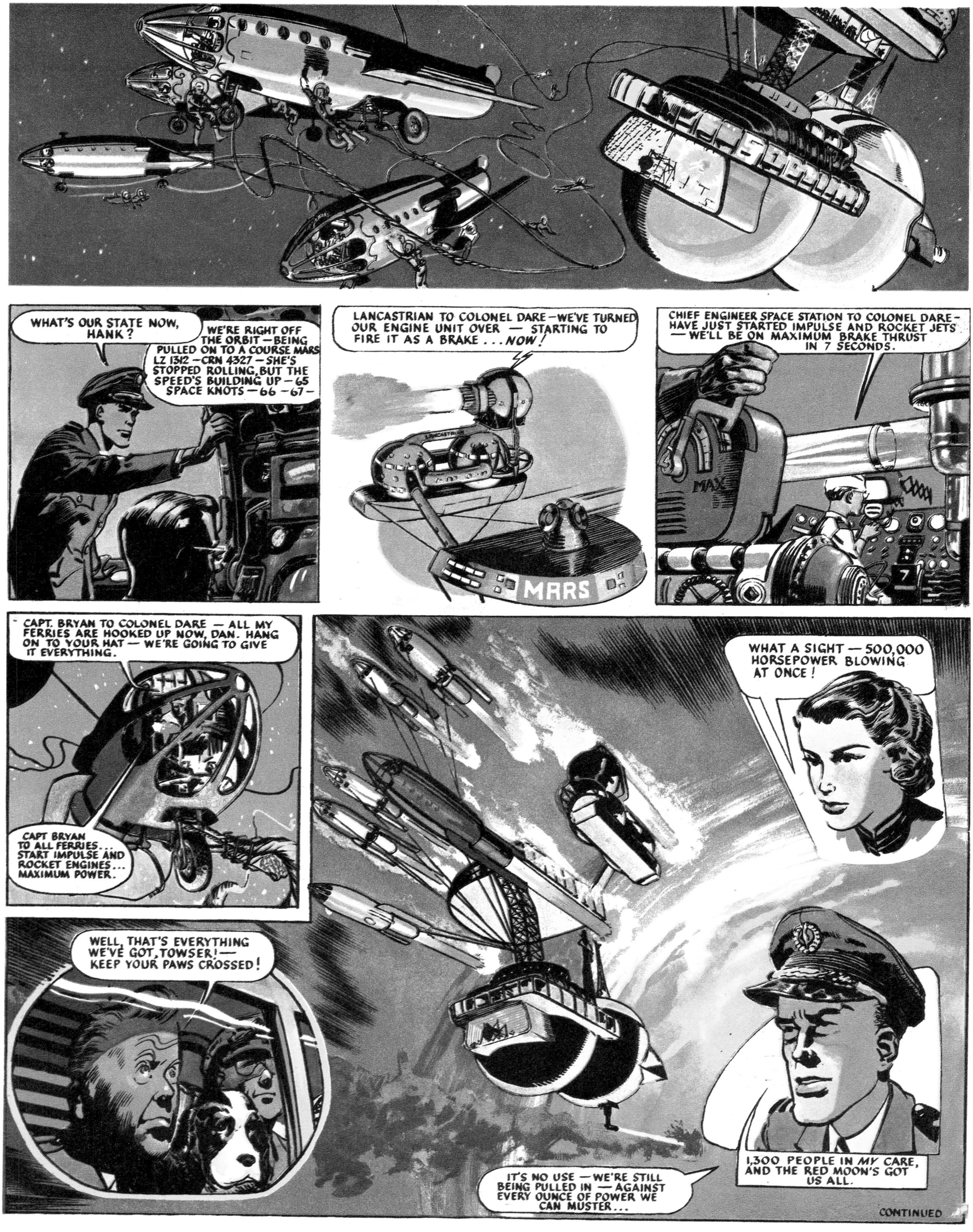

WHAT'S OUR STATE NOW, HANK?
WE'RE RIGHT OFF THE ORBIT — BEING PULLED ON TO A COURSE MARS LZ 1312 — CRN 4327 — SHE'S STOPPED ROLLING, BUT THE SPEED'S BUILDING UP — 65 SPACE KNOTS — 66 — 67 —
LANCASTRIAN TO COLONEL DARE — WE'VE TURNED OUR ENGINE UNIT OVER — STARTING TO FIRE IT AS A BRAKE ... NOW!
MARS
CHIEF ENGINEER SPACE STATION TO COLONEL DARE — HAVE JUST STARTED IMPULSE AND ROCKET JETS — WE'LL BE ON MAXIMUM BRAKE THRUST IN 7 SECONDS.
MAX
CAPT. BRYAN TO COLONEL DARE — ALL MY FERRIES ARE HOOKED UP NOW, DAN. HANG ON TO YOUR HAT — WE'RE GOING TO GIVE IT EVERYTHING.
CAPT BRYAN TO ALL FERRIES... START IMPULSE AND ROCKET ENGINES... MAXIMUM POWER.
WHAT A SIGHT — 500,000 HORSEPOWER BLOWING AT ONCE!
WELL, THAT'S EVERYTHING WE'VE GOT, TOWSER! — KEEP YOUR PAWS CROSSED!
IT'S NO USE — WE'RE STILL BEING PULLED IN — AGAINST EVERY OUNCE OF POWER WE CAN MUSTER...
1,300 PEOPLE IN MY CARE, AND THE RED MOON'S GOT US ALL.
CONTINUED

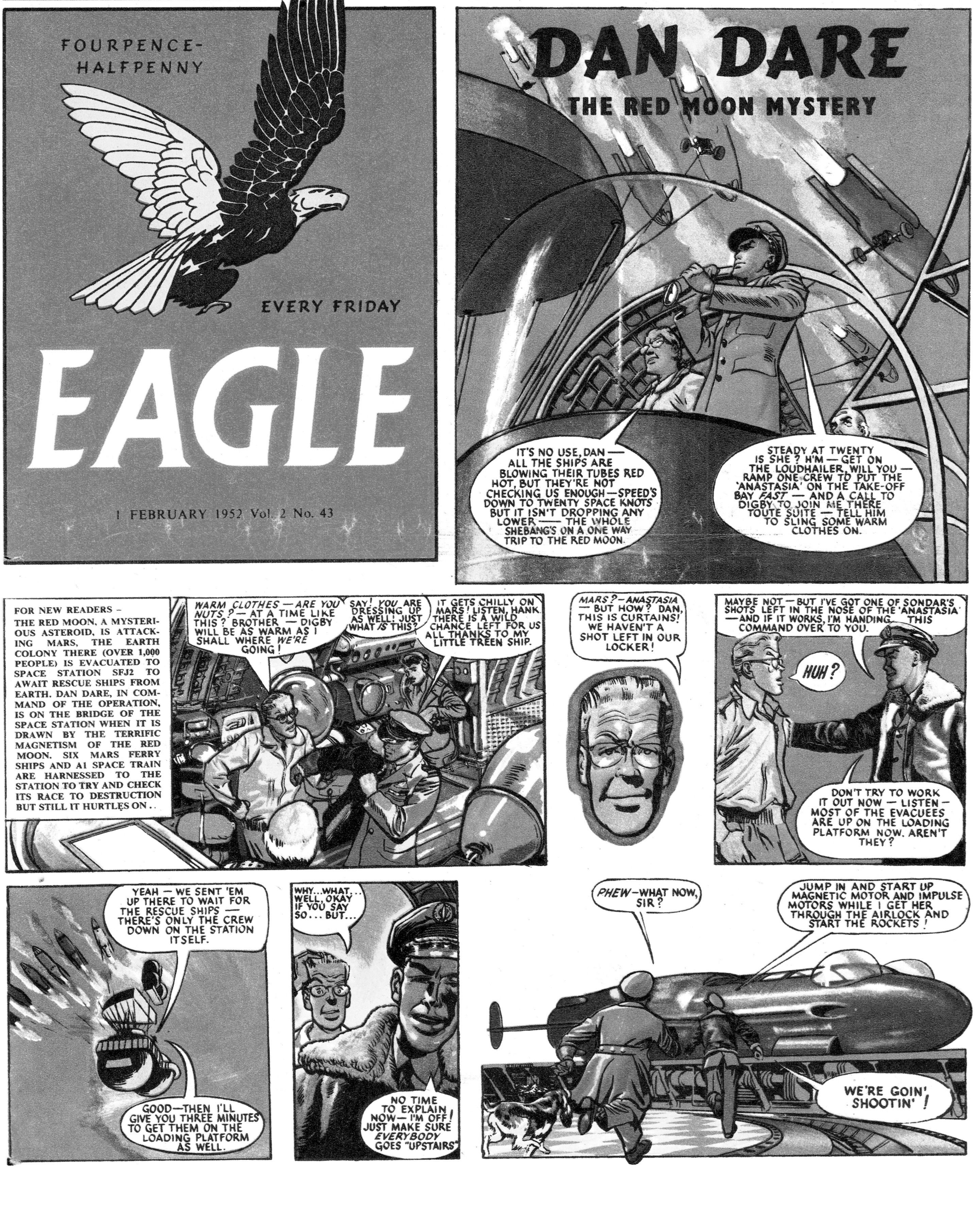
FOURPENCE-HALFPENNY
EVERY FRIDAY
EAGLE
1 FEBRUARY 1952 Vol. 2 No. 43
DAN DARE
THE RED MOON MYSTERY
IT'S NO USE, DAN — ALL THE SHIPS ARE BLOWING THEIR TUBES RED HOT, BUT THEY'RE NOT CHECKING US ENOUGH — SPEED'S DOWN TO TWENTY SPACE KNOTS BUT IT ISN'T DROPPING ANY LOWER —— THE WHOLE SHEBANG'S ON A ONE WAY TRIP TO THE RED MOON.
STEADY AT TWENTY IS SHE? H'M — GET ON THE LOUDHAILER, WILL YOU — RAMP ONE CREW TO PUT THE 'ANASTASIA' ON THE TAKE-OFF BAY FAST — AND A CALL TO DIGBY TO JOIN ME THERE TOUTE SUITE — TELL HIM TO SLING SOME WARM CLOTHES ON.
FOR NEW READERS – THE RED MOON, A MYSTERIOUS ASTEROID, IS ATTACKING MARS, THE EARTH COLONY THERE (OVER 1,000 PEOPLE) IS EVACUATED TO SPACE STATION SFJ2 TO AWAIT RESCUE SHIPS FROM EARTH. DAN DARE, IN COMMAND OF THE OPERATION, IS ON THE BRIDGE OF THE SPACE STATION WHEN IT IS DRAWN BY THE TERRIFIC MAGNETISM OF THE RED MOON. SIX MARS FERRY SHIPS AND A1 SPACE TRAIN ARE HARNESSED TO THE STATION TO TRY AND CHECK ITS RACE TO DESTRUCTION BUT STILL IT HURTLES ON . .
WARM CLOTHES — ARE YOU NUTS? — AT A TIME LIKE THIS? BROTHER — DIGBY WILL BE AS WARM AS I SHALL WHERE WE'RE GOING!
SAY! YOU ARE DRESSING UP AS WELL! JUST WHAT IS THIS?
IT GETS CHILLY ON MARS! LISTEN, HANK. THERE IS A WILD CHANCE LEFT FOR US ALL THANKS TO MY LITTLE TREEN SHIP.
MARS? — ANASTASIA — BUT HOW? DAN, THIS IS CURTAINS! WE HAVEN'T A SHOT LEFT IN OUR LOCKER!
MAYBE NOT — BUT I'VE GOT ONE OF SONDAR'S SHOTS LEFT IN THE NOSE OF THE 'ANASTASIA' — AND IF IT WORKS, I'M HANDING THIS COMMAND OVER TO YOU.
HUH?
DON'T TRY TO WORK IT OUT NOW — LISTEN — MOST OF THE EVACUEES ARE UP ON THE LOADING PLATFORM NOW, AREN'T THEY?
YEAH — WE SENT 'EM UP THERE TO WAIT FOR THE RESCUE SHIPS — THERE'S ONLY THE CREW DOWN ON THE STATION ITSELF.
GOOD — THEN I'LL GIVE YOU THREE MINUTES TO GET THEM ON THE LOADING PLATFORM AS WELL.
WHY...WHAT... WELL, OKAY IF YOU SAY SO... BUT...
NO TIME TO EXPLAIN NOW — I'M OFF! JUST MAKE SURE EVERYBODY GOES "UPSTAIRS"
PHEW — WHAT NOW, SIR?
JUMP IN AND START UP MAGNETIC MOTOR AND IMPULSE MOTORS WHILE I GET HER THROUGH THE AIRLOCK AND START THE ROCKETS!
WE'RE GOIN' SHOOTIN'!

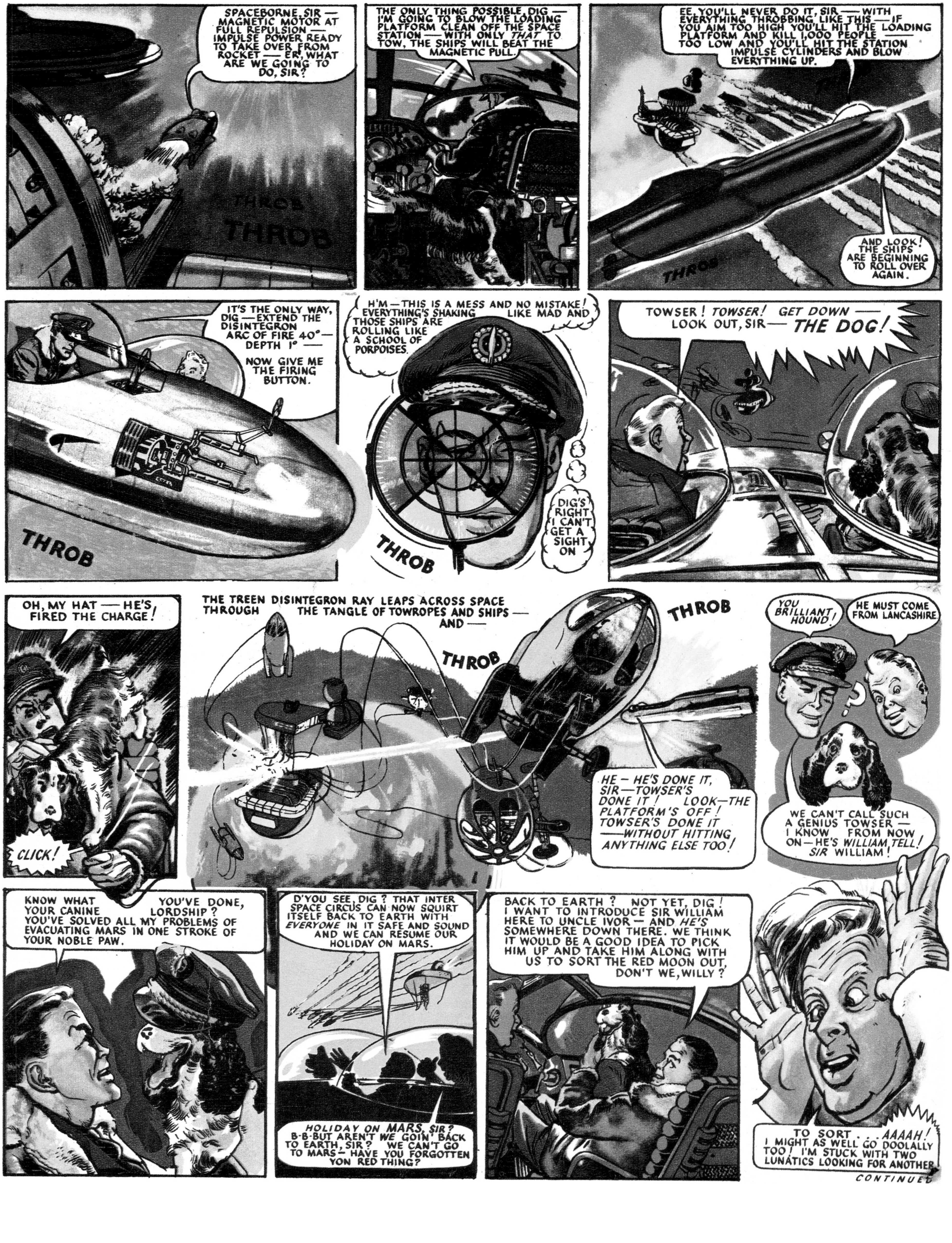

SPACEBORNE, SIR — MAGNETIC MOTOR AT FULL REPULSION — IMPULSE POWER READY TO TAKE OVER FROM ROCKET — ER, WHAT ARE WE GOING TO DO, SIR?
THROB
THROB
THE ONLY THING POSSIBLE, DIG — I'M GOING TO BLOW THE LOADING PLATFORM CLEAN OFF THE SPACE STATION — WITH ONLY THAT TO TOW, THE SHIPS WILL BEAT THE MAGNETIC PULL.
EE, YOU'LL NEVER DO IT, SIR — WITH EVERYTHING THROBBING LIKE THIS — IF YOU AIM TOO HIGH YOU'LL HIT THE LOADING PLATFORM AND KILL 1,000 PEOPLE — TOO LOW AND YOU'LL HIT THE STATION IMPULSE CYLINDERS AND BLOW EVERYTHING UP.
AND LOOK! THE SHIPS ARE BEGINNING TO ROLL OVER AGAIN.
THROB
IT'S THE ONLY WAY, DIG — EXTEND THE DISINTEGRON ARC OF FIRE 40° — DEPTH 1° — NOW GIVE ME THE FIRING BUTTON.
THROB
H'M — THIS IS A MESS AND NO MISTAKE! EVERYTHING'S SHAKING LIKE MAD AND THOSE SHIPS ARE ROLLING LIKE A SCHOOL OF PORPOISES.
DIG'S RIGHT I CAN'T GET A SIGHT ON
THROB
TOWSER! TOWSER! GET DOWN — LOOK OUT, SIR — THE DOG!
OH, MY HAT — HE'S FIRED THE CHARGE!
CLICK!
THE TREEN DISINTEGRON RAY LEAPS ACROSS SPACE THROUGH THE TANGLE OF TOWROPES AND SHIPS — AND —
THROB
THROB
HE — HE'S DONE IT, SIR — TOWSER'S DONE IT! LOOK — THE PLATFORM'S OFF! TOWSER'S DONE IT — WITHOUT HITTING ANYTHING ELSE TOO!
YOU BRILLIANT HOUND!
HE MUST COME FROM LANCASHIRE
WE CAN'T CALL SUCH A GENIUS TOWSER — I KNOW FROM NOW ON — HE'S WILLIAM TELL! SIR WILLIAM!
KNOW WHAT YOU'VE DONE, YOUR CANINE LORDSHIP? YOU'VE SOLVED ALL MY PROBLEMS OF EVACUATING MARS IN ONE STROKE OF YOUR NOBLE PAW.
D'YOU SEE, DIG? THAT INTER SPACE CIRCUS CAN NOW SQUIRT ITSELF BACK TO EARTH WITH EVERYONE IN IT SAFE AND SOUND AND WE CAN RESUME OUR HOLIDAY ON MARS.
HOLIDAY ON MARS, SIR? B-B-BUT AREN'T WE GOIN' BACK TO EARTH, SIR? WE CAN'T GO TO MARS — HAVE YOU FORGOTTEN YON RED THING?
BACK TO EARTH? NOT YET, DIG! I WANT TO INTRODUCE SIR WILLIAM HERE TO UNCLE IVOR — AND HE'S SOMEWHERE DOWN THERE. WE THINK IT WOULD BE A GOOD IDEA TO PICK HIM UP AND TAKE HIM ALONG WITH US TO SORT THE RED MOON OUT, DON'T WE, WILLY?
TO SORT . . . AAAAH! I MIGHT AS WELL GO DOOLALLY TOO! I'M STUCK WITH TWO LUNATICS LOOKING FOR ANOTHER!
CONTINUED

EAGLE-BRITAIN'S NATIONAL STRIP CARTOON WEEKLY

FOURPENCE-HALFPENNY

EVERY FRIDAY

EAGLE

8 FEBRUARY 1952 Vol. 2 No. 44

MEANWHILE, IN LONDON, SIR HUBERT GUEST IS ATTENDING A MEETING OF THE RED MOON COMMISSION.
AS FOR THE MARS EVACUATION, GENTLEMEN — WE ARE STILL IN THE DARK . . .
HULTON PRESS
THE INTENSE ELECTRICAL DISTURBANCES AROUND THE RED MOON BLANKETED ALL RADIO AND VIEWER COMMUNICATION FOUR HOURS AGO . . .
WE ARE, OF COURSE, MONITORING ALL THE TIME AND COLONEL O'REILLY IS STANDING BY AT THE ASTRAL COMMUNICATIONS ROOM WHILE I'M HERE . . .
STILL NOTHING, SMITH ?
NO, SIR, JUST CRACKLES AND THROBBING.
WAIT A MINUTE — IT'S CLEARING
I'M GETTING SIGNALS !
A NEWSPAPER OFFICE . . .
IT'S NEWS, CHIEF — RED MOON NEWS — THE STATIC'S CLEARED AND HOGAN'S COME THROUGH — ALL EVACUEES SAFE AND HOMEWARD BOUND.
DARE'S GONE DOWN TO MARS AND — WOW — THE RED MOON'S FOOTLOOSE AGAIN!
WELL DON'T JUST STAND THERE!
WHAT'S THE TROUBLE, WAYNE ? WHY THE EMERGENCY CALL ?
2345'S BROKEN HER ORBIT OF MARS, SIR, AND ALL THE ELECTRICAL PHENOMENA HAS CEASED — WE'RE PLOTTING HER NEW LINE NOW . . .
THE OBSERVATORY AT MOUNT PALOMAR
A COMMUNIQUE JUST ISSUED BY MOUNT PALOMAR STATES THAT THE ASTEROID 2345 — THE RED MOON — HAS BROKEN ITS ORBIT OF MARS, AND RESUMED ITS OLD COURSE.
WHAT DOES THAT MEAN, STINKY ?
IT MEANS THAT IT'LL HIT THE EARTH IN ABOUT A WEEK.
?
LOFT CLUB no girls
AN ATTIC IN WIGAN
YES, SIR — I'VE PICKED UP MY UNCLE — AND DORTAN'S BOX — DR. DARE IS TRYING TO OPEN IT NOW — BUT, AS YOU KNOW, THE RED MOON'S SUDDENLY GONE QUIET. THE STORMS AND THROBBING HAVE STOPPED AND SHE SEEMS TO BE MOVING AWAY. IT'S OBVIOUSLY THE TIME TO GET A GOOD LOOK AT HER AT LAST !
I TOOK OFF FIVE MINUTES AGO — AND THIS TIME I'M GOING TO LAND ON THIS WRETCHED ASTEROID — OR BUST.
VERY WELL, DAN — BUT KEEP IN TOUCH — AND BE CAREFUL.
CAREFUL ? GOSH, YES, SIR — YOU OUGHT TO SEE DIGBY !!
CONTINUED

EAGLE-BIKE-A-WEEK COMPETITION STARTS TODAY!

FOURPENCE-HALFPENNY
EVERY FRIDAY
EAGLE
15 FEBRUARY 1952 Vol. 2 No. 45
DAN DARE
THE RED MOON MYSTERY
I TELL YOU THE ANSWER'S *HERE*, DAN IN THIS BOX!
FOR NEW READERS – DAN, DIGBY AND DAN'S UNCLE IVOR, THE FAMOUS ARCHAEOLOGIST, ARE ABOUT TO EXPLORE THE MYSTERIOUS ASTEROID 2345, "THE RED MOON" WHICH, AFTER CAUSING TERRIBLE STORMS AND HAVOC ON MARS, HAS SWUNG OUT INTO SPACE AGAIN AND IS HEADING FOR THE EARTH. UNCLE IVOR HAS DUG UP A BOX FROM ANCIENT RUINS ON MARS WHICH HE IS CERTAIN WILL GIVE THEM VALUABLE INFORMATION...
WHY DON'T YOU WAIT UNTIL I OPEN IT BEFORE YOU DIVE INTO THAT THING?
JUST WHAT DO YOU EXPECT TO FIND INSIDE IT, SIR?
ANASTASIA
I DONT KNOW, DIGBY—ALL I KNOW IS THAT WHEN HIS PLANET WAS FINALLY OVERWHELMED BY THE RED MOON 200,000 YEARS AGO, THE LAST EMPEROR OF MARS PUT *SOMETHING* IN THIS BOX TO SHOW WHAT EXACTLY IT WAS THAT WIPED OUT *EVERYTHING*.
BUT THE FASTENING OF THE THING ELUDES ME — IT MUST BE A VERY SPECIAL KIND — I DON'T WANT TO DAMAGE THE BOX — IT'S UNIQUE. QUITE IRREPLACEABLE.
LOOK, UNCLE—WE DON'T KNOW HOW LONG THE RED MOON WILL STAY QUIET—WE *MUST* TAKE THE CHANCE TO EXPLORE IT *NOW*—I'LL WAIT JUST TWO MORE MINUTES FOR YOU TO OPEN THE BOX...
...BUT YOU MUST SWALLOW YOUR SCRUPLES AND LET DIGBY DO IT WITH AN OXY-CUTTER.
OH VERY WELL!
VANDAL!
THAT'S GOT IT—I'VE HIT A CATCH OR SOMETHING—SHE'LL OPEN NOW, SIR...
WELL BLOW ME DOWN WITH A JERKY JET.
THAT'S A TURNUP! WHAT IS IT?

AFTER 200,000 YEARS, DORTAN'S BOX IS OPENED AND ITS SECRET REVEALED, BUT...
IT'S JUST SOME DIRTY OLD STONE OR SOMETHING — HALF A DOZEN SLABS OF IT — NOTHING ON THEM — THEY WON'T HELP US MUCH
I-I DON'T UNDERSTAND JUST THESE — NOTHING MORE?
SORRY, UNCLE THAT SETTLES IT — HERE WE GO!
STAND BY YOUR INSTRUMENTS, DIG
SURFACE 75 MILES, SIR — 70 — 65 — GRAVITY REGISTERING ON CLARKE SCALE — 3·7 UNITS — OUTER SKIN COOLERS WORKING. SURFACE 50 MILES.
START REACTOR BRAKES!
ANY MAGNETIC PULL?
VERY SLIGHT, SIR — IT'S HARDLY BOTHERING THE MAGNETIC MOTORS. RADIO'S NOT AFFECTED, EITHER.
RIGHT — I'M SWITCHING OVER TO AIRPLANE CONTROLS — GIVE THE REACTORS A FORCE 10 BLAST FOR 2 SECONDS — THEN I'M GOING TO PULL HER OUT ON THE WINGS...
HERE WE ARE, AT LAST — THE SURFACE OF THE RED MOON.
EE, ISN'T IT QUIET. HARDLY A THROB WORTH MENTIONING. IT MUST BE SOMEBODY'S DAY OFF.
BUT I RECKON NOWT OF IT AS A "SURFACE" — CAN'T SEE A LEVEL SPOT THE SIZE OF A POSTAGE STAMP...
...AND THE RADAR BUFFER'S TYING ITSELF IN KNOTS STEERING US THROUGH THESE ROCK PINNACLES... ...OH, WAIT A MINUTE...
THERE'S A MORE REGULAR SHAPE COMING UP ON THE RADAR SCREEN, SIR — IT MIGHT BE SOMETHING WE COULD LAND ON...
WHERE? UM — YES — SWITCH ON THE SEARCHLIGHT AND STAND BY WITH THE VERTICAL LANDING JETS.
THERE IT IS — WHATEVER IT IS — ARE YOU GOING TO TRY AND GET DOWN ON IT, SIR?
YES, I THINK WE CAN MANAGE IT, DIG — I'LL CIRCLE ROUND AND COME IN THE SAME WAY AGAIN — DEAD SLOW, WITH THE LANDING JETS KEEPING US AIRBORNE...
RIGHTO, SIR. COME ON, WILLY — COME TO YOUR UNCLE DIGBY — AND KEEP YOUR PAWS CROSSED!
NOW YOU'LL SEE WHY ALL MY HAIR HAS TURNED WHITE!
CONTINUED...

EAGLE-BRITAIN'S NATIONAL STRIP CARTOON WEEKLY

FOURPENCE-HALFPENNY

EVERY FRIDAY

EAGLE

22 FEBRUARY 1952 Vol. 2 No. 46

DAN DARE
THE RED MOON MYSTERY
IT'S ALL RIGHT, DIG! — YOU CAN OPEN YOUR EYES — WE'RE DOWN.

GULP, YESSIR – NOT EXACTLY WITH A MILE TO SPARE, IS IT?
DAN, DIGBY AND UNCLE IVOR ARE INVESTIGATING ASTEROID 2345, THE MYSTERIOUS "RED MOON" WHICH IS RACING TOWARDS THE EARTH. DIVING THROUGH THE 100 MILE CLOUD, THEY ARRIVE AT THE SURFACE AND, IN A MOMENTARY BREAK IN THE SWIRLING DUST, DAN LANDS ON THE ONLY LEVEL SPOT IN SIGHT.
IT'LL BE ALL RIGHT IF YOU DON'T JUMP ABOUT, DIG — GET OUT THE TEUPEL TESTER AND SAMPLE TEMPERATURE AND ATMOSPHERE —— I'M GOING TO REPORT TO SIR HUBERT.

ON EARTH AT SPACE FLEET H.Q.
SIR HUBERT! COLONEL DARE'S ON THE VIEWER. HE'S LANDED ON THE RED MOON!
OH, GOOD SHOW.
SWITCH HIM THROUGH TO MY OFFICE.
YESSIR — WE'RE DOWN — THE TERRAIN'S TERRIBLE — PINNACLES AND CRAGS OF ROCK — WE'RE ON SOME KIND OF ARTIFICIAL STRUCTURE — NO SIGNS OF LIFE. AH, HERE'S DIG WITH THE TEUPEL READING.
H'M — NOT MUCH OXYGEN ABOUT THE PLACE —— TEMPERATURE –10° F.
TEMPERATURE –10°? HAVE YOU GOT YOUR SPACESUITS?
NOT OFFICIAL ONES, SIR — NO H.D.S. OR ANYTHING LIKE THAT — AFTER ALL, WE STARTED OUT ON A HOLIDAY —— BUT WE CAN USE OUR LIGHT MARS PLAY-SUITS —— THEY'RE PROOF TO –100°F. I SUGGEST WE HAVE A LOOK OUTSIDE IN THEM AND CALL BACK IN 10 MINUTES.
I KNEW IT! COLUMBUS STUFF!
IT'S NO USE YOU JUMPING ABOUT, WILLIE — YOU CAN'T GO WALKIES HERE.

WHAT D'YOU THINK THIS THING IS WE'VE LANDED ON, SIR?

WELL... IT'S METAL AND, I SUPPOSE, A BUILDING OF SOME SORT.

HIGH UP, AREN'T WE, DAN—CAN YOU SEE THE BOTTOM?

I CAN'T SEE OWT BUT DUST AND YON BUBBLE THINGS

EE—HAVE YOU GOT A PIN, SIR?

DIGBY, YOU ASS—DON'T TOUCH IT—IT MAY EXPLODE OR RELEASE ACID OR...

...IT MAY EVEN BE ALIVE!

THIS IS GETTING US NOWHERE—DIG, NIP BACK IN AND SWITCH THE SEARCHLIGHT ON.

H'M—THAT'S NOT EXACTLY A GREAT HELP—TRY HER WITH INFRA RED, DIG—I DON'T SUPPOSE IT'LL HELP, BUT IT MAY DO...

NO BETTER—H'M—PRETTY DIM OUTLOOK

HELLO—WHAT'S THE MATTER WITH DIGBY?

SIR! LOOK!

THE SLABS IN THE INFRA RED LIGHT—I COULD JUST SEE THEM IN THE GLOW IN THE CABIN.

THEY'VE GOT PICTURES ON THEM NOW!

SEVEN MINUTES GONE, SIR—THREE MORE AND DAN WILL REPORT AGAIN.

SIR—CAPTAIN HOGAN'S ON THE VIEWER FROM THE MARS EVACUEE CONVOY. SAYS HE MUST SPEAK TO SIR HUBERT.

HANK?—WHAT DOES HE WANT?—ALL RIGHT. I'LL GIVE HIM TWO MINUTES. SWITCH HIM THROUGH.

LIST? EVACUEES? WHAT ARE YOU TALKING ABOUT?

MISS PEABODY, SIR—SHE'S BEEN LEFT BEHIND!

IT'S ALL A TERRIBLE MISTAKE, SIR. I CHECKED THE CREW LIST, BUT OF COURSE SHE WASN'T ON THAT—AND Q CHECKED THE EVACUEE LIST—BUT SHE WAS OUT WITH DAN WHEN THAT WAS MADE UP AND SHE WASN'T PUT ON IT.

AND NOW WE CAN'T FIND HER ANYWHERE.

SHE'S STILL IN THE SPACE STATION...

...SOMEWHERE ON THE RED MOON!

CONTINUED

EAGLE-BRITAIN'S NATIONAL STRIP CARTOON WEEKLY

FOURPENCE-HALFPENNY
EVERY FRIDAY
EAGLE
29 FEBRUARY 1952 Vol. 2 No. 47

DAN DARE
THE RED MOON MYSTERY
WHAT? MISS PEABODY'S STILL IN THE SPACE STATION? —I THOUGHT YOU'D PULLED IT CLEAR.
NO, SIR—WE GOT EVERYBODY INTO THE LOADING PLATFORM—THEN DAN SHOT IT AWAY FROM THE STATION AND THE FERRIES TOWED IT.

FOR NEW READERS
AS SIR HUBERT WAITS ANXIOUSLY FOR NEWS FROM DAN, WHO HAS AT LAST MANAGED TO LAND ON THE MYSTERIOUS RED MOON, AN URGENT CALL COMES FROM HANK HOGAN (WHO HAS TAKEN COMMAND OF THE EVACUEE CONVOY FROM MARS) - REPORTING THAT MISS PEABODY IS MISSING.
BUT THE MAIN PART OF THE STATION WAS PULLED BY THE MAGNETISM TO THE RED MOON.

OF COURSE, AT THE TIME, WE THOUGHT IT WAS EMPTY...
POOR GIRL! IT'S TOO LATE TO DO ANYTHING NOW...
BUT, NOW IT SEEMS THAT MISS PEABODY MUST HAVE BEEN IN IT.

BUT, SIR—IT'S JUST POSSIBLE THAT SHE'S STILL ALIVE, AND DAN'S LANDED ON THE RED MOON—COULDN'T HE...
NO, HANK!
HE COULDN'T DO ANYTHING—HIS MISSION IS TOO VITAL FOR HIM TO BE DISTRACTED FOR ANY INDIVIDUAL—NO MATTER WHO IT IS!

WITH THE RED MOON RACING TO THE EARTH, MILLIONS OF LIVES DEPEND ON US GETTING INFORMATION—AND ONLY DAN CAN GET IT.
BUT, SIR COULDN'T I GO BACK IN ONE OF THE FERRIES AND...

NO, HANK—I'M SORRY, BUT THAT IS FINAL. NOW PLEASE SWITCH OFF—I MUST CONTACT DAN AGAIN.
BUT, SIR—IF JOCELYN IS STILL ALIVE WE'RE SENTENCING HER TO...

CAPTAIN HOGAN—
FOR THE LAST TIME—
CLEAR THAT SCREEN NOW—
I.S.F
—OR, BY THE STARS, I'LL DRUM YOU OUT OF THE SERVICE!

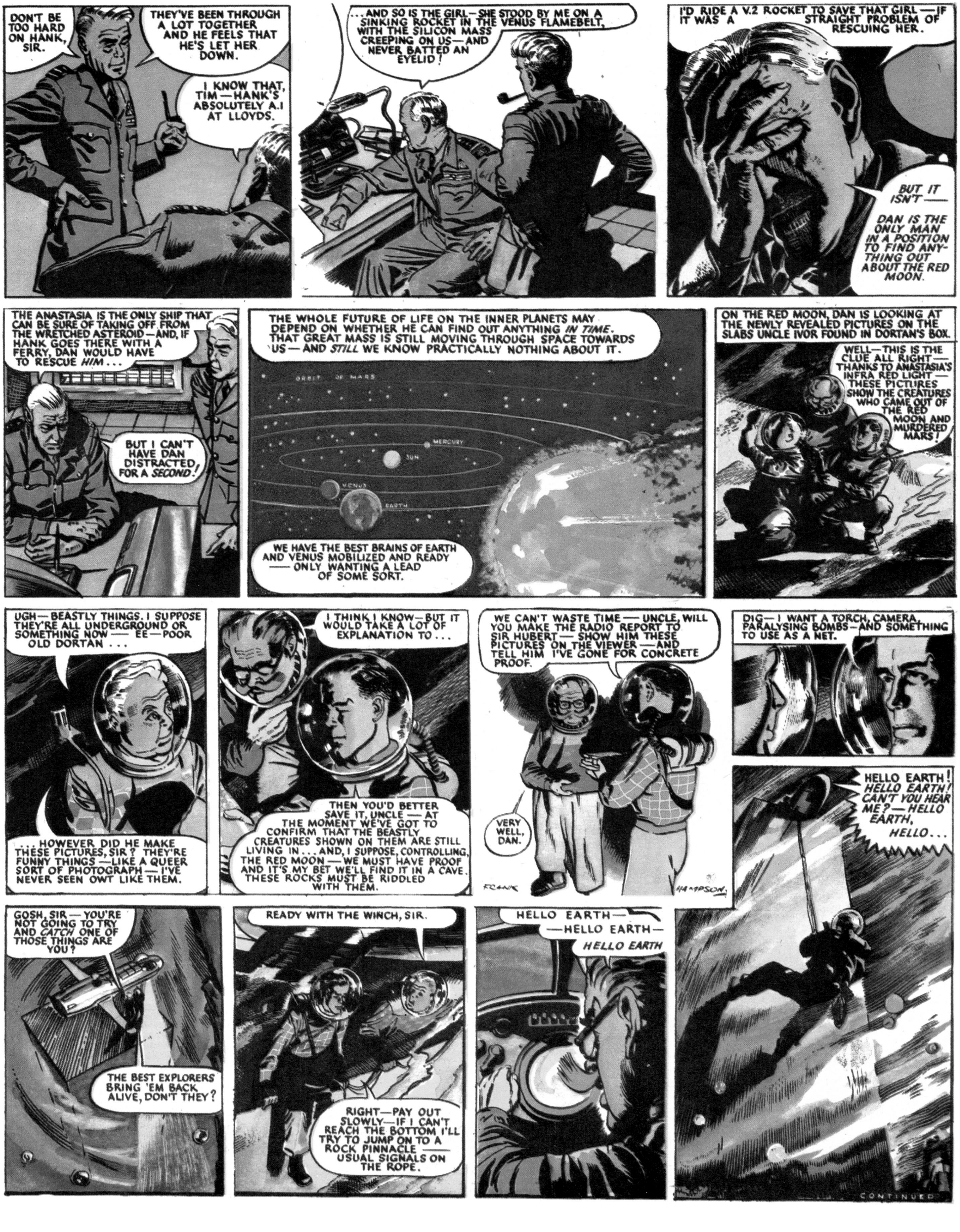
DON'T BE TOO HARD ON HANK, SIR.
THEY'VE BEEN THROUGH A LOT TOGETHER AND HE FEELS THAT HE'S LET HER DOWN.
I KNOW THAT, TIM — HANK'S ABSOLUTELY A.1 AT LLOYDS.
... AND SO IS THE GIRL — SHE STOOD BY ME ON A SINKING ROCKET IN THE VENUS FLAMEBELT, WITH THE SILICON MASS CREEPING ON US — AND NEVER BATTED AN EYELID!
I'D RIDE A V.2 ROCKET TO SAVE THAT GIRL — IF IT WAS A STRAIGHT PROBLEM OF RESCUING HER.
BUT IT ISN'T —
DAN IS THE ONLY MAN IN A POSITION TO FIND ANYTHING OUT ABOUT THE RED MOON.
THE ANASTASIA IS THE ONLY SHIP THAT CAN BE SURE OF TAKING OFF FROM THE WRETCHED ASTEROID — AND, IF HANK GOES THERE WITH A FERRY, DAN WOULD HAVE TO RESCUE HIM ...
BUT I CAN'T HAVE DAN DISTRACTED, FOR A SECOND!
THE WHOLE FUTURE OF LIFE ON THE INNER PLANETS MAY DEPEND ON WHETHER HE CAN FIND OUT ANYTHING IN TIME. THAT GREAT MASS IS STILL MOVING THROUGH SPACE TOWARDS US — AND STILL WE KNOW PRACTICALLY NOTHING ABOUT IT.
ORBIT OF MARS
MERCURY
SUN
VENUS
EARTH
WE HAVE THE BEST BRAINS OF EARTH AND VENUS MOBILIZED AND READY — ONLY WANTING A LEAD OF SOME SORT.
ON THE RED MOON, DAN IS LOOKING AT THE NEWLY REVEALED PICTURES ON THE SLABS UNCLE IVOR FOUND IN DORTAN'S BOX.
WELL — THIS IS THE CLUE ALL RIGHT — THANKS TO ANASTASIA'S INFRA RED LIGHT — THESE PICTURES SHOW THE CREATURES WHO CAME OUT OF THE RED MOON AND MURDERED MARS!
UGH — BEASTLY THINGS. I SUPPOSE THEY'RE ALL UNDERGROUND OR SOMETHING NOW — EE — POOR OLD DORTAN ...
... HOWEVER DID HE MAKE THESE PICTURES, SIR? THEY'RE FUNNY THINGS — LIKE A QUEER SORT OF PHOTOGRAPH — I'VE NEVER SEEN OWT LIKE THEM.
I THINK I KNOW — BUT IT WOULD TAKE A LOT OF EXPLANATION TO ...
THEN YOU'D BETTER SAVE IT, UNCLE — AT THE MOMENT WE'VE GOT TO CONFIRM THAT THE BEASTLY CREATURES SHOWN ON THEM ARE STILL LIVING IN ... AND, I SUPPOSE, CONTROLLING, THE RED MOON — WE MUST HAVE PROOF AND IT'S MY BET WE'LL FIND IT IN A CAVE. THESE ROCKS MUST BE RIDDLED WITH THEM.
WE CAN'T WASTE TIME — UNCLE, WILL YOU MAKE THE RADIO REPORT TO SIR HUBERT — SHOW HIM THESE PICTURES ON THE VIEWER — AND TELL HIM I'VE GONE FOR CONCRETE PROOF.
VERY WELL, DAN.
FRANK HAMPSON
DIG — I WANT A TORCH, CAMERA, PARALYSING BOMBS — AND SOMETHING TO USE AS A NET.
GOSH, SIR — YOU'RE NOT GOING TO TRY AND CATCH ONE OF THOSE THINGS ARE YOU?
THE BEST EXPLORERS BRING 'EM BACK ALIVE, DON'T THEY?
READY WITH THE WINCH, SIR.
RIGHT — PAY OUT SLOWLY — IF I CAN'T REACH THE BOTTOM I'LL TRY TO JUMP ON TO A ROCK PINNACLE — USUAL SIGNALS ON THE ROPE.
HELLO EARTH —
— HELLO EARTH —
HELLO EARTH
HELLO EARTH! HELLO EARTH! CAN'T YOU HEAR ME? — HELLO EARTH, HELLO ...
CONTINUED

EAGLE-BRITAIN'S NATIONAL STRIP CARTOON WEEKLY

FOURPENCE-HALFPENNY
EVERY FRIDAY
EAGLE
7 MARCH 1952 Vol. 2 No. 48
DAN DARE
THE RED MOON MYSTERY
CALLING ANASTASIA! — CALLING ANASTASIA ON THE RED MOON. COME IN ANASTASIA. COLONEL DARE, CAN YOU HEAR ME? -CAN YOU HEAR ME?
ASTEROID 2345, THE RED MOON, HAS BROKEN OFF ITS ATTACK ON MARS AND IS NOW RACING TOWARDS THE EARTH. DAN, DIGBY AND UNCLE IVOR HAVE LANDED ON THE ASTEROID BUT WHEN UNCLE IVOR TRIES TO RADIO A REPORT HE IS UNABLE TO GET THROUGH. ON EARTH, AT SPACE FLEET H.Q., THE OPERATORS ARE ALSO VAINLY TRYING TO ESTABLISH CONTACT.
I CAN'T UNDERSTAND IT, SIR, HE PROMISED TO CALL US BACK IN 10 MINUTES — HOURS AGO.
I CAN, TIM. I HAVE JUST HAD A SIGNAL THAT THE MARS IMPULSE RELAY STATION IS OUT OF ACTION.
A VOLUNTEER CREW WAS LEFT TO WORK IT WHEN MARS WAS EVACUATED — REMEMBER? THE POOR CHAPS MUST HAVE BEEN KNOCKED OUT IN THE RED MOON'S THIRD ORBIT OF MARS...
... BUT THE PRE-SET MACHINERY WOULD GO ON WORKING UNTIL THE CARBON RODS NEEDED REPLACEMENT... THEN THE WHOLE THING WOULD PACK UP, JUST WHEN DAN'S REPORT WAS DUE.
DAN'S SPACE RADIO IS IMPULSE POWERED, SO IT'LL BE OUT OF ACTION...
... UNTIL THE RED MOON, WITH ANASTASIA ON IT, COMES WITHIN RANGE OF THE EARTH TRANSMITTER
THAT WON'T BE LONG, SIR — AT THE SPEED SHE'S SHIFTING NOW.
NO, TIM. THE WRETCHED THING WILL BE VISIBLE SOON — WE'LL HAVE TO START THE EMERGENCY MEASURES
GET ME THE CHIEF COMMISSIONER, U.N. POLICE.
YES, SIR HUBERT, WE'RE ALL SET... I'VE ONLY TO SEND OUT THE CODE WORD, MOONRISE
... AND THE FIRST PHASE OF THE AGREED SECURITY MEASURES WILL BE PUT INTO ACTION.
HQ ALL POLICE = URGENT
+ MOONRISE +
AND SO, TO LOCAL POLICE FORCES ALL OVER THE WORLD, THE CODE WORD IS FLASHED

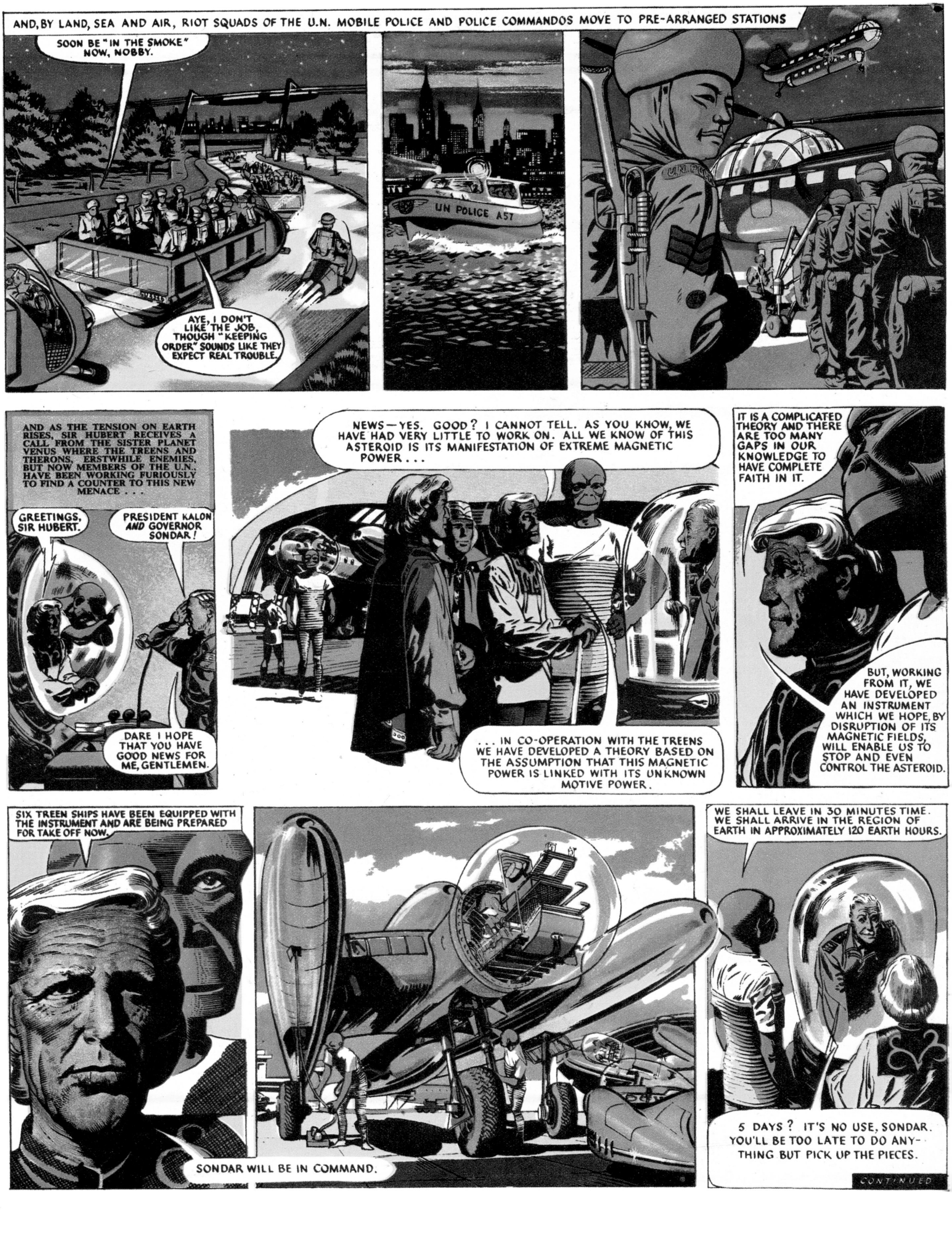

AND, BY LAND, SEA AND AIR, RIOT SQUADS OF THE U.N. MOBILE POLICE AND POLICE COMMANDOS MOVE TO PRE-ARRANGED STATIONS
SOON BE "IN THE SMOKE" NOW, NOBBY.
AYE, I DON'T LIKE THE JOB, THOUGH "KEEPING ORDER" SOUNDS LIKE THEY EXPECT REAL TROUBLE.
UN POLICE A57
AND AS THE TENSION ON EARTH RISES, SIR HUBERT RECEIVES A CALL FROM THE SISTER PLANET VENUS WHERE THE TREENS AND THERONS, ERSTWHILE ENEMIES, BUT NOW MEMBERS OF THE U.N., HAVE BEEN WORKING FURIOUSLY TO FIND A COUNTER TO THIS NEW MENACE . . .
GREETINGS, SIR HUBERT.
PRESIDENT KALON AND GOVERNOR SONDAR!
DARE I HOPE THAT YOU HAVE GOOD NEWS FOR ME, GENTLEMEN.
NEWS — YES. GOOD? I CANNOT TELL. AS YOU KNOW, WE HAVE HAD VERY LITTLE TO WORK ON. ALL WE KNOW OF THIS ASTEROID IS ITS MANIFESTATION OF EXTREME MAGNETIC POWER . . .
. . . IN CO-OPERATION WITH THE TREENS WE HAVE DEVELOPED A THEORY BASED ON THE ASSUMPTION THAT THIS MAGNETIC POWER IS LINKED WITH ITS UNKNOWN MOTIVE POWER.
IT IS A COMPLICATED THEORY AND THERE ARE TOO MANY GAPS IN OUR KNOWLEDGE TO HAVE COMPLETE FAITH IN IT.
BUT, WORKING FROM IT, WE HAVE DEVELOPED AN INSTRUMENT WHICH WE HOPE, BY DISRUPTION OF ITS MAGNETIC FIELDS, WILL ENABLE US TO STOP AND EVEN CONTROL THE ASTEROID.
SIX TREEN SHIPS HAVE BEEN EQUIPPED WITH THE INSTRUMENT AND ARE BEING PREPARED FOR TAKE OFF NOW.
SONDAR WILL BE IN COMMAND.
WE SHALL LEAVE IN 30 MINUTES TIME. WE SHALL ARRIVE IN THE REGION OF EARTH IN APPROXIMATELY 120 EARTH HOURS.
5 DAYS? IT'S NO USE, SONDAR. YOU'LL BE TOO LATE TO DO ANYTHING BUT PICK UP THE PIECES.
CONTINUED

EAGLE-BRITAIN'S NATIONAL STRIP CARTOON WEEKLY

FOURPENCE-HALFPENNY
EVERY FRIDAY
EAGLE
14 MARCH 1952 Vol. 2 No. 49

DAN DARE
THE RED MOON MYSTERY

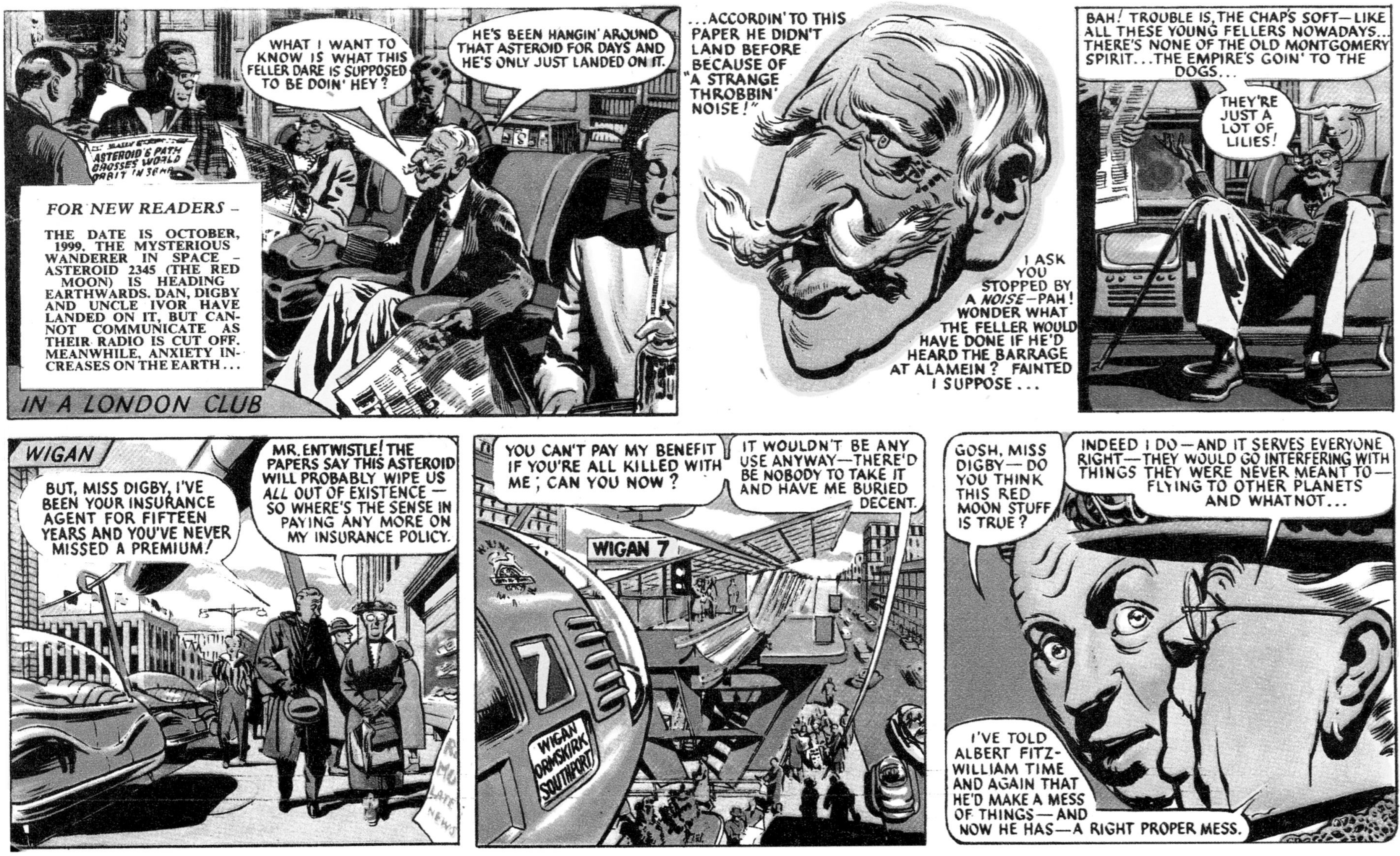

WHAT I WANT TO KNOW IS WHAT THIS FELLER DARE IS SUPPOSED TO BE DOIN' HEY?
HE'S BEEN HANGIN' AROUND THAT ASTEROID FOR DAYS AND HE'S ONLY JUST LANDED ON IT.
ASTEROID'S PATH CROSSES WORLD ORBIT
FOR NEW READERS – THE DATE IS OCTOBER, 1999. THE MYSTERIOUS WANDERER IN SPACE – ASTEROID 2345 (THE RED MOON) IS HEADING EARTHWARDS. DAN, DIGBY AND UNCLE IVOR HAVE LANDED ON IT, BUT CANNOT COMMUNICATE AS THEIR RADIO IS CUT OFF. MEANWHILE, ANXIETY INCREASES ON THE EARTH...
IN A LONDON CLUB
...ACCORDIN' TO THIS PAPER HE DIDN'T LAND BEFORE BECAUSE OF "A STRANGE THROBBIN' NOISE!"
I ASK YOU STOPPED BY A NOISE—PAH! WONDER WHAT THE FELLER WOULD HAVE DONE IF HE'D HEARD THE BARRAGE AT ALAMEIN? FAINTED I SUPPOSE...
BAH! TROUBLE IS, THE CHAP'S SOFT—LIKE ALL THESE YOUNG FELLERS NOWADAYS... THERE'S NONE OF THE OLD MONTGOMERY SPIRIT... THE EMPIRE'S GOIN' TO THE DOGS...
THEY'RE JUST A LOT OF LILIES!
WIGAN
BUT, MISS DIGBY, I'VE BEEN YOUR INSURANCE AGENT FOR FIFTEEN YEARS AND YOU'VE NEVER MISSED A PREMIUM!
MR. ENTWISTLE! THE PAPERS SAY THIS ASTEROID WILL PROBABLY WIPE US ALL OUT OF EXISTENCE — SO WHERE'S THE SENSE IN PAYING ANY MORE ON MY INSURANCE POLICY.
YOU CAN'T PAY MY BENEFIT IF YOU'RE ALL KILLED WITH ME; CAN YOU NOW?
IT WOULDN'T BE ANY USE ANYWAY—THERE'D BE NOBODY TO TAKE IT AND HAVE ME BURIED DECENT.
WIGAN 7
WIGAN ORMSKIRK SOUTHPORT
GOSH, MISS DIGBY— DO YOU THINK THIS RED MOON STUFF IS TRUE?
INDEED I DO—AND IT SERVES EVERYONE RIGHT—THEY WOULD GO INTERFERING WITH THINGS THEY WERE NEVER MEANT TO—FLYING TO OTHER PLANETS AND WHATNOT...
I'VE TOLD ALBERT FITZ-WILLIAM TIME AND AGAIN THAT HE'D MAKE A MESS OF THINGS—AND NOW HE HAS—A RIGHT PROPER MESS.

SOON THE FULL MEANING OF THE RED MOON'S APPROACH IS REALISED BY EVERYONE . . . WITH SOME SURPRISING RESULTS !
COME ON, FOLKS ! TAKE WHAT YOU WANT! EVERYTHING'S FREE!
NOBODY WILL BUY IT WITH THE WORLD ENDING IN FIVE DAYS.
DRIVER - YOU'VE TAKEN THE WRONG ROAD.
I KNOW, BUT I'VE ALWAYS WANTED TO KNOW WHAT LAY DOWN HERE AND THERE'S ONLY 5 DAYS LEFT.
YOU'RE OFF YOUR ROUTE.
BRUDDERSFORD GAZETTE
FORTUNE NOT WORTH A FARTHING!
STOCK EXCHANGE SLUMP!
LOCAL MILLIONAIRE FINDS HE'S NOT WORTH A HA'PENNY!
YOU CAN'T TAKE IT WITH YOU!
MR. GOLDBAGS
WELL, SIR — THERE DOESN'T SEEM TO BE ANY POINT IN CRAMMING FOR AN EXAM THAT CAN'T TAKE PLACE, SO I'M TAKING 3a FISHING.
INDEED, MR. WOTHERSPOON. WAIT A MINUTE — I'LL GET MY ROD
NIGHT SAFE
SORRY, SIR. ALL BANKS CLOSED.
BUT MY RENT...
AND THE FIRST SECURITY PRECAUTIONS ARE PUT INTO EFFECT.
TRAVEL AGENT
EMERGENCY ORDER
UNITED NATIONS POLICE AUTHORITY
RED MOON EMERGENCY ORDER RM/1
COMMENCING 1 OCT
ALL TRAVEL OF MORE THAN FIVE MILES BY RAIL ROAD, MONORAIL AIR & SEA IS PROHIBITED — EXCEPT BY SPECIAL PERMISSION
ALL SPACESHIP FLIGHTS ARE BANNED
MISS ...PLEASE... I MUST 'AVE A TICKET TO VENUS... LOOK.. I PAY £10,000... £20,000... £100,000 PLEASE... I BUY A SPACESHIP — NO ?
NO!
COME ALONG, SIR. OUT YOU GO !
THE PUBLIC ARE ASKED TO CO-OPERATE IN THESE SPECIAL MEASURES, WHICH ARE DESIGNED FOR EVERYONE'S PROTECTION IN THE DANGER PERIOD.
BBC
AT SPACE FLEET H.Q., SIR HUBERT CONFERS WITH THE U.N. POLICE COMMISSIONER.
HOW IS EVERYBODY TAKING IT.?
PRETTY WELL SO FAR.
BUT, OF COURSE, ALL MY POLICE ARE WATCHING LIKE EAGLES FOR THE FIRST SIGNS OF RIOTING. I'M WORRIED ABOUT THE TROPICS.
WE'VE NEVER REALLY GOT RID OF SUPERSTITION THERE. A TALE OF A NEW RED GOD IN THE SKY IS SPREADING LIKE WILDFIRE. THEY THINK IT MEANS A RETURN TO THE OLD DAYS OF DEVILS AND BLOODSHED... LAST NIGHT...
FRANK HAMPSON
... WE HAD REPORTS OF DRUMS BEATING — TOO MANY DRUMS!
IT'S GOING TO BE TICKLISH WHEN THE THING DOES APPEAR IN THE SKY — I SUPPOSE YOU'VE HEARD NO MORE FROM DAN?
NO — AND THE SANDS ARE RUNNING OUT
I'VE HAD TO IGNORE HIM NOW ... I'VE JUST GIVEN ORDERS FOR OUR DEFENCES TO GO INTO ACTION. WE'RE LOADING THREE SHIPS WITH IMPROVISED TORPEDOES ...
I'M GOING TO TRY TO ATOM BOMB THE RED MOON OFF ITS COURSE !
WITH POOR OLD DANNY SITTING ON THE TARGET, EH?
CONTINUED

EAGLE-BRITAIN'S NATIONAL STRIP CARTOON WEEKLY

FOURPENCE-HALFPENNY

EVERY FRIDAY

EAGLE

21 MARCH 1952 Vol. 2 No. 50

MEANWHILE, ON THE RED MOON...
TWO TUGS ON THE SIGNAL ROPE—THAT MEANS HE WANTS TO COME UP.
DID YOU REACH THE BOTTOM, SIR?
NO—THIS THING IS AN INCREDIBLE HEIGHT...
... BUT THERE'S A PIECE OF ROCK JUTTING VERY CLOSE, ABOUT 50 FEET DOWN.
I THINK THAT WITH A GOOD SWING WE COULD GRASP ON TO IT.
THIS IS IT, DIG!
GIVE UNCLE THE WIRE TO STOP—AND THEN WE'LL START TO SWING.
COME ON, DIG—USE YOUR WEIGHT
THIS SHOULD BE EASY FOR YOU—OR ARE YOU ONLY AN EXPERT AT SWINGING THE LEAD?
IT'S ALL RIGHT FOR YOU, SIR—YOU'RE NOT SO STOUT...I'M FLOGGING MYSELF TO DEATH ON THE SIDE OF THIS THING.
SCRAPE
IT'LL DO YOU GOOD TO FILE SOME OFF—NOW—THIS TIME I'M GOING TO GRAB.
AAH—GOT IT—DIG, SIGNAL MORE SLACK!
WE'RE THERE.
COME ALONG, MY INTREPID EXPLORER AND SET FOOT ON VIRGIN SOIL—IN THE BEST FILMS THEY ALWAYS MAKE SPEECHES—CAN YOU THINK OF ANYTHING YOU'D LIKE TO SAY?
WELL, I WISH I HAD SOME WITCHHAZEL. I BET I'M BRUISED ALL DOWN THIS SIDE.
YOU'VE NO SOUL, DIGBY. NOW, FOLLOW ME—AND KEEP YOUR CANNON HANDY.
THE INTREPID EXPLORERS WILL NOW FIND A CAVE AND CAPTURE ONE OF ITS OCCUPANTS!
LOOKS AS THOUGH THE INTREPID EXPLORERS HAVE DISCOVERED A DEAD END, SIR.
NONSENSE, DIG—YOU FORGET MY EXPLORER'S ROPE.
OH, VERY NEAT, SIR—I DIDN'T KNOW YOU WERE AN INTREPID COW PUNCHER AS WELL.
IT RUNS IN THE FAMILY. BUFFALO BILL WAS MY GREAT GRANDFATHER!
BUT YOU HAVE TO GO MUCH FURTHER BACK IN MY FAMILY TREE FOR THE ORIGIN OF THIS TRICK... IN FACT...
JUMPIN' JETS!
GREAT ROARING RACKETTING REVERBERATING ROCKETS!
DIGBY—THERE'S A LIGHT FLASHING DOWN THERE IN MORSE!
DIT DIT DA DA DIT DIT DIT DA DA DA DA DIT DIT DA DIT DA DA
CONTINUED

EAGLE-BRITAIN'S NATIONAL STRIP CARTOON WEEKLY

FOURPENCE-HALFPENNY

EVERY FRIDAY

EAGLE

28 MARCH 1952 Vol. 2 No. 51

DAN DARE

THE RED MOON MYSTERY

E-A-B-O-D-Y!
IT'S PEABODY!
PEABODY! HERE!!

FOR NEW READERS:

DAN, DIG AND UNCLE IVOR ARE ON THE RED MOON, THE MYSTERIOUS ASTEROID WHICH IS THREATENING THE EARTH. UNCLE IVOR HAS UNEARTHED SOME OLD PICTURES FROM A RUIN OF MARS, WHICH SHOW THE INHABITANTS OF THE RED MOON. TO CONFIRM THE PICTURES, DAN AND DIG ARE TRYING TO CAPTURE A SPECIMEN FROM THE CAVES WHERE THEY LIVE. CROSSING A CHASM BY ROPE, DAN SEES A SIGNAL LIGHT FLASHING IN MORSE

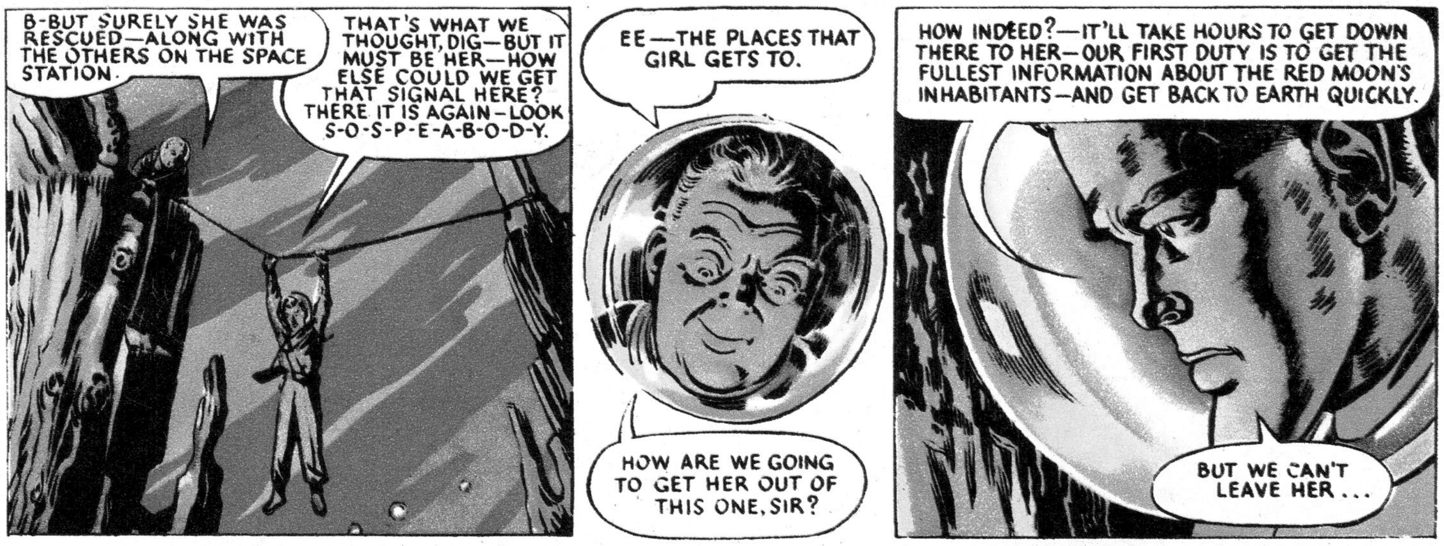
B-BUT SURELY SHE WAS RESCUED—ALONG WITH THE OTHERS ON THE SPACE STATION.
THAT'S WHAT WE THOUGHT, DIG—BUT IT MUST BE HER—HOW ELSE COULD WE GET THAT SIGNAL HERE? THERE IT IS AGAIN—LOOK S-O-S-P-E-A-B-O-D-Y.
EE—THE PLACES THAT GIRL GETS TO.
HOW ARE WE GOING TO GET HER OUT OF THIS ONE, SIR?
HOW INDEED?—IT'LL TAKE HOURS TO GET DOWN THERE TO HER—OUR FIRST DUTY IS TO GET THE FULLEST INFORMATION ABOUT THE RED MOON'S INHABITANTS—AND GET BACK TO EARTH QUICKLY.
BUT WE CAN'T LEAVE HER . . .

BUT DAN'S QUANDARY IS RESOLVED FOR HIM . . .
COME BACK, SIR—TAKE COVER!
WHAT IS IT, SIR?
CAN'T YOU GUESS, DIG?

IT'S AN ATOM BOMB — THE EARTH'S HITTING BACK!
AYE — AT US!
WOW—THERE GOES ANOTHER
THEY'RE ABOUT 40 MILES AWAY.
OUCH—THAT ONE WASN'T!...
...IT WAS ONLY 39!
QUICK, DIG—UP INTO ANASTASIA—THIS GIVES US A CHANCE.
WHAT'S HAPPENING, DAN?
INTO THE SHIP, UNCLE—THERE ARE MORE BOMBS TO COME—I HOPE.
YOU HOPE?
AND OUT IN SPACE, THE EARTH BOMBERS CONTINUE THEIR ACTION IN AN ATTEMPT TO SWERVE THE RED MOON OFF ITS COURSE.
NO. 1 SHIP BOMBS GONE.
NO. 2 SHIP READY!
NO. 2 SHIP ON TARGET...
FIRE—PORT AND STARBOARD
FIRE—PORT AND STARBOARD
BOMBS AWAY!
CONTINUED

EAGLE-NEW RIDERS OF THE RANGE STORY STARTS TODAY

FOURPENCE-HALFPENNY

EVERY FRIDAY

EAGLE

4 APRIL 1952 Vol. 2 No. 52

DAN DARE
THE RED MOON MYSTERY
SAY WHAT YOU LIKE, SIR ... THAT LAST BOMB WAS TOO CLOSE.

For New Readers -
Dan & Co are exploring the Red Moon – the mysterious asteroid which is threatening the Earth. Cut off from radio contact, they do not know that orders have been given for spaceships to fire atom bombs at the asteroid in an attempt to try and change its course. They see an S.O.S. signal from Miss Peabody, who is marooned on the Red Moon, just as the first atom bombs explode . . .
DON'T NATTER, DIG - WE'RE ONLY ON THE FRINGE OF THEM, AND THE BLAST IS DOING WHAT I HOPED IT WOULD.

SEE – IT'S ROLLING THE DUST UP FOR MILES – LOOK! THE VALLEY'S NEARLY CLEAR!
GOSH, SIR – IT'S A BUILT UP AREA. LET'S GET OUT OF IT!

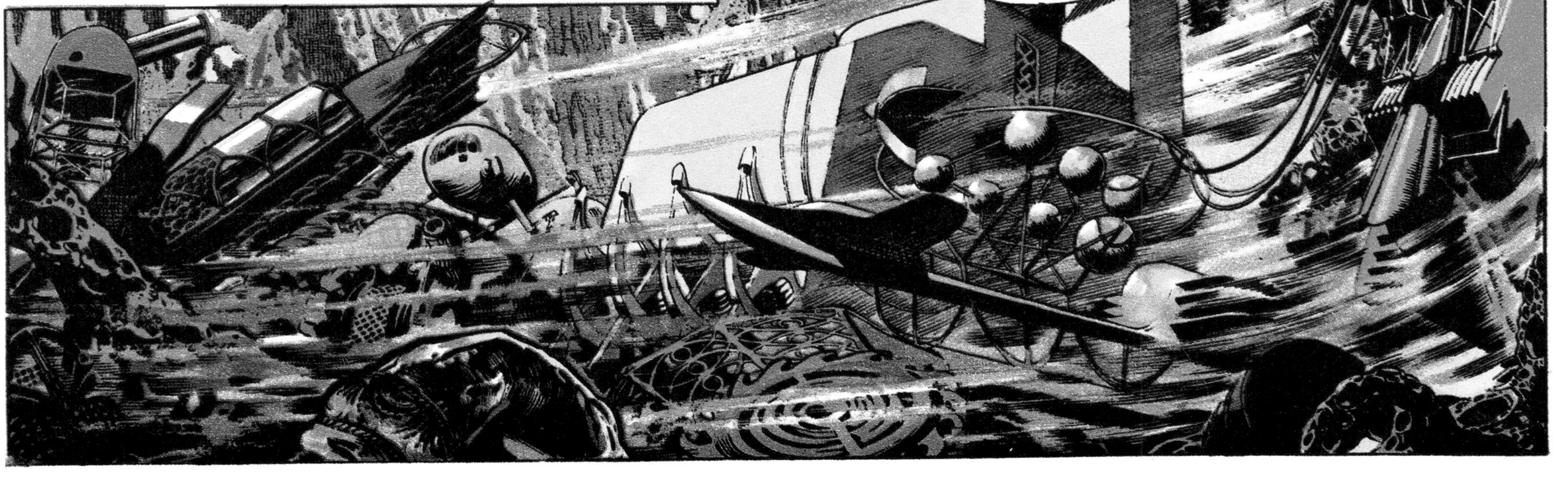

NO, IT ISN'T, DIG — IT'S A JUNK HEAP — A GRAVEYARD — A SARGASSO SEA OF SPACE.
DON'T YOU SEE? THEY'RE ALL METAL OBJECTS PULLED TO THE RED MOON BY ITS INSANE MAGNETISM — FROM PLANETS WHICH IT HAS ATTACKED.
WE'RE PROBABLY LOOKING AT THE REMAINS OF SCORES OF CIVILIZATIONS.
THIS IS WONDERFUL. OH, THE KNOWLEDGE THAT MUST BE DOWN THERE — I MUST INVESTIGATE.
OH, NO YOU DON'T, UNCLE.
THERE'S JUST ONE THING WE'RE GOING TO INVESTIGATE...
...AND WE SHOULD FIND IT NEAR THE PLACE WHERE WE SAW THE SIGNAL.
THERE IT IS! THE SPACE STATION! STAND BY WITH THE LANDING JETS, DIG!
THERE'S SOMETHING UP THERE, DIG — LOOK, ON THE DECK GALLERY TOP.
IT'S HER, SIR — IT'S MISS PEABODY.
GOOD GIRL — SHE'D GOT HERSELF INTO A SPACE SUIT AND DUG OUT AN ALDIS SIGNAL LAMP.
SHE'S FAINTED — SHOCK OR SLIGHT BLAST CONCUSSION — BRING THE "ANASTASIA" UP CLOSE, DIG. GET THE WING UNDER HERE AND I'LL SLIDE THE PROF. DOWN...
SHE MUST HAVE SEEN OUR SEARCH-LIGHT WHEN WE CIRCLED TO LAND ON THE TOWER.
NOW WE'LL GET AWAY FROM HERE.
WHAT ABOUT THE SPECIMEN RED MOON-ITE, SIR — AREN'T YOU AFTER ONE NOW?
USE YOUR HEAD, DIG! — WE ONLY STOOD A CHANCE OF GETTING ONE BY SNEAKING UP ON IT UNAWARES. THOSE BOMBS WILL HAVE STIRRED UP A HORNET'S NEST NOW — AS SOON AS THEY GET OVER THE SHOCK THEY'LL BE SWARMING OUT IN THOUSANDS
IN ANY CASE THE BOMB ATTACK MEANS WE'RE GETTING TOO CLOSE TO EARTH. WE'VE GOT TO GET AWAY WITH THE EVIDENCE WE HAVE.
GOSH — MORE ATOM BOMBS — WE'VE BOUGHT IT THIS TIME!
CONTINUED

EAGLE - SPECIAL SECOND-BIRTHDAY NUMBER

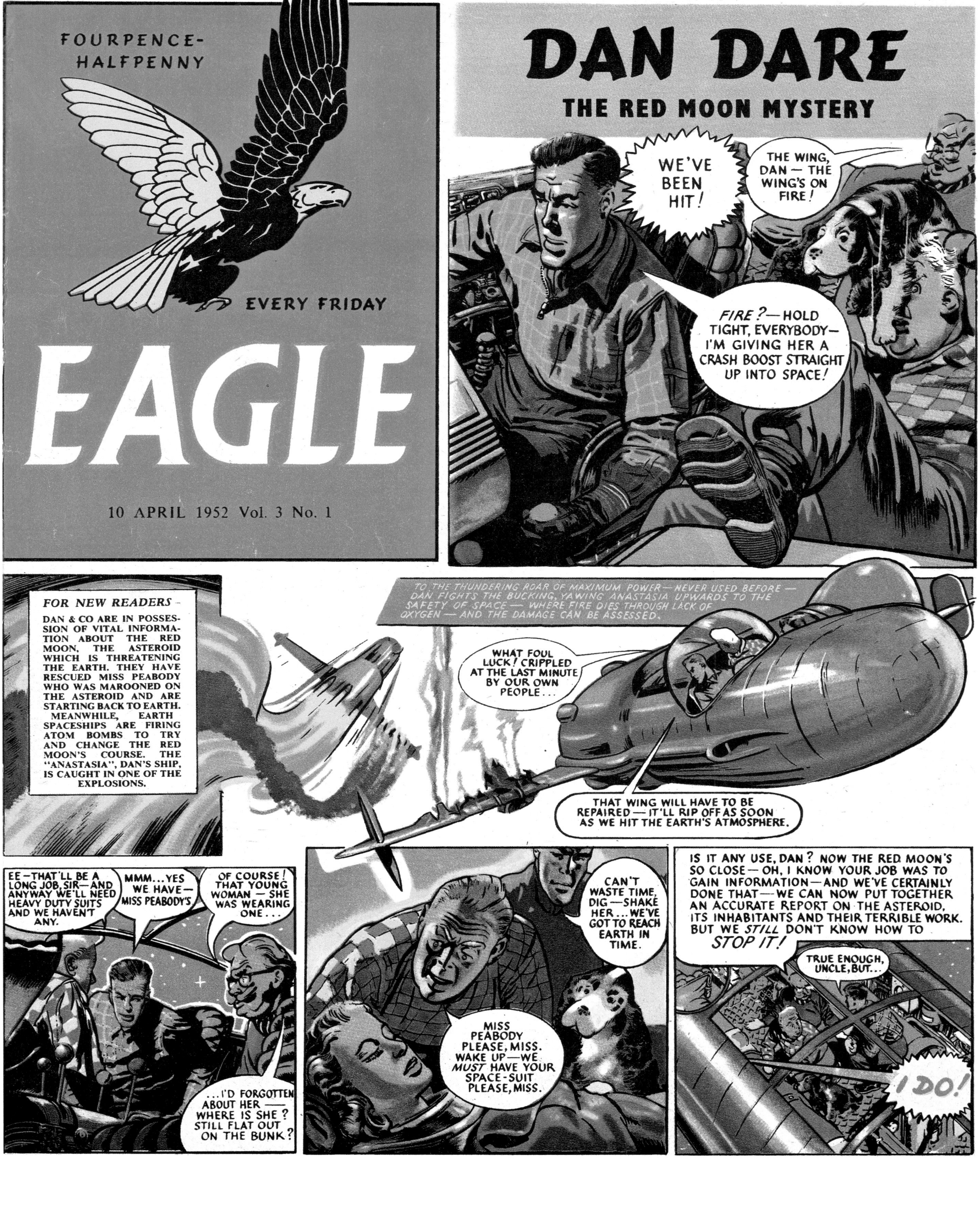

FOURPENCE-HALFPENNY
EVERY FRIDAY
EAGLE
10 APRIL 1952 Vol. 3 No. 1
DAN DARE
THE RED MOON MYSTERY
WE'VE BEEN HIT!
THE WING, DAN — THE WING'S ON FIRE!
FIRE?— HOLD TIGHT, EVERYBODY— I'M GIVING HER A CRASH BOOST STRAIGHT UP INTO SPACE!
FOR NEW READERS - DAN & CO ARE IN POSSESSION OF VITAL INFORMATION ABOUT THE RED MOON, THE ASTEROID WHICH IS THREATENING THE EARTH. THEY HAVE RESCUED MISS PEABODY WHO WAS MAROONED ON THE ASTEROID AND ARE STARTING BACK TO EARTH. MEANWHILE, EARTH SPACESHIPS ARE FIRING ATOM BOMBS TO TRY AND CHANGE THE RED MOON'S COURSE. THE "ANASTASIA", DAN'S SHIP, IS CAUGHT IN ONE OF THE EXPLOSIONS.
TO THE THUNDERING ROAR OF MAXIMUM POWER — NEVER USED BEFORE — DAN FIGHTS THE BUCKING, YAWING ANASTASIA UPWARDS TO THE SAFETY OF SPACE — WHERE FIRE DIES THROUGH LACK OF OXYGEN — AND THE DAMAGE CAN BE ASSESSED.
WHAT FOUL LUCK! CRIPPLED AT THE LAST MINUTE BY OUR OWN PEOPLE...
THAT WING WILL HAVE TO BE REPAIRED — IT'LL RIP OFF AS SOON AS WE HIT THE EARTH'S ATMOSPHERE.
EE — THAT'LL BE A LONG JOB, SIR — AND ANYWAY WE'LL NEED HEAVY DUTY SUITS AND WE HAVEN'T ANY.
MMM... YES WE HAVE — MISS PEABODY'S.
OF COURSE! THAT YOUNG WOMAN — SHE WAS WEARING ONE...
...I'D FORGOTTEN ABOUT HER — WHERE IS SHE? STILL FLAT OUT ON THE BUNK?
CAN'T WASTE TIME, DIG — SHAKE HER... WE'VE GOT TO REACH EARTH IN TIME.
MISS PEABODY PLEASE, MISS. WAKE UP — WE MUST HAVE YOUR SPACE-SUIT PLEASE, MISS.
IS IT ANY USE, DAN? NOW THE RED MOON'S SO CLOSE — OH, I KNOW YOUR JOB WAS TO GAIN INFORMATION — AND WE'VE CERTAINLY DONE THAT — WE CAN NOW PUT TOGETHER AN ACCURATE REPORT ON THE ASTEROID, ITS INHABITANTS AND THEIR TERRIBLE WORK. BUT WE STILL DON'T KNOW HOW TO STOP IT!
TRUE ENOUGH, UNCLE, BUT...
I DO!

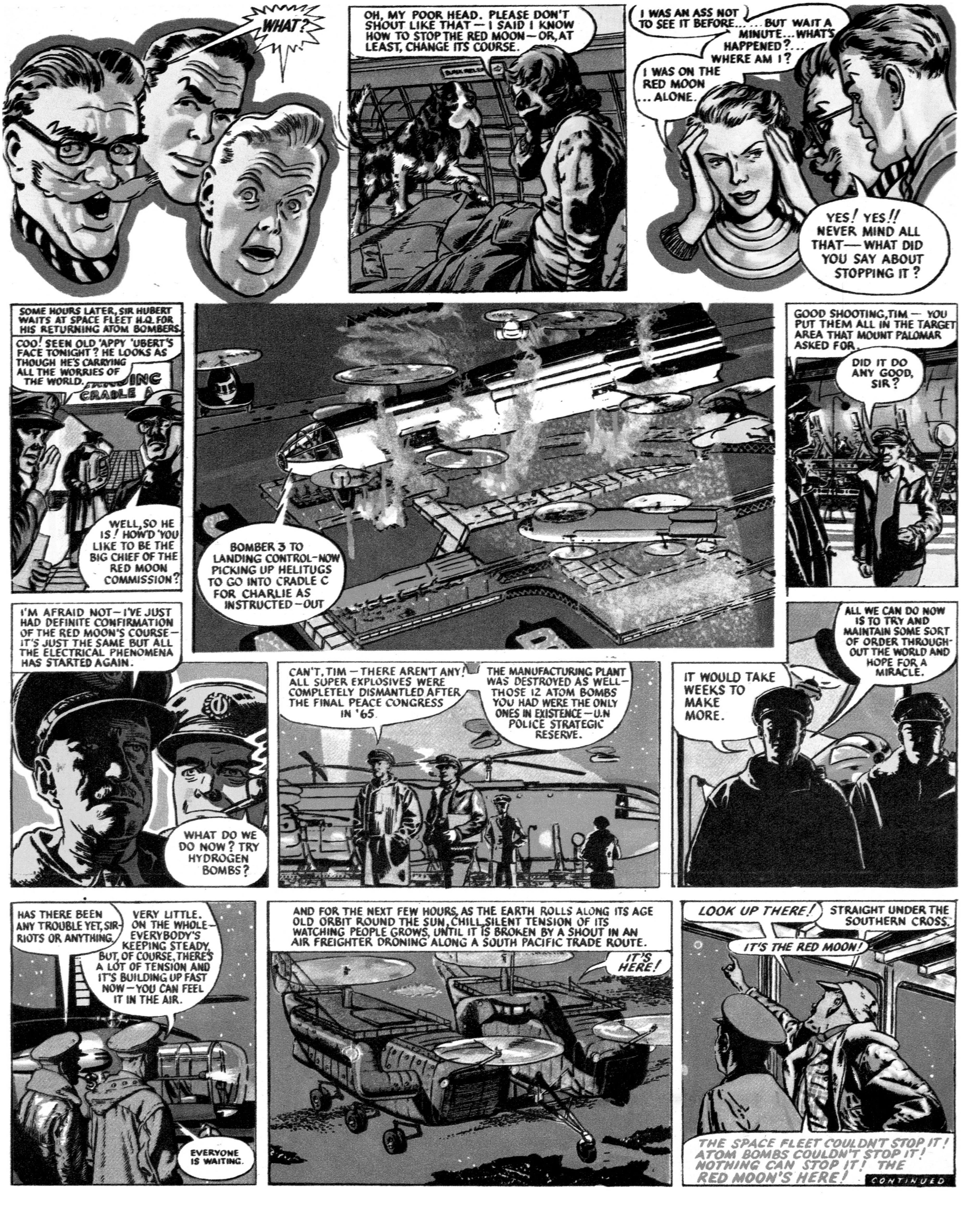

WHAT?
OH, MY POOR HEAD. PLEASE DON'T SHOUT LIKE THAT — I SAID I KNOW HOW TO STOP THE RED MOON — OR, AT LEAST, CHANGE ITS COURSE.
I WAS AN ASS NOT TO SEE IT BEFORE... ...BUT WAIT A MINUTE... WHAT'S HAPPENED?... WHERE AM I?
I WAS ON THE RED MOON ...ALONE.
YES! YES!! NEVER MIND ALL THAT — WHAT DID YOU SAY ABOUT STOPPING IT?
SOME HOURS LATER, SIR HUBERT WAITS AT SPACE FLEET H.Q. FOR HIS RETURNING ATOM BOMBERS.
COO! SEEN OLD 'APPY 'UBERT'S FACE TONIGHT? HE LOOKS AS THOUGH HE'S CARRYING ALL THE WORRIES OF THE WORLD.
WELL, SO HE IS! HOW'D 'YOU LIKE TO BE THE BIG CHIEF OF THE RED MOON COMMISSION?
BOMBER 3 TO LANDING CONTROL — NOW PICKING UP HELITUGS TO GO INTO CRADLE C FOR CHARLIE AS INSTRUCTED — OUT
GOOD SHOOTING, TIM — YOU PUT THEM ALL IN THE TARGET AREA THAT MOUNT PALOMAR ASKED FOR.
DID IT DO ANY GOOD, SIR?
I'M AFRAID NOT — I'VE JUST HAD DEFINITE CONFIRMATION OF THE RED MOON'S COURSE — IT'S JUST THE SAME BUT ALL THE ELECTRICAL PHENOMENA HAS STARTED AGAIN.
WHAT DO WE DO NOW? TRY HYDROGEN BOMBS?
CAN'T, TIM — THERE AREN'T ANY! ALL SUPER EXPLOSIVES WERE COMPLETELY DISMANTLED AFTER THE FINAL PEACE CONGRESS IN '65.
THE MANUFACTURING PLANT WAS DESTROYED AS WELL — THOSE 12 ATOM BOMBS YOU HAD WERE THE ONLY ONES IN EXISTENCE — U.N POLICE STRATEGIC RESERVE.
IT WOULD TAKE WEEKS TO MAKE MORE.
ALL WE CAN DO NOW IS TO TRY AND MAINTAIN SOME SORT OF ORDER THROUGHOUT THE WORLD AND HOPE FOR A MIRACLE.
HAS THERE BEEN ANY TROUBLE YET, SIR; RIOTS OR ANYTHING.
VERY LITTLE. ON THE WHOLE — EVERYBODY'S KEEPING STEADY, BUT, OF COURSE, THERE'S A LOT OF TENSION AND IT'S BUILDING UP FAST NOW — YOU CAN FEEL IT IN THE AIR.
EVERYONE IS WAITING.
AND FOR THE NEXT FEW HOURS, AS THE EARTH ROLLS ALONG ITS AGE OLD ORBIT ROUND THE SUN, CHILL, SILENT TENSION OF ITS WATCHING PEOPLE GROWS, UNTIL IT IS BROKEN BY A SHOUT IN AN AIR FREIGHTER DRONING ALONG A SOUTH PACIFIC TRADE ROUTE.
IT'S HERE!
LOOK UP THERE!
STRAIGHT UNDER THE SOUTHERN CROSS.
IT'S THE RED MOON!
THE SPACE FLEET COULDN'T STOP IT! ATOM BOMBS COULDN'T STOP IT! NOTHING CAN STOP IT! THE RED MOON'S HERE!
CONTINUED

EAGLE-BRITAIN'S NATIONAL STRIP CARTOON WEEKLY

FOURPENCE-HALFPENNY

EVERY FRIDAY

EAGLE

18 APRIL 1952 Vol. 3 No. 2

SUDDENLY, SIMULTANEOUSLY AROUND THE GLOBE, THE CRASH AND CRACKLE OF LIGHTNING HERALDS THE FIRST LASH OF THE RED MOON'S FURY.
WHILE TIDAL WAVES ROAR MILES INLAND...
...AIRCREWS OF THE U.N. WEATHER SERVICE FIGHT THEIR 'PLANES OUT OVER THE TURBULENT SEA TO SPOT FRESH TROUBLE AS IT BEGINS.
WEATHER 'PLANE W.E.7 TO EMERGENCY WEATHER CONTROL... WARN BRITISH ISLES OF HURRICANES FROM S.W. MOVING IN FROM THE ATLANTIC...
...DOZENS OF 'EM!
AND IN SPACE FLEET H.Q.'s OWN WEATHER BUREAU
YES, SIR HUBERT, THEY'RE TYPICAL MAGNETIC STORMS, SIMILAR TO THOSE WE GET WITH A SUN SPOT CYCLE, BUT MUCH MORE SEVERE. YOU WILL NOTICE THAT THE MAGNETIC HORIZONTAL INTENSITY SHOT UP IN THE FIRST FEW MINUTES AND THEN STARTED TO DESCEND RAPIDLY. THE WORST PART OF THE STORM WILL START WHEN IT REACHES BOTTOM
HORIZONTAL INTENSITY
...IF IT EVER DOES. IT SEEMS TO BE HEADING STRAIGHT THROUGH THE FLOOR.
THE STORMS ARE DEFINITELY BEING CAUSED BY DISRUPTIONS OF THE EARTH'S MAGNETIC FIELD FROM OUTSIDE. YOUR RED ASTEROID IS A SLY ENEMY—IT'S USING OUR OWN WEATHER AGAINST US—AND IF I'M NOT MISTAKEN, IT'S ABOUT TO LET GO WITH A STRAIGHT LEFT. LET'S LOOK AT THE SEISMOGRAPH
WE DON'T NEED TO—I CAN FEEL IT!
EARTHQUAKES!
TIM! LOOK! THAT SHIP! WE MUST GET THEM OFF THE RAMPS BEFORE THE WHOLE PLACE IS WRECKED—COME ON!
GOSH! THERE'S A 'PLANE COMING THROUGH IT ALL—
IT'S THE PRIME MINISTER.
SIR HUBERT! I HAD TO COME AND SEE YOU PERSONALLY. THIS THING IS TERRIBLE. ALREADY THE DAMAGE IS COLOSSAL. ROTTERDAM IS UNDER WATER AND CAPE TOWN IS ON FIRE—IS THERE NOTHING THE SPACE FLEET CAN DO?
IF YOU WISH, SIR, I WILL LEAD THE FLEET OUT AND RAM THE ASTEROID WITH EVERY SHIP WE HAVE — BUT IT WILL HAVE NO EFFECT.
NO! NO USELESS HEROISM. BESIDES IT WOULD BE UNWISE NOW TO LAUNCH ANY SPACE SHIPS WITHOUT A VERY GOOD REASON. SOME ONE WILL BE SURE TO THINK THAT V.I.P.s ARE ESCAPING TO VENUS IN THEM.
AND WE CAN'T AFFORD TO LET THAT SORT OF TALE GET ABOUT. EVERYBODY'S TAKING IT WONDERFULLY WELL SO FAR—WE MUSTN'T TRY THEM TOO MUCH.
THEN THERE IS ONLY ONE THING I CAN SUGGEST, SIR.
WHAT'S THAT, SIR HUBERT?
PRAY!
THAT'S WHAT I'M GOING TO DO!
CONTINUED

EAGLE-BRITAIN'S NATIONAL STRIP CARTOON WEEKLY

FOURPENCE-HALFPENNY

EVERY FRIDAY

EAGLE

25 APRIL 1952 Vol. 3 No. 3

DAN DARE
THE RED MOON MYSTERY

For New Readers
The Earth's attack with atom bombs on Asteroid 2345, the Red Moon, has failed to change its course and it has started to circle the Earth. Its disruptive effect on the Earth's magnetic field causes terrible electrical storms and other disturbances. On the afternoon of Oct. 4th, 1999, it looms over a London partly submerged by a tidal wave roaring up the Thames.
GOSH! — LOOK WHAT'S COMING NOW — GOOD OLD LONDON TRANSPORT!
I WON'T ARGUE ABOUT THE FARE THIS TRIP.
TOURS
LONDON TRANSPORT
AND SIMULTANEOUSLY THE REST OF THE WORLD REELS UNDER THE BLOWS OF THE FIRST ORBIT OF THE MYSTERIOUS RED GLOBE.
NEW YORK CALLING EMERGENCY CONTROL. THE LAST TREMOR SURE SHOOK THINGS UP! MANHATTAN ISN'T AN ISLAND ANY MORE — THE EAST RIVER'S DRY AS A BONE...
ALLEZ! VITE! LA — TREMBLEMENT DE TERRE!
PAS DE CALAIS
CROIX ROUGE
AMBULANCE
CAPETOWN FIRE DEPT

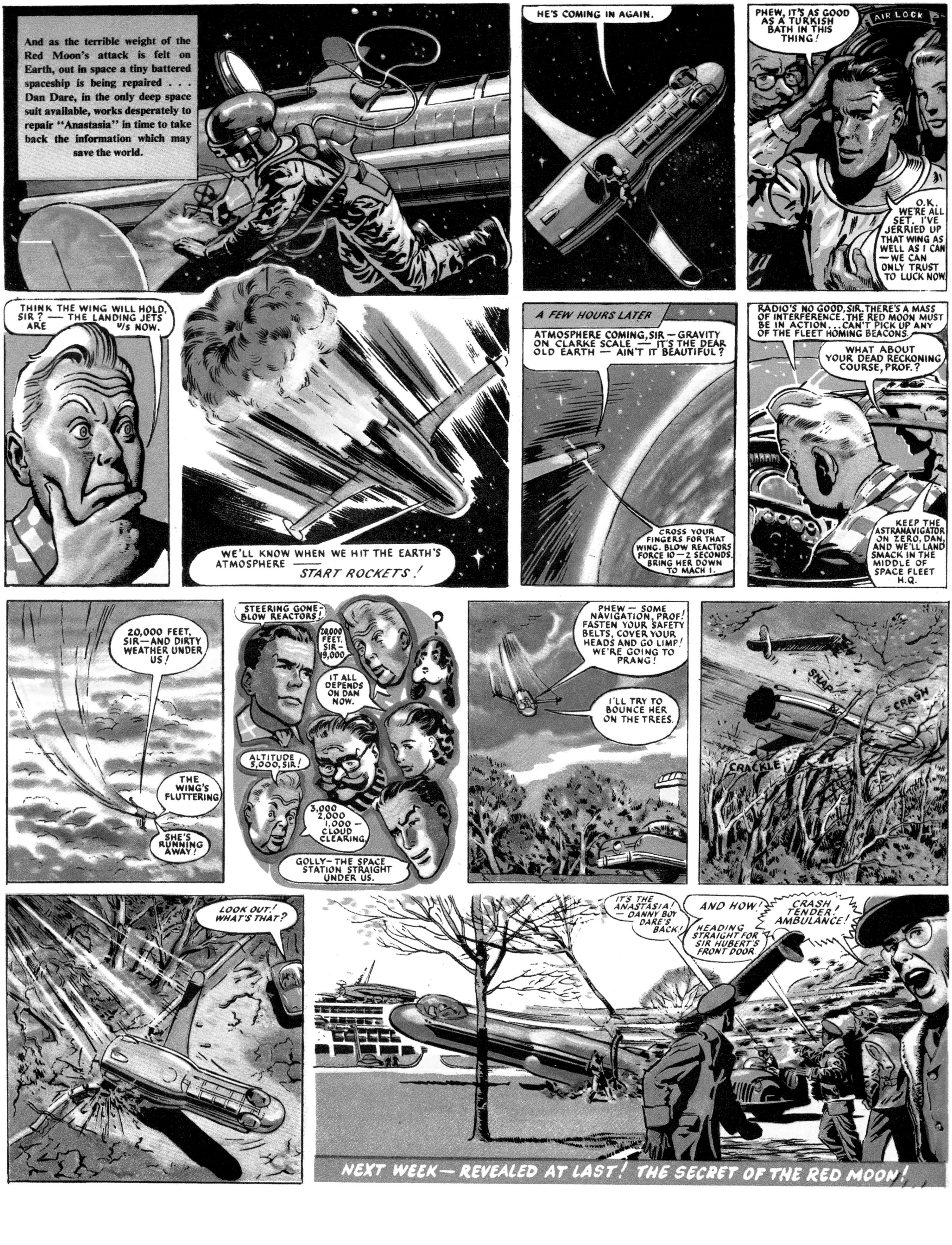

And as the terrible weight of the Red Moon's attack is felt on Earth, out in space a tiny battered spaceship is being repaired . . . Dan Dare, in the only deep space suit available, works desperately to repair "Anastasia" in time to take back the information which may save the world.
HE'S COMING IN AGAIN.
PHEW, IT'S AS GOOD AS A TURKISH BATH IN THIS THING!
AIR LOCK
O.K. WE'RE ALL SET. I'VE JERRIED UP THAT WING AS WELL AS I CAN — WE CAN ONLY TRUST TO LUCK NOW.
THINK THE WING WILL HOLD, SIR? — THE LANDING JETS ARE U/S NOW.
WE'LL KNOW WHEN WE HIT THE EARTH'S ATMOSPHERE — START ROCKETS!
A FEW HOURS LATER
ATMOSPHERE COMING, SIR — GRAVITY ON CLARKE SCALE — IT'S THE DEAR OLD EARTH — AIN'T IT BEAUTIFUL?
CROSS YOUR FINGERS FOR THAT WING. BLOW REACTORS FORCE 10 — 2 SECONDS. BRING HER DOWN TO MACH 1.
RADIO'S NO GOOD, SIR. THERE'S A MASS OF INTERFERENCE. THE RED MOON MUST BE IN ACTION. . . CAN'T PICK UP ANY OF THE FLEET HOMING BEACONS.
WHAT ABOUT YOUR DEAD RECKONING COURSE, PROF.?
KEEP THE ASTRANAVIGATOR ON ZERO, DAN, AND WE'LL LAND SMACK IN THE MIDDLE OF SPACE FLEET H.Q.
20,000 FEET, SIR — AND DIRTY WEATHER UNDER US!
THE WING'S FLUTTERING.
SHE'S RUNNING AWAY!
STEERING GONE — BLOW REACTORS!
20,000 FEET. SIR — 19,000
?
IT ALL DEPENDS ON DAN NOW.
ALTITUDE 5,000, SIR!
3,000 2,000 1,000 — CLOUD CLEARING.
GOLLY — THE SPACE STATION STRAIGHT UNDER US.
PHEW — SOME NAVIGATION, PROF! FASTEN YOUR SAFETY BELTS, COVER YOUR HEADS AND GO LIMP! WE'RE GOING TO PRANG!
I'LL TRY TO BOUNCE HER ON THE TREES.
SNAP
CRASH
CRACKLE
LOOK OUT! WHAT'S THAT?
IT'S THE ANASTASIA! — DANNY BOY DARE'S BACK!
AND HOW!
HEADING STRAIGHT FOR SIR HUBERT'S FRONT DOOR.
CRASH TENDER. AMBULANCE!
NEXT WEEK — REVEALED AT LAST! THE SECRET OF THE RED MOON!

EAGLE-BRITAIN'S NATIONAL STRIP CARTOON WEEKLY

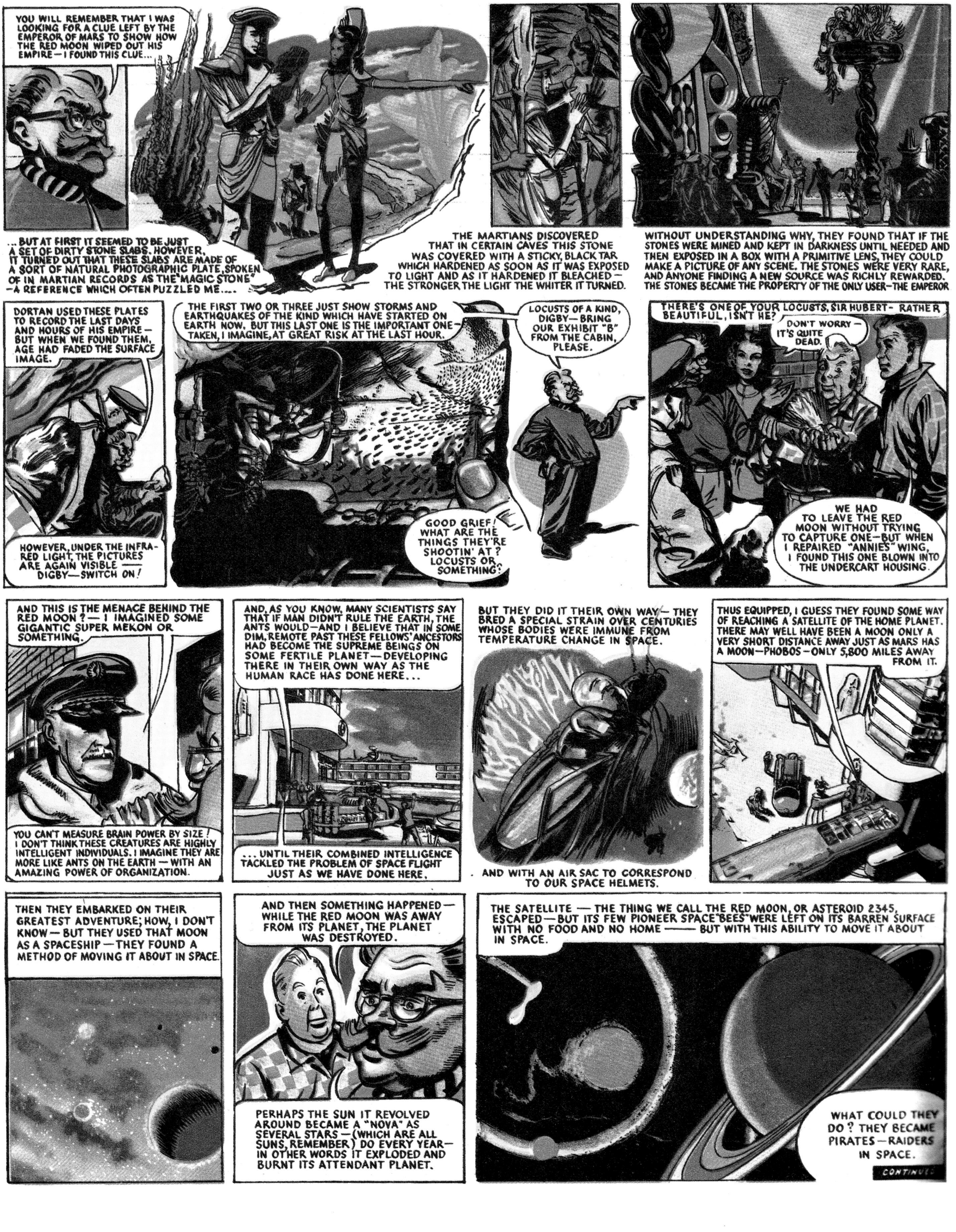

YOU WILL REMEMBER THAT I WAS LOOKING FOR A CLUE LEFT BY THE EMPEROR OF MARS TO SHOW HOW THE RED MOON WIPED OUT HIS EMPIRE—I FOUND THIS CLUE...
... BUT AT FIRST IT SEEMED TO BE JUST A SET OF DIRTY STONE SLABS. HOWEVER, IT TURNED OUT THAT THESE SLABS ARE MADE OF A SORT OF NATURAL PHOTOGRAPHIC PLATE, SPOKEN OF IN MARTIAN RECORDS AS THE "MAGIC STONE" —A REFERENCE WHICH OFTEN PUZZLED ME....
THE MARTIANS DISCOVERED THAT IN CERTAIN CAVES THIS STONE WAS COVERED WITH A STICKY, BLACK TAR WHICH HARDENED AS SOON AS IT WAS EXPOSED TO LIGHT AND AS IT HARDENED IT BLEACHED— THE STRONGER THE LIGHT THE WHITER IT TURNED.
WITHOUT UNDERSTANDING WHY, THEY FOUND THAT IF THE STONES WERE MINED AND KEPT IN DARKNESS UNTIL NEEDED AND THEN EXPOSED IN A BOX WITH A PRIMITIVE LENS, THEY COULD MAKE A PICTURE OF ANY SCENE. THE STONES WERE VERY RARE, AND ANYONE FINDING A NEW SOURCE WAS RICHLY REWARDED. THE STONES BECAME THE PROPERTY OF THE ONLY USER—THE EMPEROR
DORTAN USED THESE PLATES TO RECORD THE LAST DAYS AND HOURS OF HIS EMPIRE— BUT WHEN WE FOUND THEM, AGE HAD FADED THE SURFACE IMAGE.
HOWEVER, UNDER THE INFRA-RED LIGHT, THE PICTURES ARE AGAIN VISIBLE — DIGBY—SWITCH ON!
THE FIRST TWO OR THREE JUST SHOW STORMS AND EARTHQUAKES OF THE KIND WHICH HAVE STARTED ON EARTH NOW. BUT THIS LAST ONE IS THE IMPORTANT ONE- TAKEN, I IMAGINE, AT GREAT RISK AT THE LAST HOUR.
GOOD GRIEF! WHAT ARE THE THINGS THEY'RE SHOOTIN' AT? LOCUSTS OR SOMETHING?
LOCUSTS OF A KIND, DIGBY—BRING OUR EXHIBIT "B" FROM THE CABIN, PLEASE.
THERE'S ONE OF YOUR LOCUSTS, SIR HUBERT- RATHER BEAUTIFUL, ISN'T HE?
DON'T WORRY— IT'S QUITE DEAD.
WE HAD TO LEAVE THE RED MOON WITHOUT TRYING TO CAPTURE ONE—BUT WHEN I REPAIRED "ANNIES" WING, I FOUND THIS ONE BLOWN INTO THE UNDERCART HOUSING.
AND THIS IS THE MENACE BEHIND THE RED MOON?— I IMAGINED SOME GIGANTIC SUPER MEKON OR SOMETHING.
YOU CAN'T MEASURE BRAIN POWER BY SIZE! I DON'T THINK THESE CREATURES ARE HIGHLY INTELLIGENT INDIVIDUALS. I IMAGINE THEY ARE MORE LIKE ANTS ON THE EARTH — WITH AN AMAZING POWER OF ORGANIZATION.
AND, AS YOU KNOW, MANY SCIENTISTS SAY THAT IF MAN DIDN'T RULE THE EARTH, THE ANTS WOULD—AND I BELIEVE THAT IN SOME DIM, REMOTE PAST THESE FELLOWS' ANCESTORS HAD BECOME THE SUPREME BEINGS ON SOME FERTILE PLANET—DEVELOPING THERE IN THEIR OWN WAY AS THE HUMAN RACE HAS DONE HERE...
... UNTIL THEIR COMBINED INTELLIGENCE TACKLED THE PROBLEM OF SPACE FLIGHT JUST AS WE HAVE DONE HERE.
BUT THEY DID IT THEIR OWN WAY— THEY BRED A SPECIAL STRAIN OVER CENTURIES WHOSE BODIES WERE IMMUNE FROM TEMPERATURE CHANGE IN SPACE.
AND WITH AN AIR SAC TO CORRESPOND TO OUR SPACE HELMETS.
THUS EQUIPPED, I GUESS THEY FOUND SOME WAY OF REACHING A SATELLITE OF THE HOME PLANET. THERE MAY WELL HAVE BEEN A MOON ONLY A VERY SHORT DISTANCE AWAY JUST AS MARS HAS A MOON—PHOBOS—ONLY 5,800 MILES AWAY FROM IT.
THEN THEY EMBARKED ON THEIR GREATEST ADVENTURE; HOW, I DON'T KNOW—BUT THEY USED THAT MOON AS A SPACESHIP—THEY FOUND A METHOD OF MOVING IT ABOUT IN SPACE.
AND THEN SOMETHING HAPPENED— WHILE THE RED MOON WAS AWAY FROM ITS PLANET, THE PLANET WAS DESTROYED.
PERHAPS THE SUN IT REVOLVED AROUND BECAME A "NOVA" AS SEVERAL STARS—(WHICH ARE ALL SUNS, REMEMBER) DO EVERY YEAR— IN OTHER WORDS IT EXPLODED AND BURNT ITS ATTENDANT PLANET.
THE SATELLITE — THE THING WE CALL THE RED MOON, OR ASTEROID 2345, ESCAPED—BUT ITS FEW PIONEER SPACE "BEES" WERE LEFT ON ITS BARREN SURFACE WITH NO FOOD AND NO HOME —— BUT WITH THIS ABILITY TO MOVE IT ABOUT IN SPACE.
WHAT COULD THEY DO? THEY BECAME PIRATES—RAIDERS IN SPACE.
CONTINUE

THRILLING NEW FOREIGN LEGION STORY STARTS TODAY!

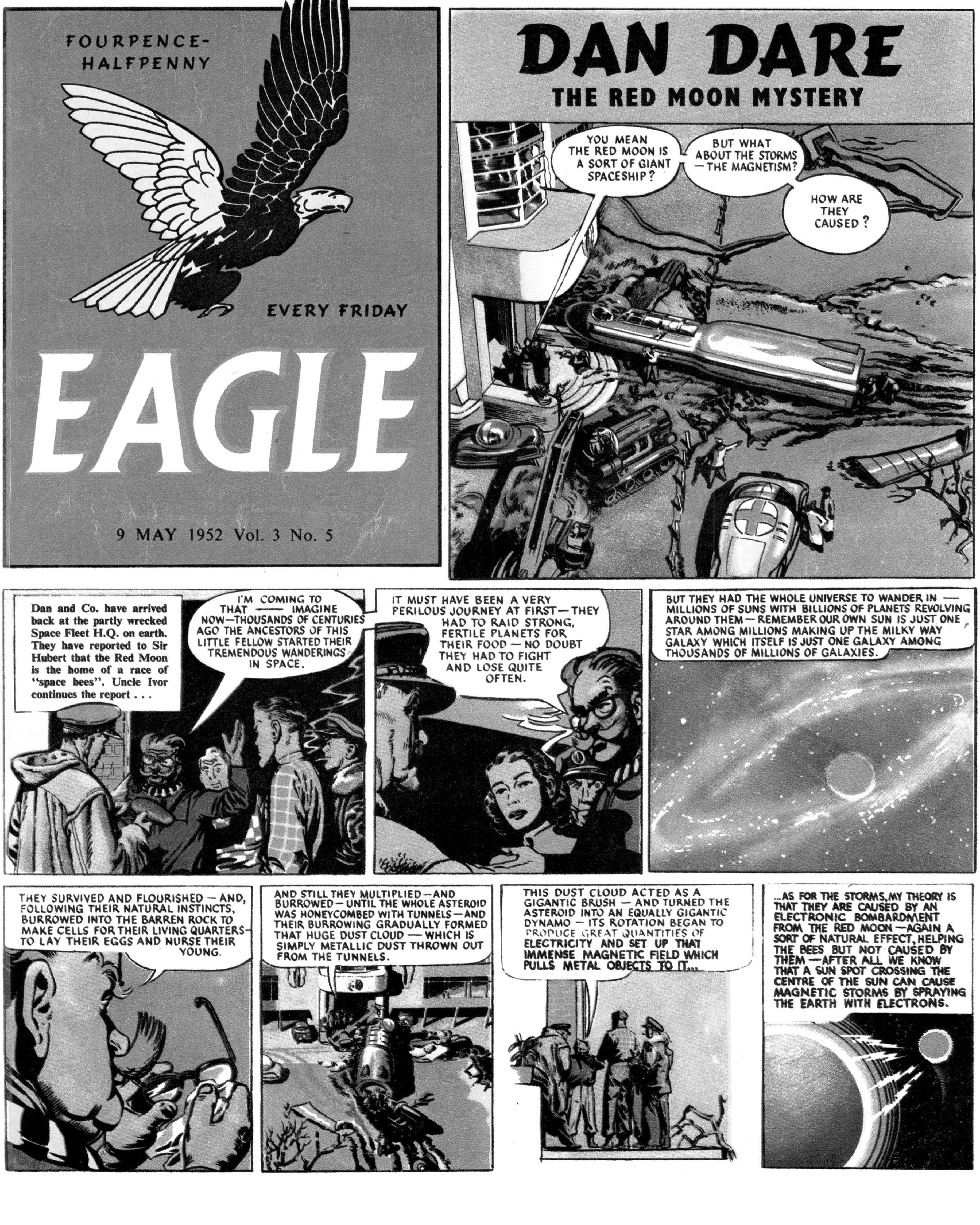
FOURPENCE-HALFPENNY
EVERY FRIDAY
EAGLE
9 MAY 1952 Vol. 3 No. 5
DAN DARE
THE RED MOON MYSTERY
YOU MEAN THE RED MOON IS A SORT OF GIANT SPACESHIP?
BUT WHAT ABOUT THE STORMS — THE MAGNETISM?
HOW ARE THEY CAUSED?
Dan and Co. have arrived back at the partly wrecked Space Fleet H.Q. on earth. They have reported to Sir Hubert that the Red Moon is the home of a race of "space bees". Uncle Ivor continues the report . . .
I'M COMING TO THAT — IMAGINE NOW—THOUSANDS OF CENTURIES AGO THE ANCESTORS OF THIS LITTLE FELLOW STARTED THEIR TREMENDOUS WANDERINGS IN SPACE.
IT MUST HAVE BEEN A VERY PERILOUS JOURNEY AT FIRST—THEY HAD TO RAID STRONG, FERTILE PLANETS FOR THEIR FOOD — NO DOUBT THEY HAD TO FIGHT AND LOSE QUITE OFTEN.
BUT THEY HAD THE WHOLE UNIVERSE TO WANDER IN — MILLIONS OF SUNS WITH BILLIONS OF PLANETS REVOLVING AROUND THEM — REMEMBER OUR OWN SUN IS JUST ONE STAR AMONG MILLIONS MAKING UP THE MILKY WAY GALAXY WHICH ITSELF IS JUST ONE GALAXY AMONG THOUSANDS OF MILLIONS OF GALAXIES.
THEY SURVIVED AND FLOURISHED — AND, FOLLOWING THEIR NATURAL INSTINCTS, BURROWED INTO THE BARREN ROCK TO MAKE CELLS FOR THEIR LIVING QUARTERS — TO LAY THEIR EGGS AND NURSE THEIR YOUNG.
AND STILL THEY MULTIPLIED—AND BURROWED— UNTIL THE WHOLE ASTEROID WAS HONEYCOMBED WITH TUNNELS—AND THEIR BURROWING GRADUALLY FORMED THAT HUGE DUST CLOUD — WHICH IS SIMPLY METALLIC DUST THROWN OUT FROM THE TUNNELS.
THIS DUST CLOUD ACTED AS A GIGANTIC BRUSH — AND TURNED THE ASTEROID INTO AN EQUALLY GIGANTIC DYNAMO — ITS ROTATION BEGAN TO PRODUCE GREAT QUANTITIES OF ELECTRICITY AND SET UP THAT IMMENSE MAGNETIC FIELD WHICH PULLS METAL OBJECTS TO IT...
...AS FOR THE STORMS, MY THEORY IS THAT THEY ARE CAUSED BY AN ELECTRONIC BOMBARDMENT FROM THE RED MOON—AGAIN A SORT OF NATURAL EFFECT, HELPING THE BEES BUT NOT CAUSED BY THEM—AFTER ALL WE KNOW THAT A SUN SPOT CROSSING THE CENTRE OF THE SUN CAN CAUSE MAGNETIC STORMS BY SPRAYING THE EARTH WITH ELECTRONS.

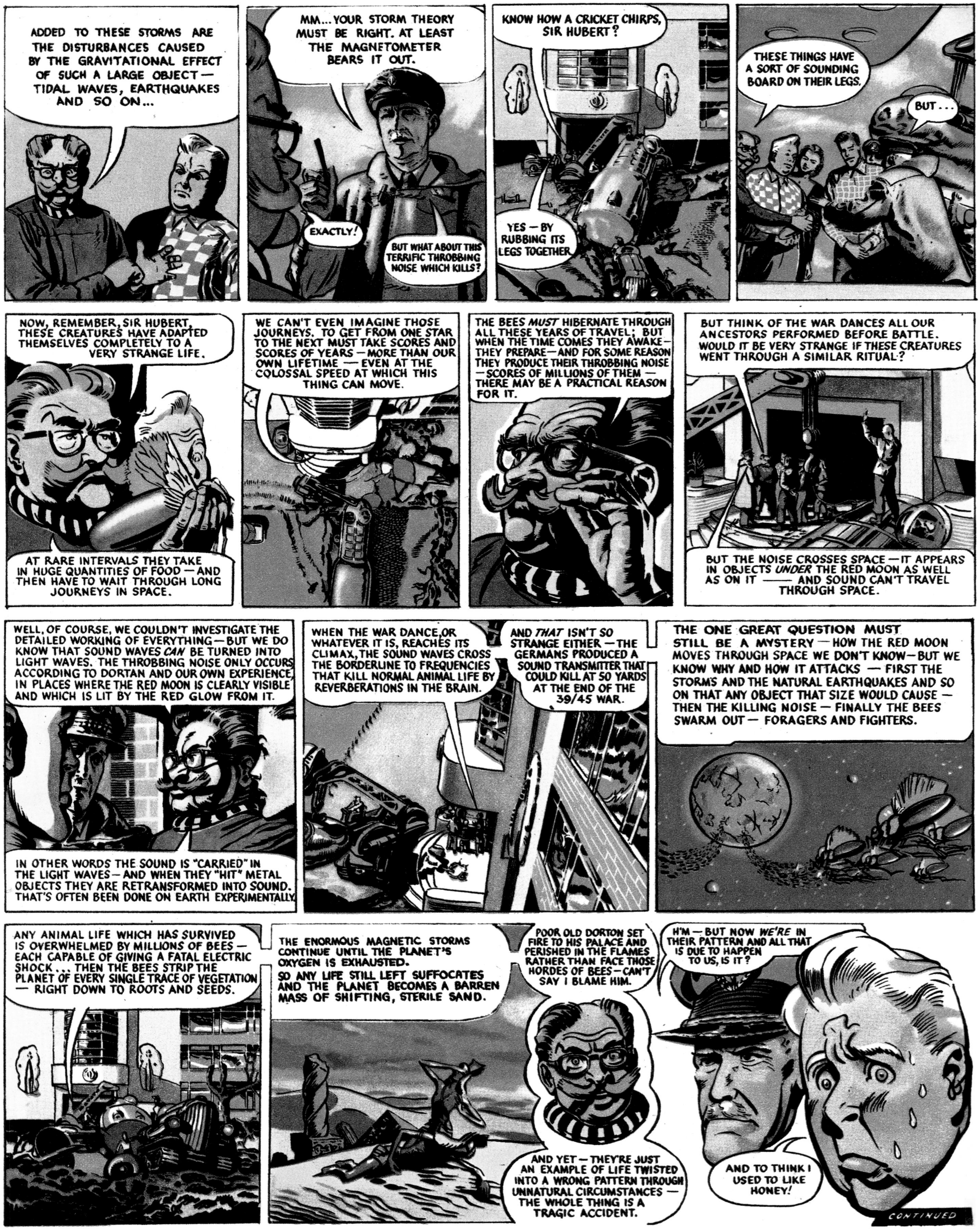

ADDED TO THESE STORMS ARE THE DISTURBANCES CAUSED BY THE GRAVITATIONAL EFFECT OF SUCH A LARGE OBJECT — TIDAL WAVES, EARTHQUAKES AND SO ON...
MM... YOUR STORM THEORY MUST BE RIGHT. AT LEAST THE MAGNETOMETER BEARS IT OUT.
EXACTLY!
BUT WHAT ABOUT THIS TERRIFIC THROBBING NOISE WHICH KILLS?
KNOW HOW A CRICKET CHIRPS, SIR HUBERT?
YES — BY RUBBING ITS LEGS TOGETHER.
THESE THINGS HAVE A SORT OF SOUNDING BOARD ON THEIR LEGS.
BUT...
NOW, REMEMBER, SIR HUBERT, THESE CREATURES HAVE ADAPTED THEMSELVES COMPLETELY TO A VERY STRANGE LIFE.
AT RARE INTERVALS THEY TAKE IN HUGE QUANTITIES OF FOOD — AND THEN HAVE TO WAIT THROUGH LONG JOURNEYS IN SPACE.
WE CAN'T EVEN IMAGINE THOSE JOURNEYS. TO GET FROM ONE STAR TO THE NEXT MUST TAKE SCORES AND SCORES OF YEARS — MORE THAN OUR OWN LIFETIME — EVEN AT THE COLOSSAL SPEED AT WHICH THIS THING CAN MOVE.
THE BEES MUST HIBERNATE THROUGH ALL THESE YEARS OF TRAVEL; BUT WHEN THE TIME COMES THEY AWAKE — THEY PREPARE — AND FOR SOME REASON THEY PRODUCE THEIR THROBBING NOISE — SCORES OF MILLIONS OF THEM — THERE MAY BE A PRACTICAL REASON FOR IT.
BUT THINK OF THE WAR DANCES ALL OUR ANCESTORS PERFORMED BEFORE BATTLE. WOULD IT BE VERY STRANGE IF THESE CREATURES WENT THROUGH A SIMILAR RITUAL?
BUT THE NOISE CROSSES SPACE — IT APPEARS IN OBJECTS UNDER THE RED MOON AS WELL AS ON IT —— AND SOUND CAN'T TRAVEL THROUGH SPACE.
WELL, OF COURSE, WE COULDN'T INVESTIGATE THE DETAILED WORKING OF EVERYTHING — BUT WE DO KNOW THAT SOUND WAVES CAN BE TURNED INTO LIGHT WAVES. THE THROBBING NOISE ONLY OCCURS ACCORDING TO DORTAN AND OUR OWN EXPERIENCE IN PLACES WHERE THE RED MOON IS CLEARLY VISIBLE AND WHICH IS LIT BY THE RED GLOW FROM IT.
IN OTHER WORDS THE SOUND IS "CARRIED" IN THE LIGHT WAVES — AND WHEN THEY "HIT" METAL OBJECTS THEY ARE RETRANSFORMED INTO SOUND. THAT'S OFTEN BEEN DONE ON EARTH EXPERIMENTALLY.
WHEN THE WAR DANCE, OR WHATEVER IT IS, REACHES ITS CLIMAX, THE SOUND WAVES CROSS THE BORDERLINE TO FREQUENCIES THAT KILL NORMAL ANIMAL LIFE BY REVERBERATIONS IN THE BRAIN.
AND THAT ISN'T SO STRANGE EITHER — THE GERMANS PRODUCED A SOUND TRANSMITTER THAT COULD KILL AT 50 YARDS AT THE END OF THE 39/45 WAR.
THE ONE GREAT QUESTION MUST STILL BE A MYSTERY — HOW THE RED MOON MOVES THROUGH SPACE WE DON'T KNOW — BUT WE KNOW WHY AND HOW IT ATTACKS — FIRST THE STORMS AND THE NATURAL EARTHQUAKES AND SO ON THAT ANY OBJECT THAT SIZE WOULD CAUSE — THEN THE KILLING NOISE — FINALLY THE BEES SWARM OUT — FORAGERS AND FIGHTERS.
ANY ANIMAL LIFE WHICH HAS SURVIVED IS OVERWHELMED BY MILLIONS OF BEES — EACH CAPABLE OF GIVING A FATAL ELECTRIC SHOCK... THEN THE BEES STRIP THE PLANET OF EVERY SINGLE TRACE OF VEGETATION — RIGHT DOWN TO ROOTS AND SEEDS.
THE ENORMOUS MAGNETIC STORMS CONTINUE UNTIL THE PLANET'S OXYGEN IS EXHAUSTED.
SO ANY LIFE STILL LEFT SUFFOCATES AND THE PLANET BECOMES A BARREN MASS OF SHIFTING, STERILE SAND.
POOR OLD DORTON SET FIRE TO HIS PALACE AND PERISHED IN THE FLAMES RATHER THAN FACE THOSE HORDES OF BEES — CAN'T SAY I BLAME HIM.
AND YET — THEY'RE JUST AN EXAMPLE OF LIFE TWISTED INTO A WRONG PATTERN THROUGH UNNATURAL CIRCUMSTANCES — THE WHOLE THING IS A TRAGIC ACCIDENT.
H'M — BUT NOW WE'RE IN THEIR PATTERN AND ALL THAT IS DUE TO HAPPEN TO US, IS IT?
AND TO THINK I USED TO LIKE HONEY!
CONTINUED

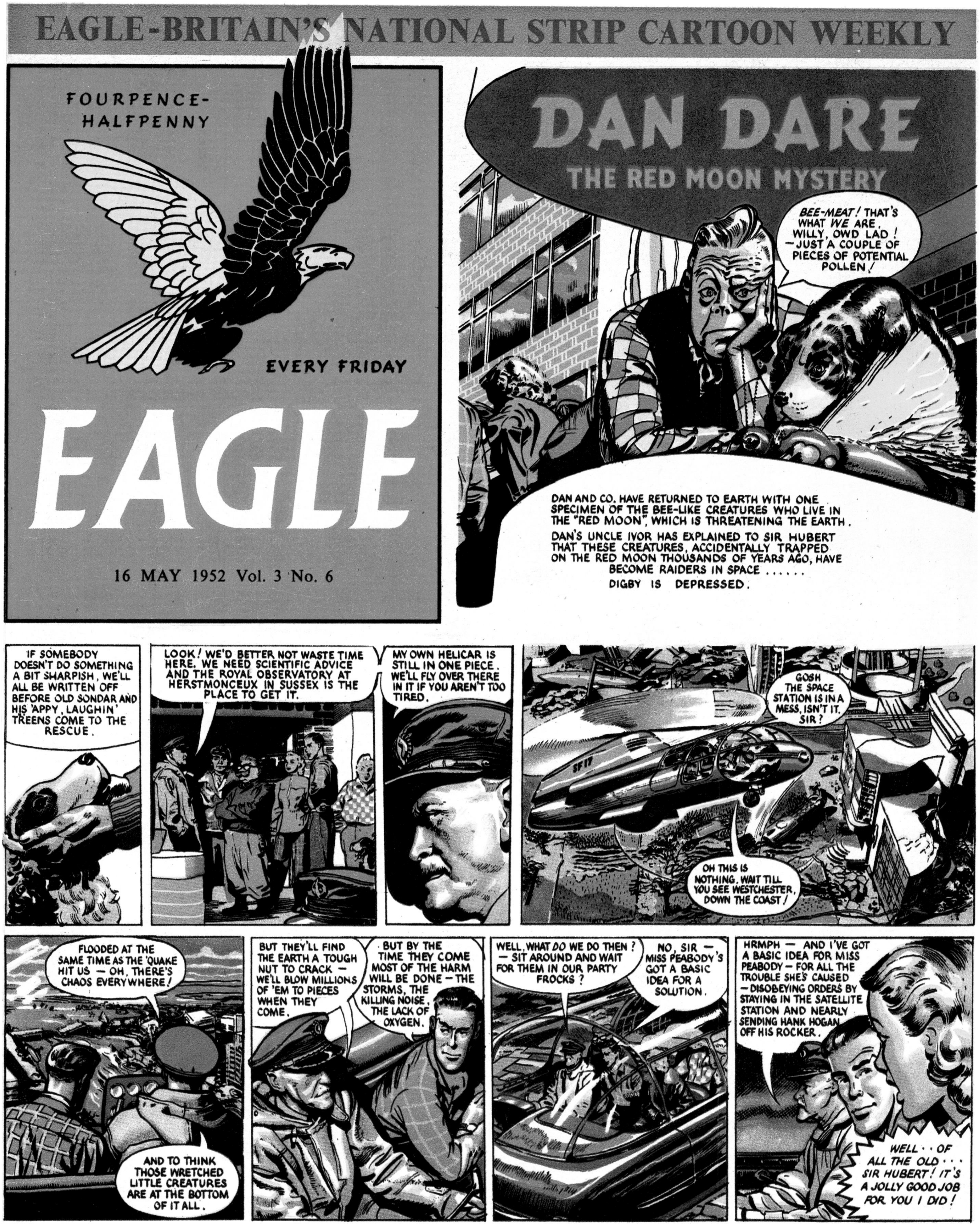
EAGLE-BRITAIN'S NATIONAL STRIP CARTOON WEEKLY
FOURPENCE-HALFPENNY
EVERY FRIDAY
EAGLE
16 MAY 1952 Vol. 3 No. 6
DAN DARE
THE RED MOON MYSTERY
BEE-MEAT! THAT'S WHAT WE ARE, WILLY, OWD LAD! — JUST A COUPLE OF PIECES OF POTENTIAL POLLEN!
DAN AND CO. HAVE RETURNED TO EARTH WITH ONE SPECIMEN OF THE BEE-LIKE CREATURES WHO LIVE IN THE "RED MOON", WHICH IS THREATENING THE EARTH.
DAN'S UNCLE IVOR HAS EXPLAINED TO SIR HUBERT THAT THESE CREATURES, ACCIDENTALLY TRAPPED ON THE RED MOON THOUSANDS OF YEARS AGO, HAVE BECOME RAIDERS IN SPACE ......
DIGBY IS DEPRESSED.
IF SOMEBODY DOESN'T DO SOMETHING A BIT SHARPISH, WE'LL ALL BE WRITTEN OFF BEFORE OLD SONDAR AND HIS 'APPY, LAUGHIN' TREENS COME TO THE RESCUE.
LOOK! WE'D BETTER NOT WASTE TIME HERE. WE NEED SCIENTIFIC ADVICE AND THE ROYAL OBSERVATORY AT HERSTMONCEUX IN SUSSEX IS THE PLACE TO GET IT.
MY OWN HELICAR IS STILL IN ONE PIECE. WE'LL FLY OVER THERE IN IT IF YOU AREN'T TOO TIRED.
GOSH THE SPACE STATION IS IN A MESS, ISN'T IT, SIR?
OH THIS IS NOTHING. WAIT TILL YOU SEE WESTCHESTER, DOWN THE COAST!
FLOODED AT THE SAME TIME AS THE 'QUAKE HIT US — OH, THERE'S CHAOS EVERYWHERE!
AND TO THINK THOSE WRETCHED LITTLE CREATURES ARE AT THE BOTTOM OF IT ALL.
BUT THEY'LL FIND THE EARTH A TOUGH NUT TO CRACK — WE'LL BLOW MILLIONS OF 'EM TO PIECES WHEN THEY COME.
BUT BY THE TIME THEY COME MOST OF THE HARM WILL BE DONE — THE STORMS, THE KILLING NOISE, THE LACK OF OXYGEN.
WELL, WHAT DO WE DO THEN? — SIT AROUND AND WAIT FOR THEM IN OUR PARTY FROCKS?
NO, SIR — MISS PEABODY'S GOT A BASIC IDEA FOR A SOLUTION.
HRMPH — AND I'VE GOT A BASIC IDEA FOR MISS PEABODY — FOR ALL THE TROUBLE SHE'S CAUSED — DISOBEYING ORDERS BY STAYING IN THE SATELLITE STATION AND NEARLY SENDING HANK HOGAN OFF HIS ROCKER.
WELL · · OF ALL THE OLD · · · SIR HUBERT! IT'S A JOLLY GOOD JOB FOR YOU I DID!

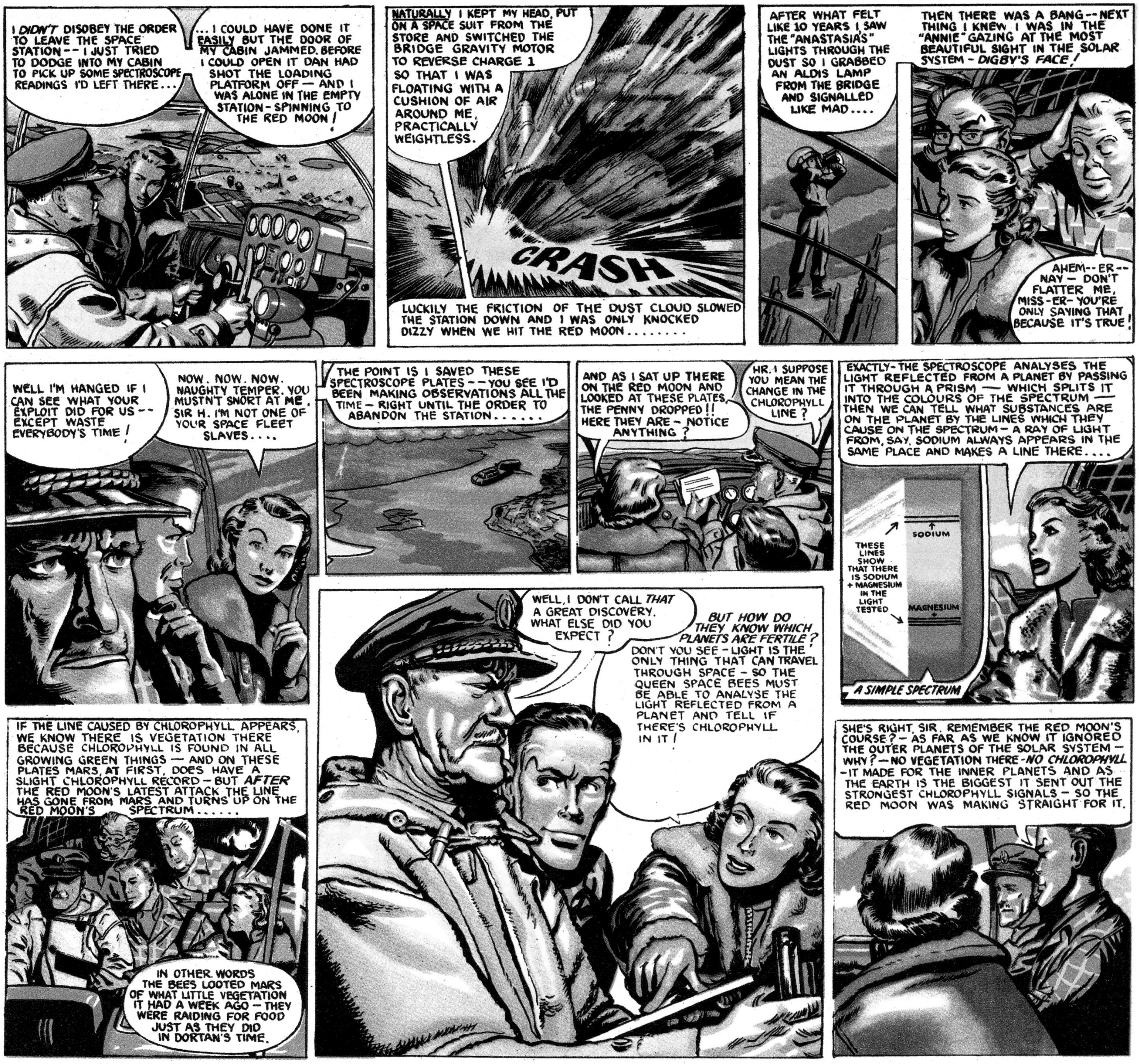
I DIDN'T DISOBEY THE ORDER TO LEAVE THE SPACE STATION -- I JUST TRIED TO DODGE INTO MY CABIN TO PICK UP SOME SPECTROSCOPE READINGS I'D LEFT THERE...
...I COULD HAVE DONE IT EASILY BUT THE DOOR OF MY CABIN JAMMED. BEFORE I COULD OPEN IT DAN HAD SHOT THE LOADING PLATFORM OFF — AND I WAS ALONE IN THE EMPTY STATION - SPINNING TO THE RED MOON!
NATURALLY I KEPT MY HEAD, PUT ON A SPACE SUIT FROM THE STORE AND SWITCHED THE BRIDGE GRAVITY MOTOR TO REVERSE CHARGE 1 SO THAT I WAS FLOATING WITH A CUSHION OF AIR AROUND ME, PRACTICALLY WEIGHTLESS.
CRASH
LUCKILY THE FRICTION OF THE DUST CLOUD SLOWED THE STATION DOWN AND I WAS ONLY KNOCKED DIZZY WHEN WE HIT THE RED MOON........
AFTER WHAT FELT LIKE 10 YEARS I SAW THE "ANASTASIA'S" LIGHTS THROUGH THE DUST SO I GRABBED AN ALDIS LAMP FROM THE BRIDGE AND SIGNALLED LIKE MAD....
THEN THERE WAS A BANG -- NEXT THING I KNEW I WAS IN THE "ANNIE" GAZING AT THE MOST BEAUTIFUL SIGHT IN THE SOLAR SYSTEM - DIGBY'S FACE!
AHEM -- ER -- NAY — DON'T FLATTER ME, MISS - ER - YOU'RE ONLY SAYING THAT BECAUSE IT'S TRUE!
WELL I'M HANGED IF I CAN SEE WHAT YOUR EXPLOIT DID FOR US -- EXCEPT WASTE EVERYBODY'S TIME!
NOW. NOW. NOW. NAUGHTY TEMPER. YOU MUSTN'T SNORT AT ME, SIR H. I'M NOT ONE OF YOUR SPACE FLEET SLAVES....
THE POINT IS I SAVED THESE SPECTROSCOPE PLATES -- YOU SEE I'D BEEN MAKING OBSERVATIONS ALL THE TIME - RIGHT UNTIL THE ORDER TO ABANDON THE STATION......
AND AS I SAT UP THERE ON THE RED MOON AND LOOKED AT THESE PLATES, THE PENNY DROPPED!! HERE THEY ARE - NOTICE ANYTHING?
HR. I SUPPOSE YOU MEAN THE CHANGE IN THE CHLOROPHYLL LINE?
EXACTLY - THE SPECTROSCOPE ANALYSES THE LIGHT REFLECTED FROM A PLANET BY PASSING IT THROUGH A PRISM — WHICH SPLITS IT INTO THE COLOURS OF THE SPECTRUM — THEN WE CAN TELL WHAT SUBSTANCES ARE ON THE PLANET BY THE LINES WHICH THEY CAUSE ON THE SPECTRUM - A RAY OF LIGHT FROM, SAY, SODIUM ALWAYS APPEARS IN THE SAME PLACE AND MAKES A LINE THERE....
THESE LINES SHOW THAT THERE IS SODIUM + MAGNESIUM IN THE LIGHT TESTED
SODIUM
MAGNESIUM
A SIMPLE SPECTRUM
IF THE LINE CAUSED BY CHLOROPHYLL APPEARS, WE KNOW THERE IS VEGETATION THERE BECAUSE CHLOROPHYLL IS FOUND IN ALL GROWING GREEN THINGS — AND ON THESE PLATES MARS, AT FIRST, DOES HAVE A SLIGHT CHLOROPHYLL RECORD - BUT AFTER THE RED MOON'S LATEST ATTACK THE LINE HAS GONE FROM MARS AND TURNS UP ON THE RED MOON'S SPECTRUM.....
IN OTHER WORDS THE BEES LOOTED MARS OF WHAT LITTLE VEGETATION IT HAD A WEEK AGO - THEY WERE RAIDING FOR FOOD JUST AS THEY DID IN DORTAN'S TIME.
WELL, I DON'T CALL THAT A GREAT DISCOVERY. WHAT ELSE DID YOU EXPECT?
BUT HOW DO THEY KNOW WHICH PLANETS ARE FERTILE?
DON'T YOU SEE - LIGHT IS THE ONLY THING THAT CAN TRAVEL THROUGH SPACE - SO THE QUEEN SPACE BEES MUST BE ABLE TO ANALYSE THE LIGHT REFLECTED FROM A PLANET AND TELL IF THERE'S CHLOROPHYLL IN IT!
SHE'S RIGHT, SIR. REMEMBER THE RED MOON'S COURSE? - AS FAR AS WE KNOW IT IGNORED THE OUTER PLANETS OF THE SOLAR SYSTEM - WHY? - NO VEGETATION THERE - NO CHLOROPHYLL - IT MADE FOR THE INNER PLANETS AND AS THE EARTH IS THE BIGGEST IT SENT OUT THE STRONGEST CHLOROPHYLL SIGNALS - SO THE RED MOON WAS MAKING STRAIGHT FOR IT.
BUT LOOK - HERES A SKETCH OF THE RED MOON'S COURSE AND THE PLANETS POSITIONS. AT THE ANGLE IT CAME IT PASSED VERY CLOSE TO MARS - AND ALTHOUGH MARS IS PRETTY BARREN THERE IS SOME VEGETATION THERE - ALL THAT SCRUBBY GORSE IN THE GREEN PATCHES AND THE PLANTATIONS WE TRIED TO CULTIVATE IN '95 AND '96
PATH OF RED MOON
MARS 299°
EARTH 4°
VENUS 28°
SUN
MERCURY 255°
INNER PLANETS 29 SEP 99
WHEN IT WAS SO CLOSE THE CHLOROPHYLL SIGNALS FROM MARS SWAMPED THOSE OF EARTH AND SO THE RED MOON TURNED AND ATTACKED IT.....
BUT THERE WAS SO LITTLE THERE THAT THE ATTACK FINISHED AT THE END OF THE THIRD DAY, THE BEES HIBERNATED AGAIN AND IT CAME ON TO THE EARTH!
UM - MAYBE - BUT I STILL DON'T SEE...
OH! HOW STUPID CAN A MAN GET? THAT'S THE ANSWER OF COURSE! WE'VE GOT TO SWAMP THE EARTH SIGNALS AGAIN! WE'VE GOT TO DECOY THE RED MOON AWAY BY TRAILING ANOTHER, TASTIER PLANET IN FRONT OF IT!
A TASTIER? PLANET? PLANET? WHAT ON EARTH? ANOTHER PLANET?
YOU'VE GONE MAD!
MY POOR GIRL!
KNOW WHAT A PLANET IS?
MERCURY'S THE SMALLEST!
ONLY 3,000 MILES DIAMETER.
TIE HER DOWN SOMEONE - SHE'S RAVING! TRAIL A PLANET!! HA HA, WHY NOT THE SUN?!!

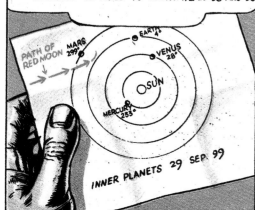

CONTINUED

TEN BICYCLES AND OTHER THRILLING PRIZES TO BE WON!

THAT SOUNDS MORE PRACTICAL—OH, HERE WE ARE—WE'LL SOON HAVE AN EXPERT OPINION ON YOUR IDEAS... NOT SURE WE DON'T REALLY WANT A MENTAL SPECIALIST!
BRONSTEIN HAPPENED TO BE IN ENGLAND WHEN THIS THING BROKE SO HE CAME DOWN HERE TO TRY AND MAKE SENSE OF IT—SO FAR HE'S HAD NOTHING TO WORK ON.
SF17
BRONSTEIN? HE'S RATHER IMPORTANT ISN'T HE?
INDEED, YES—ISAAC BRONSTEIN, MATHEMATICIAN, STELLAR PHYSICIST. AS SUPREME, PERHAPS, IN HIS OWN FIELD AS I AM IN MARTIAN HISTORY.
I WONDER IF HE'S AS MODEST?
AND SO YOU THINK THESE LITTLE CHAPS ARE RESPONSIBLE FOR ALL THIS DO YOU?
THAT'S THE THEORY, ISAAC, BUT WHAT DO YOU THINK?
H'M—I'LL JUST SWITCH ON THIS ELECTRO MAGNET IF YOU DON'T MIND.
THAT SEEMS TO BEAR OUT YOUR ELECTRICITY THEORIES AND SHOWS HOW THE BEES MOVE—THESE SAILS ARE "SPUN" BY THE BEE AS A SPIDER SPINS HIS WEB—THEY'RE MAGNETIZED—RED SIDE REPELS A NORTH POLE CHARGE—YELLOW ATTRACTS—ALL THEY DO IS TO TURN THE APPROPRIATE SIDE TO THEIR MOON AND SAIL TO AND FROM IT.
THEIR ANATOMY, AIR SAC AND SO ON, ALSO SUPPORTS THE IDEA.
FOR THE REST, IT IS TOO MUCH SURMISE AND NOT ENOUGH FACT FOR ME TO CONFIRM EVEN AS A THEORY—BUT... IT COULD BE RIGHT—AND YOUR REMEDY COULD BE RIGHT—AS WE HAVE NO OTHER IT WOULD BE FOOLISH NOT TO TRY IT...
SF17
YOU MEAN WE CAN FOOL THE RED MOON INTO THINKING THERE'S ANOTHER PLANET THERE—BY SHOWING A CHLOROPHYLL LIGHT?
ALAS, NO—I CAN'T GUARANTEE THAT YOU WILL DECEIVE IT—BUT I CAN SAY THAT IT IS PERFECTLY PRACTICABLE TO BUILD A CHLOROPHYLL LIGHT IN SPACE THAT WILL SWAMP THE CHLOROPHYLL SIGNALS FROM EARTH.
IF YOUR THEORY IS CORRECT THEN I SEE NO REASON WHY THE SPACEBEES SHOULD NOT ASSUME THAT THE CHLOROPHYLL SIGNALS IT EMITS ARE COMING FROM ANOTHER PLANET LARGER THAN THE EARTH.
YIPPEE—ACTION!
THAT'S ENOUGH FOR ME. COME ON, DIG, WE'VE GOT TO GET ANNIE KNOCKED INTO ONE PIECE AGAIN.
OPERATOR—CLEAR THE SWITCHBOARD! I WANT EVERY LINE THAT'S STILL WORKING.
HOOLIGANS!
WUFF!
WUFF!
CONTINUED

SUPER BICYCLES AND WRIST WATCHES TO BE WON - *see p.11*

FOURPENCE-HALFPENNY

EVERY FRIDAY

EAGLE

30 MAY 1952 Vol. 3 No. 8

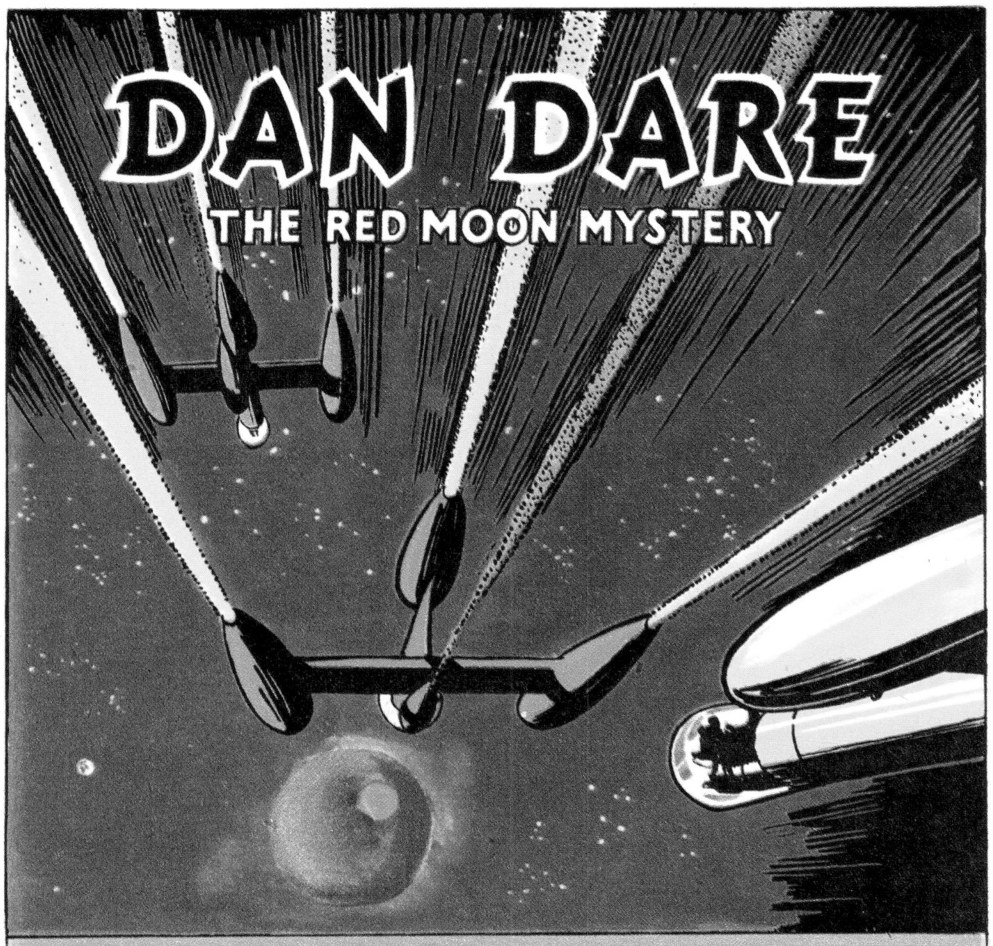
DAN DARE
THE RED MOON MYSTERY

As the Red Moon circles the Earth on its second orbit, leaving a trail of death and destruction in its wake, the relief fleet from Venus races on – still 3 flying days away. Its crew of Treens and Atlantines are helpless spectators of the fate of their sister planet.

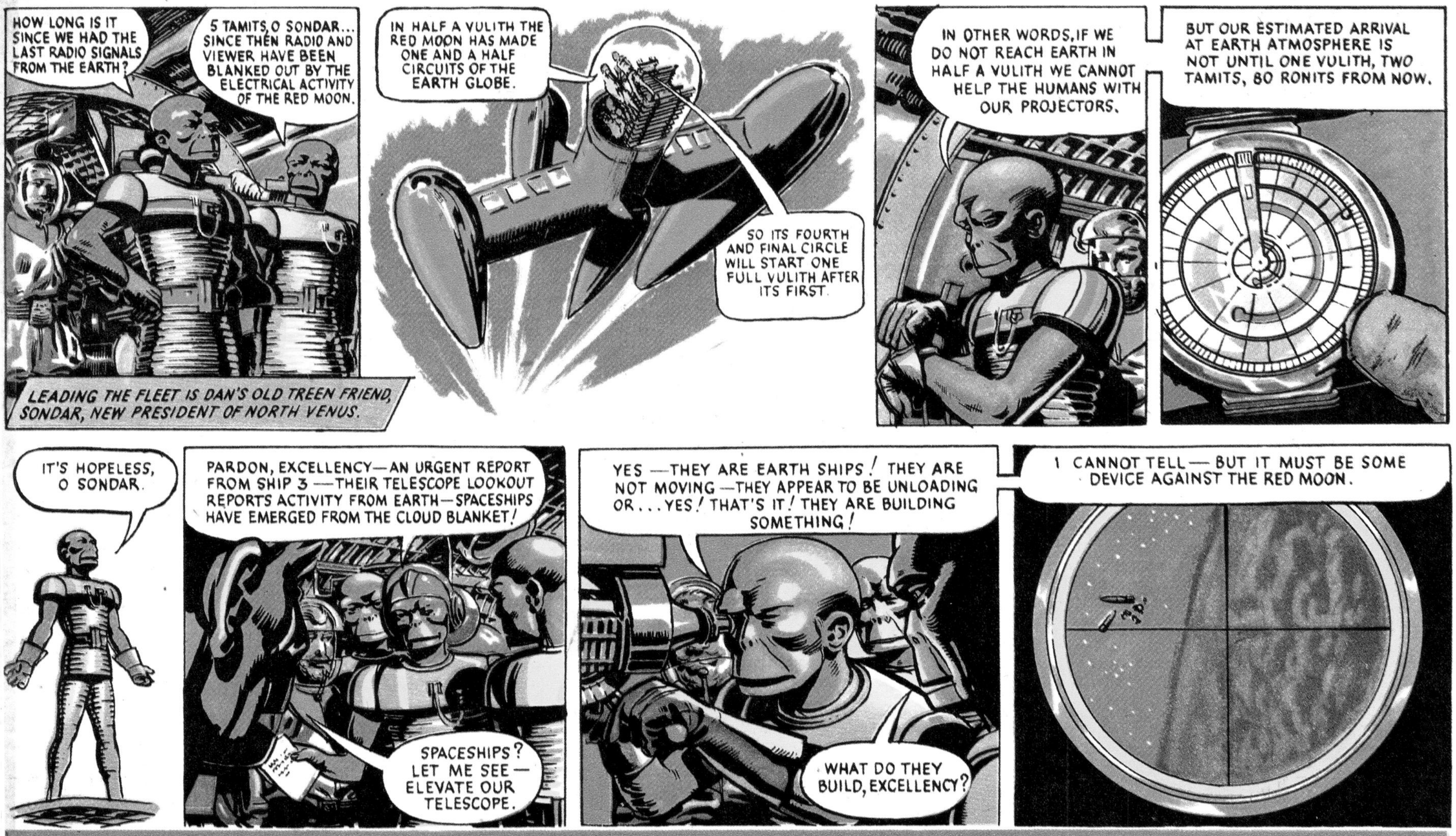
HOW LONG IS IT SINCE WE HAD THE LAST RADIO SIGNALS FROM THE EARTH?
5 TAMITS, O SONDAR... SINCE THEN RADIO AND VIEWER HAVE BEEN BLANKED OUT BY THE ELECTRICAL ACTIVITY OF THE RED MOON.
LEADING THE FLEET IS DAN'S OLD TREEN FRIEND, SONDAR, NEW PRESIDENT OF NORTH VENUS.
IN HALF A VULITH THE RED MOON HAS MADE ONE AND A HALF CIRCUITS OF THE EARTH GLOBE.
SO ITS FOURTH AND FINAL CIRCLE WILL START ONE FULL VULITH AFTER ITS FIRST.
IN OTHER WORDS, IF WE DO NOT REACH EARTH IN HALF A VULITH WE CANNOT HELP THE HUMANS WITH OUR PROJECTORS.
BUT OUR ESTIMATED ARRIVAL AT EARTH ATMOSPHERE IS NOT UNTIL ONE VULITH, TWO TAMITS, 80 RONITS FROM NOW.
IT'S HOPELESS, O SONDAR.
PARDON, EXCELLENCY—AN URGENT REPORT FROM SHIP 3 —THEIR TELESCOPE LOOKOUT REPORTS ACTIVITY FROM EARTH—SPACESHIPS HAVE EMERGED FROM THE CLOUD BLANKET!
SPACESHIPS? LET ME SEE— ELEVATE OUR TELESCOPE.
YES —THEY ARE EARTH SHIPS! THEY ARE NOT MOVING —THEY APPEAR TO BE UNLOADING OR... YES! THAT'S IT! THEY ARE BUILDING SOMETHING!
WHAT DO THEY BUILD, EXCELLENCY?
I CANNOT TELL— BUT IT MUST BE SOME DEVICE AGAINST THE RED MOON.

VENUSIAN TIME —— 1 RONIT = 2 MINUTES. 120 RONITS = 1 TAMIT. 15 TAMITS = 1 VULITH. 8 VULITHS = 1 VENUSIAN DAY = 480 EARTH HOURS

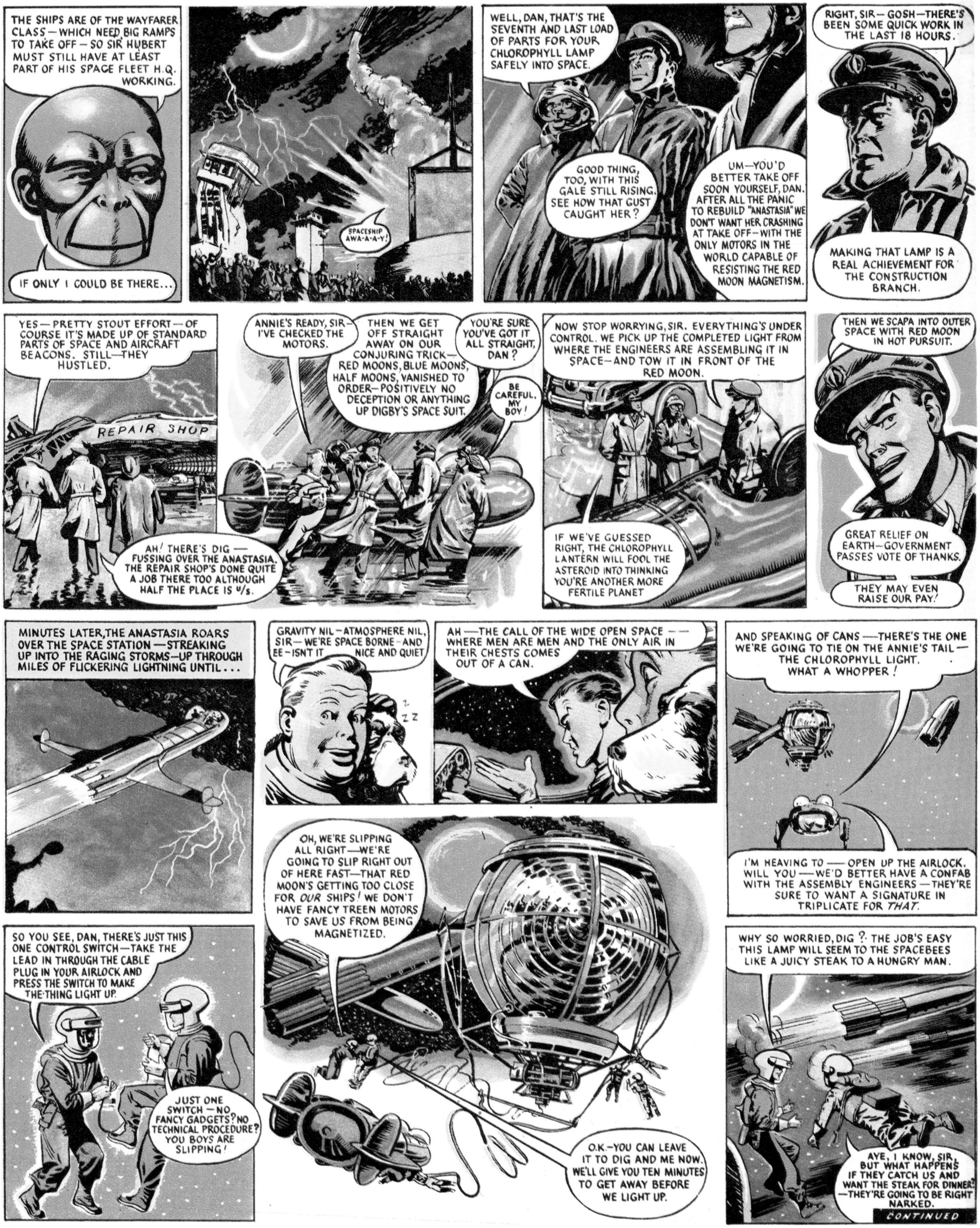

THE SHIPS ARE OF THE WAYFARER CLASS — WHICH NEED BIG RAMPS TO TAKE OFF — SO SIR HUBERT MUST STILL HAVE AT LEAST PART OF HIS SPACE FLEET H.Q. WORKING.
IF ONLY I COULD BE THERE...
SPACESHIP AWA-A-A-Y!
WELL, DAN, THAT'S THE SEVENTH AND LAST LOAD OF PARTS FOR YOUR CHLOROPHYLL LAMP SAFELY INTO SPACE.
GOOD THING, TOO, WITH THIS GALE STILL RISING. SEE HOW THAT GUST CAUGHT HER?
UM—YOU'D BETTER TAKE OFF SOON YOURSELF, DAN. AFTER ALL THE PANIC TO REBUILD "ANASTASIA" WE DON'T WANT HER CRASHING AT TAKE OFF—WITH THE ONLY MOTORS IN THE WORLD CAPABLE OF RESISTING THE RED MOON MAGNETISM.
RIGHT, SIR—GOSH—THERE'S BEEN SOME QUICK WORK IN THE LAST 18 HOURS.
MAKING THAT LAMP IS A REAL ACHIEVEMENT FOR THE CONSTRUCTION BRANCH.
YES—PRETTY STOUT EFFORT—OF COURSE IT'S MADE UP OF STANDARD PARTS OF SPACE AND AIRCRAFT BEACONS. STILL—THEY HUSTLED.
REPAIR SHOP
AH! THERE'S DIG — FUSSING OVER THE ANASTASIA. THE REPAIR SHOP'S DONE QUITE A JOB THERE TOO ALTHOUGH HALF THE PLACE IS u/s.
ANNIE'S READY, SIR—I'VE CHECKED THE MOTORS.
THEN WE GET OFF STRAIGHT AWAY ON OUR CONJURING TRICK—RED MOONS, BLUE MOONS, HALF MOONS, VANISHED TO ORDER—POSITIVELY NO DECEPTION OR ANYTHING UP DIGBY'S SPACE SUIT.
YOU'RE SURE YOU'VE GOT IT ALL STRAIGHT, DAN?
BE CAREFUL, MY BOY!
NOW STOP WORRYING, SIR. EVERYTHING'S UNDER CONTROL. WE PICK UP THE COMPLETED LIGHT FROM WHERE THE ENGINEERS ARE ASSEMBLING IT IN SPACE—AND TOW IT IN FRONT OF THE RED MOON.
IF WE'VE GUESSED RIGHT, THE CHLOROPHYLL LANTERN WILL FOOL THE ASTEROID INTO THINKING YOU'RE ANOTHER MORE FERTILE PLANET
THEN WE SCAPA INTO OUTER SPACE WITH RED MOON IN HOT PURSUIT.
GREAT RELIEF ON EARTH—GOVERNMENT PASSES VOTE OF THANKS.
THEY MAY EVEN RAISE OUR PAY!
MINUTES LATER, THE ANASTASIA ROARS OVER THE SPACE STATION—STREAKING UP INTO THE RAGING STORMS—UP THROUGH MILES OF FLICKERING LIGHTNING UNTIL...
GRAVITY NIL—ATMOSPHERE NIL, SIR—WE'RE SPACE BORNE—AND EE-ISN'T IT NICE AND QUIET
Z Z Z
AH—THE CALL OF THE WIDE OPEN SPACE — WHERE MEN ARE MEN AND THE ONLY AIR IN THEIR CHESTS COMES OUT OF A CAN.
AND SPEAKING OF CANS—THERE'S THE ONE WE'RE GOING TO TIE ON THE ANNIE'S TAIL—THE CHLOROPHYLL LIGHT. WHAT A WHOPPER!
I'M HEAVING TO — OPEN UP THE AIRLOCK, WILL YOU — WE'D BETTER HAVE A CONFAB WITH THE ASSEMBLY ENGINEERS — THEY'RE SURE TO WANT A SIGNATURE IN TRIPLICATE FOR THAT.
SO YOU SEE, DAN, THERE'S JUST THIS ONE CONTROL SWITCH—TAKE THE LEAD IN THROUGH THE CABLE PLUG IN YOUR AIRLOCK AND PRESS THE SWITCH TO MAKE THE THING LIGHT UP.
JUST ONE SWITCH—NO FANCY GADGETS? NO TECHNICAL PROCEDURE? YOU BOYS ARE SLIPPING!
OH, WE'RE SLIPPING ALL RIGHT—WE'RE GOING TO SLIP RIGHT OUT OF HERE FAST—THAT RED MOON'S GETTING TOO CLOSE FOR OUR SHIPS! WE DON'T HAVE FANCY TREEN MOTORS TO SAVE US FROM BEING MAGNETIZED.
O.K.—YOU CAN LEAVE IT TO DIG AND ME NOW. WE'LL GIVE YOU TEN MINUTES TO GET AWAY BEFORE WE LIGHT UP.
WHY SO WORRIED, DIG? THE JOB'S EASY THIS LAMP WILL SEEM TO THE SPACEBEES LIKE A JUICY STEAK TO A HUNGRY MAN.
AYE, I KNOW, SIR, BUT WHAT HAPPENS IF THEY CATCH US AND WANT THE STEAK FOR DINNER? —THEY'RE GOING TO BE RIGHT NARKED.
CONTINUED

EXCITING COMPETITION INSIDE WITH HANDSOME PRIZES

FOURPENCE-HALFPENNY

EVERY FRIDAY

EAGLE

6 JUNE 1952 Vol. 3 No. 9

DAN DARE
THE RED MOON MYSTERY
HERE WE GO! ALADDIN DARE AND HIS WONDERFUL LAMP.
NOT TO MENTION DIGBY—THE UTILITY GENIE!
Straight across the Red Moon's path, Dan sweeps with the 'bait', the chlorophyll light which should make the 'space bees' think another, more fertile, planet is passing between their home and earth . . .

THINK IT'S GOING TO WORK, DAN?
EEK!
PEABODY! WHERE DID YOU SPRING FROM?
THAT LITTLE CUBBY HOLE BEHIND THE AIRLOCK—AND YOU REALLY OUGHT TO CLEAN IT OUT—YOU'LL HAVE MICE IN THERE IF YOU DON'T.
WUFF
YOU SURELY DIDN'T THINK I'D MISS ALL THE FUN FROM MY OWN IDEA, DID YOU? BUT I KNEW SIR HUBERT WOULDN'T GIVE ME PERMISSION TO COME . . .
SO I JUST STOWED AWAY.
ON EARTH AT HURSTMONCEUX OBSERVATORY, SIR HUBERT WATCHES ANXIOUSLY IN AN OPERATIONS ROOM HASTILY RIGGED UP WITH INSTRUMENTS SALVAGED FROM THE BATTERED SPACE FLEET H.Q.
ANYTHING HAPPENED YET?
TELESCOPE VISIBILITY NIL, SIR.
ASTRARADAR SHOWS RED MOON CLOSING EARTH ON SECOND CIRCUIT.
ANASTASIA MOVING OUT ON COURSE AC 17/29 BL/2391
DAN'S STARTED—KEEP YOUR FINGERS CROSSED, SIR.
RED MOON STILL CLOSING EARTH.
ANASTASIA CLOSING RED MOON!
SHE'S STOPPED... RED MOON'S STOPPED COMING NEARER.
BUT SHE ISN'T MOVING AWAY EITHER.

INCREDIBLE—SHE'S HANGING OUT THERE MAINTAINING THE SAME SPEED AS EARTH.
WHAT'S HAPPENING?
THEY'RE PUZZLED, SIR HUBERT—THE SPACE BEES—THEY DON'T KNOW WHAT TO MAKE OF THE CHLOROPHYLL LIGHT.
ANASTASIA'S CUT HER ENGINES, SIR—COLONEL DARE IS KEEPING THE BAIT IN FRONT OF THE RED MOON.
TWO HOURS—AND THEY'RE STILL STUCK OUT THERE — I'M AGEING TEN YEARS EVERY MINUTE —THAT THING'S GOT TO JUMP ONE WAY OR THE OTHER.
SOON I WON'T MIND WHICH.
AND OUT IN SPACE...
I'M BEGINNING TO THINK WE'RE STUCK HERE FOR GOOD.
RUMPELSTILTSKIN O COULD HE SEW COULD HE SEW
WHATEVER ARE YOU DOING, DIG?
IMPROVING THE SHINING HOUR, MISS—JUST FINISHING OFF A LITTLE SPACE SUIT FOR WILLY... ...FOR THE NEXT TIME WE LAND IN TROUBLE...
I'LL HELP YOU, DIG—LET'S GO IN AND DO IT NOW.
ALL I HAVE TO DO NOW IS MAKE HIM LIKE IT.
THERE'S A GOOD DOG—NOW COME ON—THAT'S REET—EE—LOOKS RIGHT COMFY IN IT, DOESN'T HE, MISS?
H'M—A LITTLE PUZZLED PERHAPS.
ACTION!!—START UP, DIG—SHE'S MOVING!
AIR LOCK
IT WORKED, MES ENFANTS, THE RED MOON'S AFTER US NOW!
RED MOON'S MOVING OUT, SIR!
SHE'S MOVING OUT—SHE'S MOVING OUT!
HE'S DONE IT! DAN'S DONE IT! IT'S SWALLOWED THE BAIT!
HOORAY!
RADIO'S CLEARING, SIR I'M THROUGH TO THE TREEN FLEET AGAIN.
OH, GOOD—LET ME SPEAK TO SONDAR.
I UNDERSTAND, SIR HUBERT. I WILL CHANGE COURSE TO MEET COLONEL DARE IN DEEP SPACE.
WHAT'S SONDAR GOT ON THOSE SHIPS OF HIS?
SOME NEW DEVICE—A SORT OF RAY—WHICH THEY THINK ON VENUS WILL STOP THE RED MOON'S MOTION AND PARALYSE THE SPACE BEES.
IF DAN CAN KEEP AHEAD OF THE THING THEY'LL MEET IN 72 HOURS.
AND FOR THE NEXT THREE DAYS, EVERY ASTRA VIEWER AND TELESCOPE ON EARTH THAT CAN BE BROUGHT TO BEAR FOLLOWS THE DRAMA MOVING TO ITS CLIMAX IN THE VELVETY DEPTHS OF SPACE, AS THE TREEN FLEET RACES TO MEET
THE ANASTASIA, PLUGGING GRIMLY ALONG WITH ITS HEAVY BURDEN—AND ITS TERRIBLE PURSUER...
UNTIL...
GOOD OLD SONDAR!
TREEN FLEET IN SIGHT—CAST OFF OUR NIGHT LIGHT, DIG.
CALLING TREEN FLEET—CALLING TREEN FLEET—HELLO, SONDAR, YOU OLD GREEN HORROR—ONE RED MOON FOR YOU AS PER SCHEDULE.
CAN WE COME ABOARD AND WATCH THE FUN?
SALUTATIONS, O DAN. COME ALONGSIDE AND WE'LL PICK YOU UP.
FLEET TO ACTION STATIONS—CIRCLE THE RED MOON.
CONTINUED

EAGLE-BRITAIN'S NATIONAL STRIP CARTOON WEEKLY

FOURPENCE-HALFPENNY

EVERY FRIDAY

EAGLE

13 JUNE 1952 Vol. 3 No. 10

DAN DARE
THE RED MOON MYSTERY

BE STILL, WILLY!

Dan and Co's plan to lure the Red Moon away from Earth with a chlorophyll light has succeeded and now, having met the Treen Fleet, they are transferring to Sondar's ship to watch the Treens attack the asteroid with their projectors.

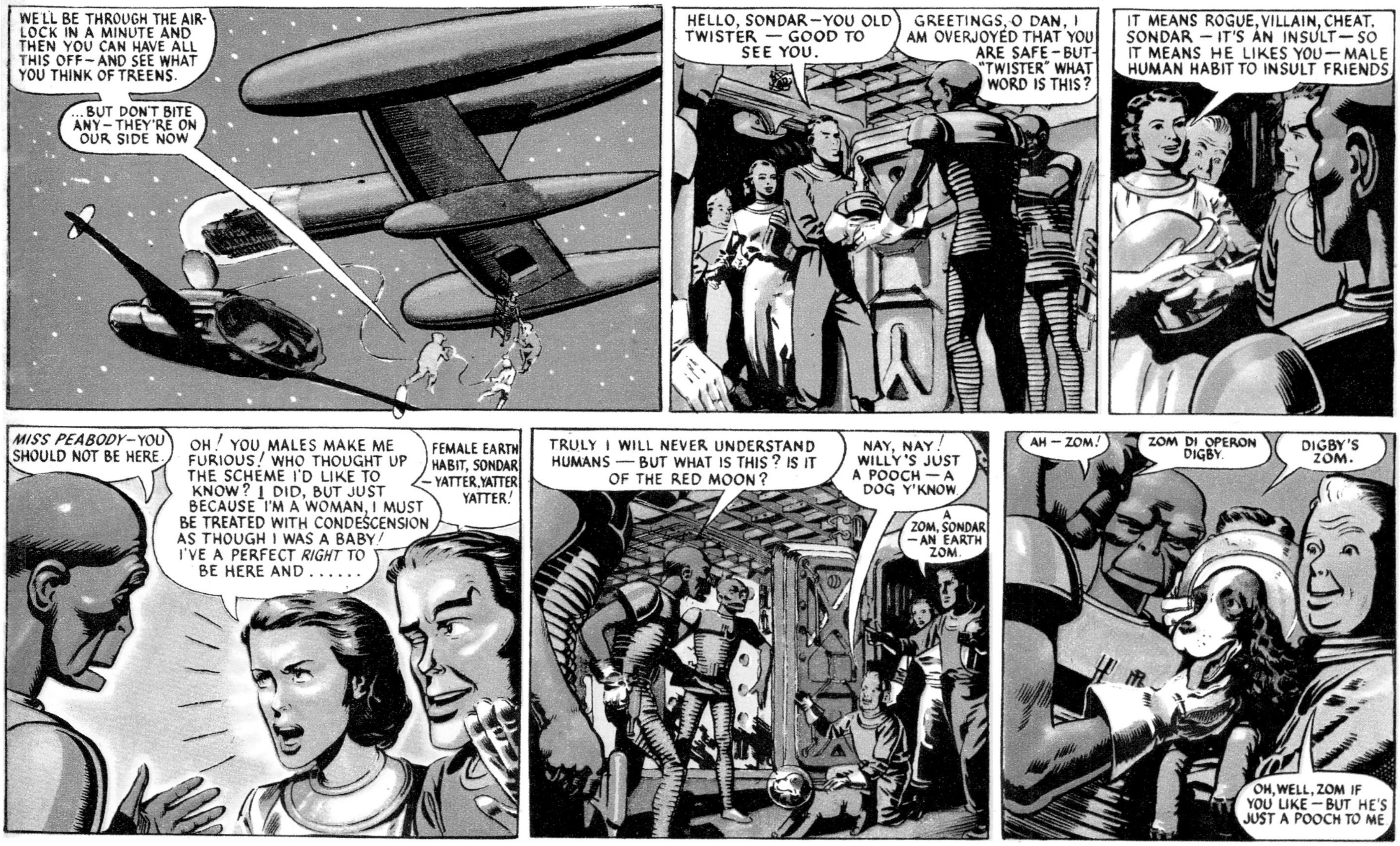

WE'LL BE THROUGH THE AIR-LOCK IN A MINUTE AND THEN YOU CAN HAVE ALL THIS OFF—AND SEE WHAT YOU THINK OF TREENS.
...BUT DON'T BITE ANY—THEY'RE ON OUR SIDE NOW
HELLO, SONDAR—YOU OLD TWISTER — GOOD TO SEE YOU.
GREETINGS, O DAN, I AM OVERJOYED THAT YOU ARE SAFE—BUT-"TWISTER" WHAT WORD IS THIS?
IT MEANS ROGUE, VILLAIN, CHEAT. SONDAR — IT'S AN INSULT — SO IT MEANS HE LIKES YOU — MALE HUMAN HABIT TO INSULT FRIENDS
MISS PEABODY—YOU SHOULD NOT BE HERE.
OH! YOU MALES MAKE ME FURIOUS! WHO THOUGHT UP THE SCHEME I'D LIKE TO KNOW? I DID, BUT JUST BECAUSE I'M A WOMAN, I MUST BE TREATED WITH CONDESCENSION AS THOUGH I WAS A BABY! I'VE A PERFECT RIGHT TO BE HERE AND ......
FEMALE EARTH HABIT, SONDAR —YATTER, YATTER, YATTER!
TRULY I WILL NEVER UNDERSTAND HUMANS — BUT WHAT IS THIS? IS IT OF THE RED MOON?
NAY, NAY! WILLY'S JUST A POOCH — A DOG Y'KNOW.
A ZOM, SONDAR —AN EARTH ZOM.
AH — ZOM!
ZOM DI OPERON DIGBY.
DIGBY'S ZOM.
OH, WELL, ZOM IF YOU LIKE—BUT HE'S JUST A POOCH TO ME

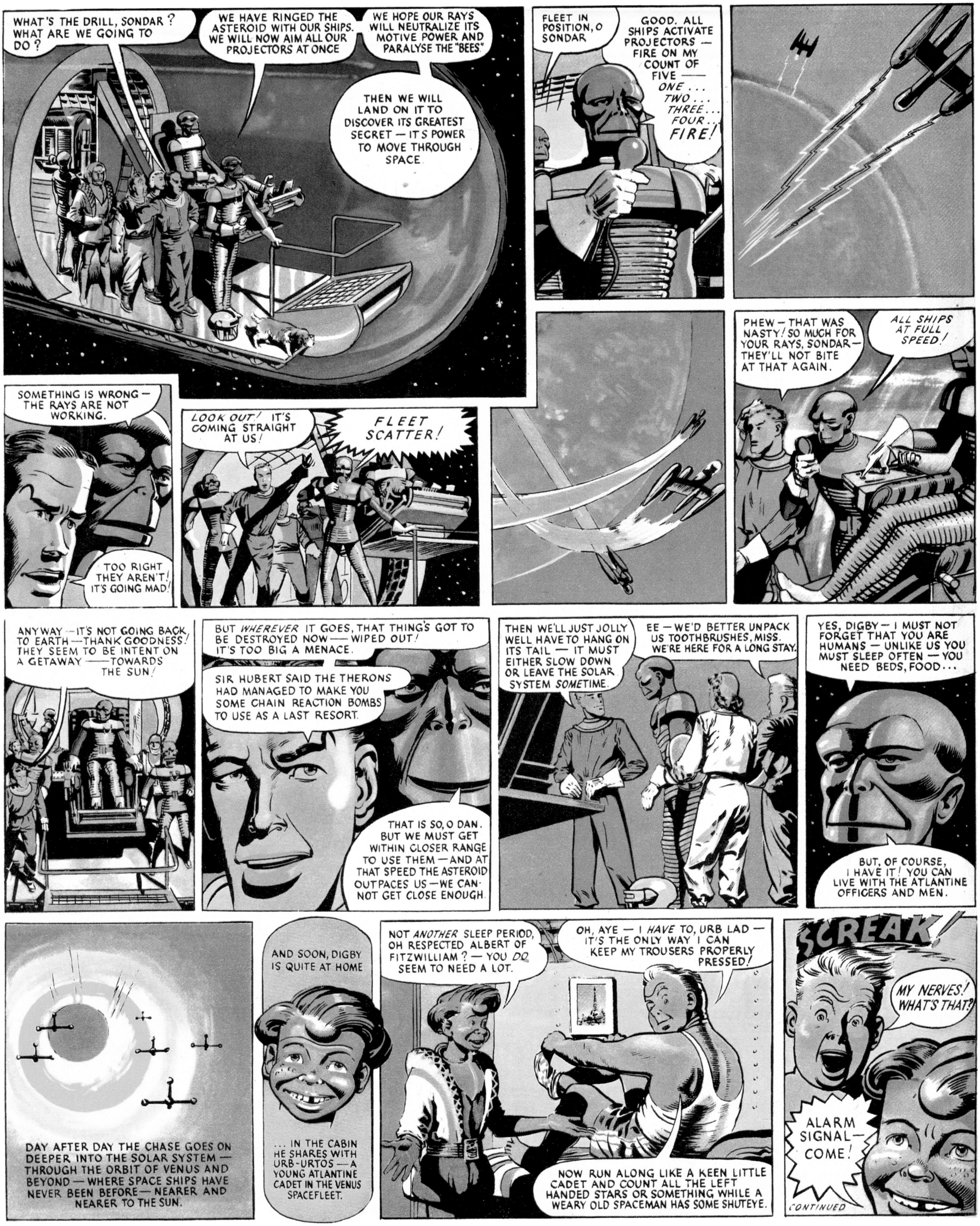
WHAT'S THE DRILL, SONDAR? WHAT ARE WE GOING TO DO?
WE HAVE RINGED THE ASTEROID WITH OUR SHIPS. WE WILL NOW AIM ALL OUR PROJECTORS AT ONCE
WE HOPE OUR RAYS WILL NEUTRALIZE ITS MOTIVE POWER AND PARALYSE THE "BEES"
THEN WE WILL LAND ON IT TO DISCOVER ITS GREATEST SECRET — IT'S POWER TO MOVE THROUGH SPACE
FLEET IN POSITION, O SONDAR
GOOD. ALL SHIPS ACTIVATE PROJECTORS — FIRE ON MY COUNT OF FIVE —— ONE ... TWO ... THREE ... FOUR ... FIRE!
SOMETHING IS WRONG — THE RAYS ARE NOT WORKING.
TOO RIGHT THEY AREN'T! IT'S GOING MAD!
LOOK OUT! IT'S COMING STRAIGHT AT US!
FLEET SCATTER!
PHEW — THAT WAS NASTY! SO MUCH FOR YOUR RAYS, SONDAR — THEY'LL NOT BITE AT THAT AGAIN.
ALL SHIPS AT FULL SPEED!
ANYWAY — IT'S NOT GOING BACK TO EARTH — THANK GOODNESS! THEY SEEM TO BE INTENT ON A GETAWAY —— TOWARDS THE SUN!
BUT WHEREVER IT GOES, THAT THING'S GOT TO BE DESTROYED NOW — WIPED OUT! IT'S TOO BIG A MENACE.
SIR HUBERT SAID THE THERONS HAD MANAGED TO MAKE YOU SOME CHAIN REACTION BOMBS TO USE AS A LAST RESORT.
THAT IS SO, O DAN. BUT WE MUST GET WITHIN CLOSER RANGE TO USE THEM — AND AT THAT SPEED THE ASTEROID OUTPACES US — WE CANNOT GET CLOSE ENOUGH.
THEN WE'LL JUST JOLLY WELL HAVE TO HANG ON ITS TAIL — IT MUST EITHER SLOW DOWN OR LEAVE THE SOLAR SYSTEM SOMETIME.
EE — WE'D BETTER UNPACK US TOOTHBRUSHES, MISS. WE'RE HERE FOR A LONG STAY.
YES, DIGBY — I MUST NOT FORGET THAT YOU ARE HUMANS — UNLIKE US YOU MUST SLEEP OFTEN — YOU NEED BEDS, FOOD ...
BUT, OF COURSE, I HAVE IT! YOU CAN LIVE WITH THE ATLANTINE OFFICERS AND MEN.
DAY AFTER DAY THE CHASE GOES ON DEEPER INTO THE SOLAR SYSTEM — THROUGH THE ORBIT OF VENUS AND BEYOND — WHERE SPACE SHIPS HAVE NEVER BEEN BEFORE — NEARER AND NEARER TO THE SUN.
AND SOON, DIGBY IS QUITE AT HOME
... IN THE CABIN HE SHARES WITH URB-URTOS — A YOUNG ATLANTINE CADET IN THE VENUS SPACEFLEET.
NOT ANOTHER SLEEP PERIOD, OH RESPECTED ALBERT OF FITZWILLIAM? — YOU DO SEEM TO NEED A LOT.
OH, AYE — I HAVE TO, URB LAD — IT'S THE ONLY WAY I CAN KEEP MY TROUSERS PROPERLY PRESSED!
NOW RUN ALONG LIKE A KEEN LITTLE CADET AND COUNT ALL THE LEFT HANDED STARS OR SOMETHING WHILE A WEARY OLD SPACEMAN HAS SOME SHUTEYE.
SCREAK!
MY NERVES! WHAT'S THAT?
ALARM SIGNAL — COME!
CONTINUED

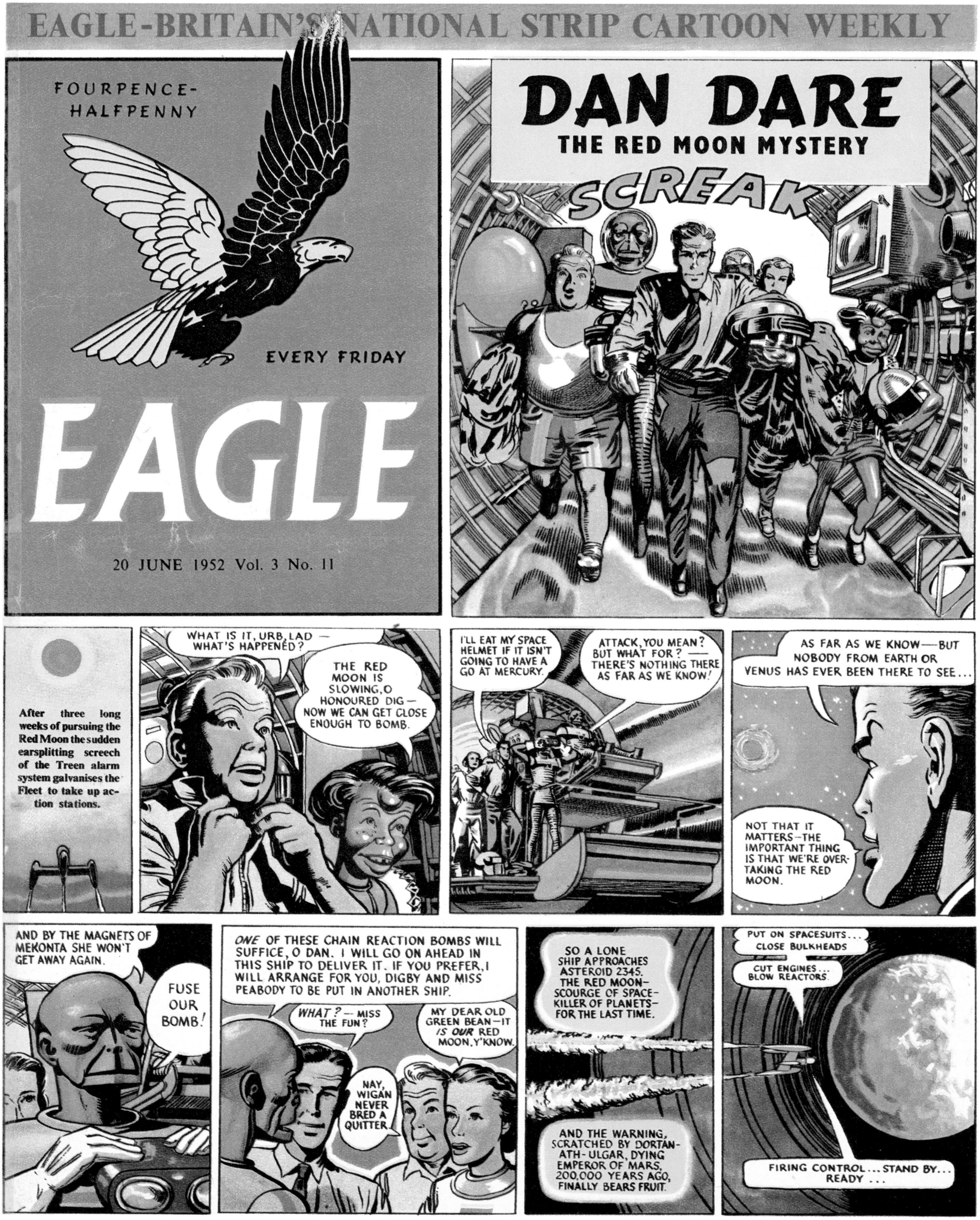

EAGLE-BRITAIN'S NATIONAL STRIP CARTOON WEEKLY
FOURPENCE-HALFPENNY
EVERY FRIDAY
EAGLE
20 JUNE 1952 Vol. 3 No. 11
DAN DARE
THE RED MOON MYSTERY
SCREAK
After three long weeks of pursuing the Red Moon the sudden earsplitting screech of the Treen alarm system galvanises the Fleet to take up action stations.
WHAT IS IT, URB, LAD — WHAT'S HAPPENED?
THE RED MOON IS SLOWING, O HONOURED DIG — NOW WE CAN GET CLOSE ENOUGH TO BOMB.
I'LL EAT MY SPACE HELMET IF IT ISN'T GOING TO HAVE A GO AT MERCURY.
ATTACK, YOU MEAN? BUT WHAT FOR? — THERE'S NOTHING THERE AS FAR AS WE KNOW!
AS FAR AS WE KNOW — BUT NOBODY FROM EARTH OR VENUS HAS EVER BEEN THERE TO SEE...
NOT THAT IT MATTERS — THE IMPORTANT THING IS THAT WE'RE OVER-TAKING THE RED MOON.
AND BY THE MAGNETS OF MEKONTA SHE WON'T GET AWAY AGAIN.
FUSE OUR BOMB!
ONE OF THESE CHAIN REACTION BOMBS WILL SUFFICE, O DAN. I WILL GO ON AHEAD IN THIS SHIP TO DELIVER IT. IF YOU PREFER, I WILL ARRANGE FOR YOU, DIGBY AND MISS PEABODY TO BE PUT IN ANOTHER SHIP.
WHAT? — MISS THE FUN?
MY DEAR OLD GREEN BEAN — IT IS OUR RED MOON, Y'KNOW.
NAY, WIGAN NEVER BRED A QUITTER.
SO A LONE SHIP APPROACHES ASTEROID 2345. THE RED MOON — SCOURGE OF SPACE — KILLER OF PLANETS — FOR THE LAST TIME.
AND THE WARNING, SCRATCHED BY DORTAN-ATH-ULGAR, DYING EMPEROR OF MARS, 200,000 YEARS AGO, FINALLY BEARS FRUIT.
PUT ON SPACESUITS... CLOSE BULKHEADS
CUT ENGINES... BLOW REACTORS.
FIRING CONTROL... STAND BY... READY...

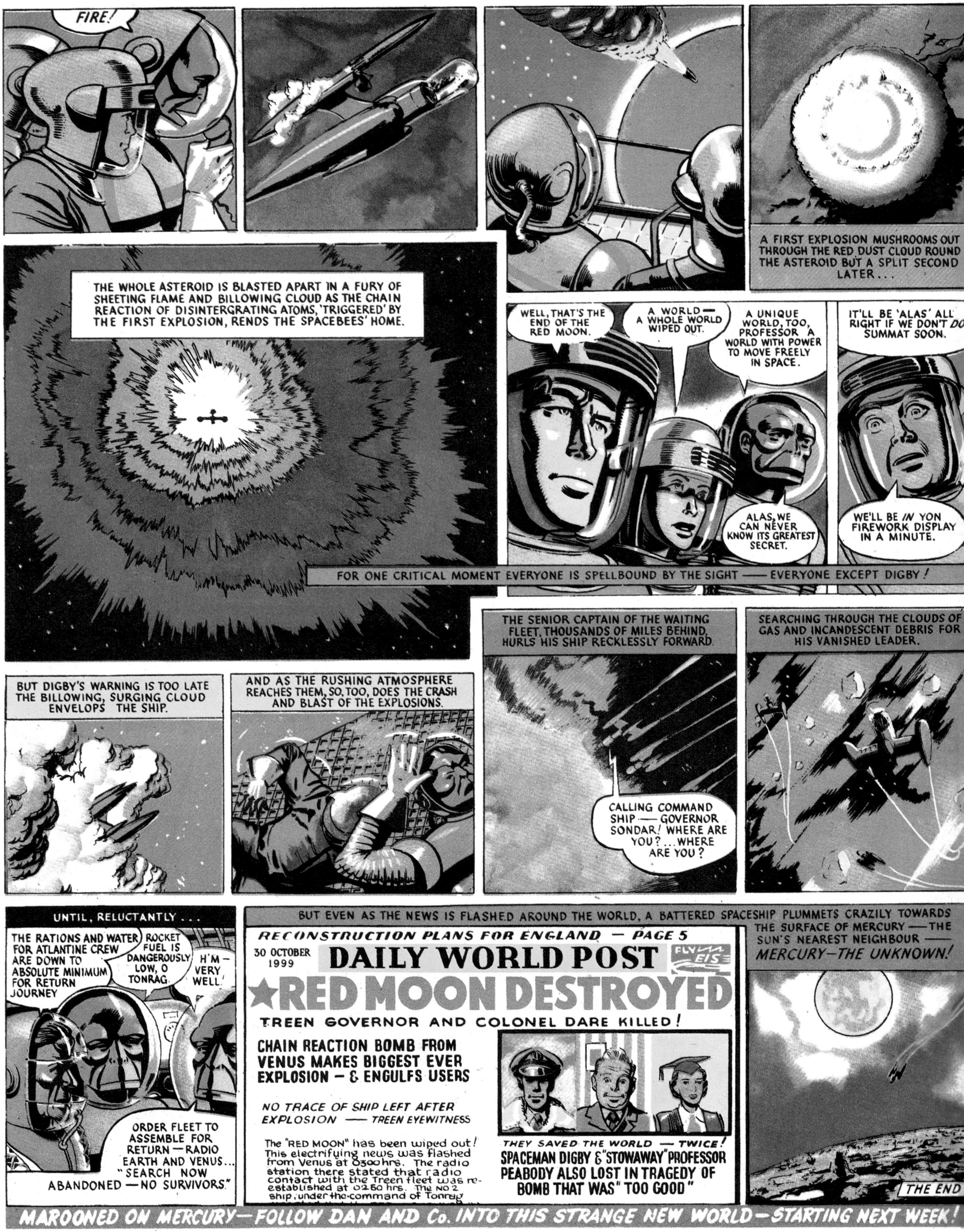

A FIRST EXPLOSION MUSHROOMS OUT THROUGH THE RED DUST CLOUD ROUND THE ASTEROID BUT A SPLIT SECOND LATER...

THE WHOLE ASTEROID IS BLASTED APART IN A FURY OF SHEETING FLAME AND BILLOWING CLOUD AS THE CHAIN REACTION OF DISINTERGRATING ATOMS, 'TRIGGERED' BY THE FIRST EXPLOSION, RENDS THE SPACEBEES' HOME.

WELL, THAT'S THE END OF THE RED MOON.

A WORLD — A WHOLE WORLD WIPED OUT.

A UNIQUE WORLD, TOO, PROFESSOR A WORLD WITH POWER TO MOVE FREELY IN SPACE.

ALAS, WE CAN NEVER KNOW ITS GREATEST SECRET.

IT'LL BE 'ALAS' ALL RIGHT IF WE DON'T DO SUMMAT SOON.

WE'LL BE IN YON FIREWORK DISPLAY IN A MINUTE.

FOR ONE CRITICAL MOMENT EVERYONE IS SPELLBOUND BY THE SIGHT — EVERYONE EXCEPT DIGBY!

THE SENIOR CAPTAIN OF THE WAITING FLEET, THOUSANDS OF MILES BEHIND, HURLS HIS SHIP RECKLESSLY FORWARD.

SEARCHING THROUGH THE CLOUDS OF GAS AND INCANDESCENT DEBRIS FOR HIS VANISHED LEADER.

BUT DIGBY'S WARNING IS TOO LATE THE BILLOWING, SURGING CLOUD ENVELOPS THE SHIP.

AND AS THE RUSHING ATMOSPHERE REACHES THEM, SO, TOO, DOES THE CRASH AND BLAST OF THE EXPLOSIONS.

CALLING COMMAND SHIP — GOVERNOR SONDAR! WHERE ARE YOU? ...WHERE ARE YOU?

UNTIL, RELUCTANTLY ...

THE RATIONS AND WATER FOR ATLANTINE CREW ARE DOWN TO ABSOLUTE MINIMUM FOR RETURN JOURNEY

ROCKET FUEL IS DANGEROUSLY LOW, O TONRAG.

H'M — VERY WELL.

ORDER FLEET TO ASSEMBLE FOR RETURN — RADIO EARTH AND VENUS... "SEARCH NOW ABANDONED — NO SURVIVORS."

BUT EVEN AS THE NEWS IS FLASHED AROUND THE WORLD, A BATTERED SPACESHIP PLUMMETS CRAZILY TOWARDS THE SURFACE OF MERCURY — THE SUN'S NEAREST NEIGHBOUR — MERCURY—THE UNKNOWN!

RECONSTRUCTION PLANS FOR ENGLAND — PAGE 5

30 OCTOBER 1999

DAILY WORLD POST

FLY EIS

★RED MOON DESTROYED

TREEN GOVERNOR AND COLONEL DARE KILLED!

CHAIN REACTION BOMB FROM VENUS MAKES BIGGEST EVER EXPLOSION — & ENGULFS USERS

NO TRACE OF SHIP LEFT AFTER EXPLOSION — TREEN EYEWITNESS

The "RED MOON" has been wiped out! This electrifying news was flashed from Venus at 0300hrs. The radio station there stated that radio contact with the Treen fleet was re-established at 0250 hrs. The NO 2 ship, under the command of Tonrag

THEY SAVED THE WORLD — TWICE!
SPACEMAN DIGBY & "STOWAWAY" PROFESSOR PEABODY ALSO LOST IN TRAGEDY OF BOMB THAT WAS" TOO GOOD"

THE END

MAROONED ON MERCURY—FOLLOW DAN AND Co. INTO THIS STRANGE NEW WORLD—STARTING NEXT WEEK!

EAGLE—THRILLING NEW *DAN DARE* STORY STARTS TO-DAY

FOURPENCE-HALFPENNY
EVERY FRIDAY
EAGLE
27 JUNE 1952 Vol. 3 No. 12

DAN DARE
PILOT OF THE FUTURE
MAROONED ON MERCURY
The Earth is mourning the death of Dan Dare and his friends, presumed lost after their successful attack on the Red Moon. But far away towards the centre of the solar system, strange watchers on the planet Mercury track the approach of a battered space-ship . . .
REE-MAH LEE-DAH RAH DAY-RAY-RAY RAW-RAY. SAW-RAY RAH-FAY. = THEY'RE FALLING STRAIGHT FOR THE LAKE OF MOLTEN LEAD—THEY'LL BE BURNT ALIVE!
RAH-FAY FEE-FAH. TAH-LOO SAH FAW-RAY! = THEY'LL BE DEAD ALREADY, I EXPECT. THE SHIP'S BADLY KNOCKED ABOUT.
SEE-FAH! FEE-MAH LEE-DAH, RAH FAY. = WE MUST GET THEM OUT—DEAD OR ALIVE—RUN! AS FAST AS YOU CAN.
CRUMP
TOO-TOO! SEE-FAH GEE-DAH SAW-RAY FAW DAW-MEE = THEY'VE CRASHED INTO THE SHORE. HURRY! THEY CAN'T STAND THE HEAT FOR LONG
RAW DAH-FAY LEE-DAH. MEE-MAH GAW-RAY . . . = THEY LOOK DEAD ENOUGH. LAY THEM IN THE SHADE OF THE SHIP.
AND SO MERCURY'S STRANGE INHABITANTS CARRY OUT THE BODIES OF DAN AND HIS FRIENDS . . .
WHAT THE ?—I'M GOING CRAZY! IT'S SONDAR—BUT WHAT THE DICKENS ARE *THOSE* THINGS?

DEE-MAN REE-FAN DAY. MOO-LAW!
=
ONE OF THEM IS MOVING! GET HOLD OF HIM—TIE HIM UP!
WHERE AM I? WHAT...
I'M GOING CRAZY— CHUNKS OF CRYSTAL WALKING ABOUT!
HEY! WHAT ARE YOU DOING? LET GO!
GOSH— WAKE UP, URB LAD— ACTION!
AH—COLONEL DARE IS IN FIGHT!—WE MUST HELP, NO?
AYE, LAD, COME ON—BUT WATCH YOUR STEP. THE GRAVITY HERE FEELS VERY LOW.
READY— NOW!
HANG ON, SIR!— HELP COMING!
DIG—GET BACK. IT'S NO USE—THESE THINGS ARE AS STRONG AS GORILLAS!
AND AS QUICK AS GREASED LIGHTNING! LOOK OUT BEHIND!
WE'VE JUST GOT TO LIE DOGGO FOR A BIT AND SEE WHAT THEY'RE UP TO. THEY HAVEN'T TAKEN OUR GUNS SO THEY MAY NOT KNOW WHAT THEY ARE...
WELL! THEY'VE EVEN TIED POOR OLD WILLIE UP, SITHEE! WHO ARE THEY, ANYWAY, AND HOW DID WE GET HERE? T' LAST THING I REMEMBER WAS YON RED MOON BLOWING UP. CRASH! BANG! WALLOP!
THAT'S IT, DIG. IT CRASHED US INTO BYE-BYES, BANGED US ALONG AND WALLOPED US ON TO HERE—WHICH I THINK IS MERCURY, EH, SONDAR?
THE EVIDENCE INDEED POINTS TO MERCURY, O DAN —— ON THE SIDE FACING THE SUN —— THE OTHER SIDE IS ALWAYS FROZEN. IF WE WERE NOT IN THE SHADE WE SHOULD FEEL WARM EVEN IN OUR SPACE SUITS—THE NORMAL HEAT HERE IS 400° CENTIGRADE.
WARM? YOU'RE TELLING US, SONDAR!— WE'D FRY! THAT LAKE IS MOLTEN LEAD—JUST FROM THE SUN'S HEAT.
FRY OR FREEZE, EH?—WE'VE GOT OURSELVES IN A RIGHT PICKLE HERE, URB!
BUT, O VALIANT FITZALBERT DIGBY, IS THIS NOT AN ADVENTURE OF EXCITEMENT?
WE ARE EXPLORATORS OF UNKNOWN PLANET!
I AM TO BECOMING A REAL SPACE MAN—LIKE YOU!
ALL IS BETTER THAN GOOD!
THAT'S THE SPIRIT, URB— BUT KEEP YOUR EYES PEELED—THOSE GOONS ARE UP TO SOMETHING —YES, LOOK— A CARRIER...
LOOKS MORE LIKE A TRAVELLING CIGARETTE BOX!
CHUMP—IT'S MADE OF CRYSTAL FOR PROTECTION FROM THE HEAT.
WHAT DO THEY THINK WE ARE—SARDINES? THEY'LL BE FRYING US NEXT.
PERHAPS THEY WILL, O DIGBY— BUT IT MAY BE AN AMBULANCE— OR A PRISON CAR!
AND AT LEAST WE CAN TALK—WE CAN'T UNDERSTAND THESE FELLOW'S LINGO BUT THEY CAN'T UNDERSTAND OURS EITHER.
BUT ON ANOTHER PART OF MERCURY...
NO, COLONEL DARE—YOU ARE RIGHT—THEY CAN'T UNDERSTAND YOU —BUT I CAN!
CONTINUED

BEGIN THIS EXCITING NEW *DAN DARE* STORY TODAY!

FOURPENCE-HALFPENNY
EVERY FRIDAY
EAGLE
4 JULY 1952 Vol. 3 No. 13

DAN DARE
MAROONED ON MERCURY
SO! THEY CRASH INTO MOLTEN LEAD—AND LIVE! THE HUMAN HERO, COLONEL DARE, HAS A CHARMED LIFE INDEED. BUT HE WILL NOT FIND IT EASY THIS TIME—NOR THE TRAITOR, SONDAR.
After their successful attack on the Red Moon, Dan and his friends crash-land their battered space-ship on to the torrid wastes of Mercury – only to be taken prisoner by the strange rock-like inhabitants of the mystery planet. Meanwhile, in another part of the planet . . .

YOU AND YOUR FRIENDS ARE ALONE, COLONEL—THE EARTH HAS GIVEN YOU UP FOR DEAD! YOU ARE MAROONED, COLONEL MAROONED ON MERCURY.

CAN'T YOU HITCH UP A BIT, DIG? YOU TAKE MORE THAN YOUR FAIR SHARE IN THE FRYING PAN.
AT LEAST I'M NOT ALL CORNERS, LIKE SOME PEOPLE! COME ON THEN—"WHEN FATHER SAYS TURN—WE ALL TURN."

TO WHERE DO YOU THINK THESE ROCK-PEOPLE TAKE US, O COLONEL DARE, SIR EXCELLENCY?
SOMEWHERE WHERE LEAD ISN'T MOLTEN I HOPE, URB.

YES, LOOK! THE SUN!—IT'S QUITE LOW ON THE HORIZON—WE'RE GETTING AWAY FROM THE TORRID ZONE.

THERE IS A NARROW TEMPERATE BELT BETWEEN THE TWO ZONES...
MAYBE THEY'LL UNPACK US THERE. LETS HOPE THEY'VE GOT AIR WE CAN BREATHE. OUR OXYGEN CAN'T LAST FOR EVER.

THERE CAN ONLY BE VERY THIN AIR—IF ANY—AND GRAVITY A QUARTER OF YOUR EARTH GRAVITY.
SO WE'RE HALE AND HEARTY IF WE DON'T FRY, UNLESS WE CAN'T BREATHE, SUPPOSING WE DON'T FREEZE ON T'OTHER SIDE O'T' PLANET, IT'S A FINE LIFE BEING A SPACEMAN, URB, ME BOY.

HELLO—WE'RE GETTING SOMEWHERE.

LOOKS LIKE THE END OF THE LINE, SPACE-MATES!

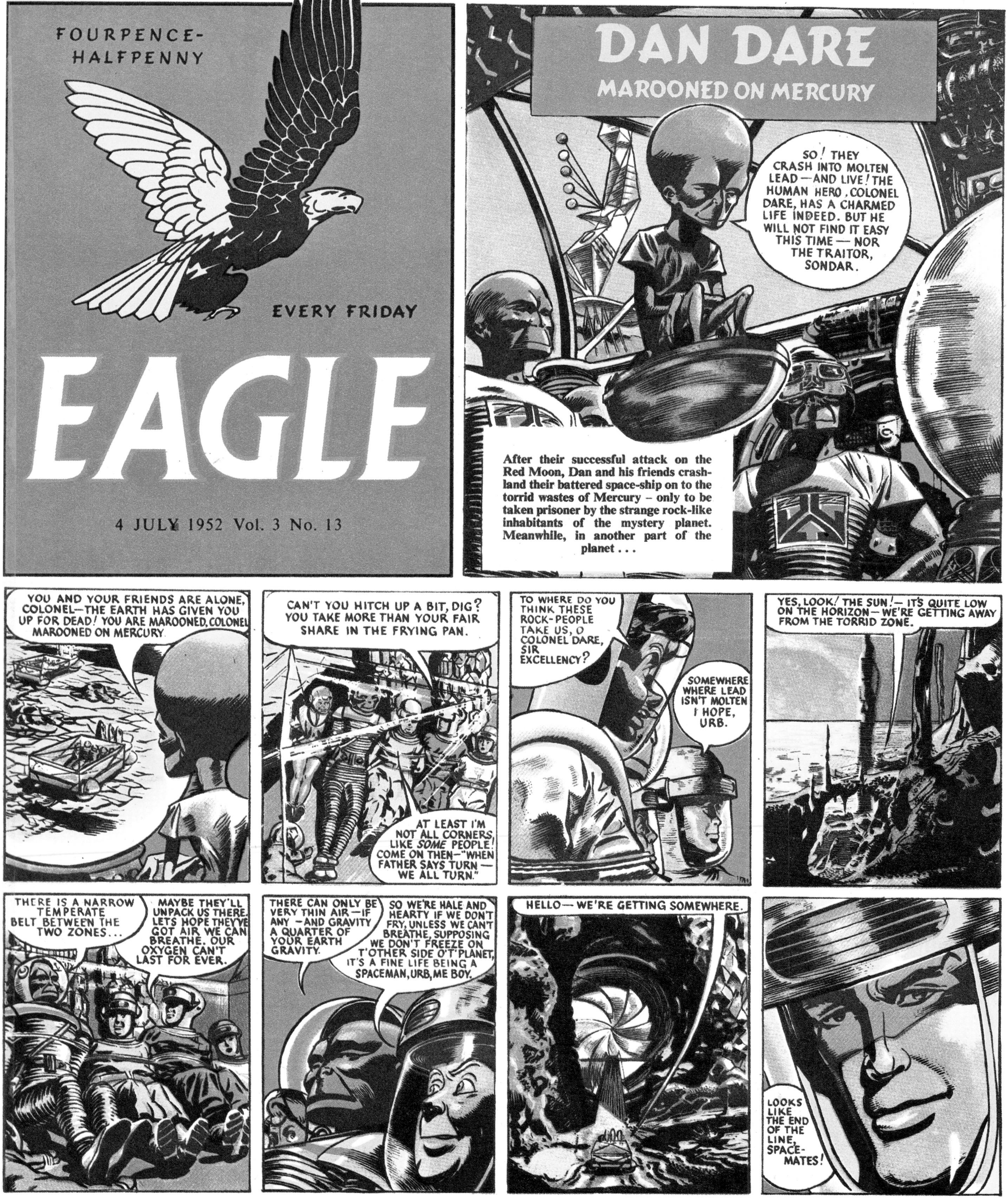

EE, BY GUM, THATS CLEVER! LOOK—IT'S OPENING—IT'S A DOOR!
WORKED LIKE A CAMERA SHUTTER! THESE CREATURES AREN'T STUPID.
LOOKS LIKE WE'VE ARRIVED—NOW KEEP CALM EVERYBODY!—WE DON'T KNOW WHAT THEY'RE UP TO AND AT THE MOMENT THEY HOLD ALL THE ACES, BUT THERE'S A CHANCE THEY MAY BE FRIENDLY.
FRIENDLY? ABOUT AS FRIENDLY AS A BUNCH OF BARNACLES!
DAN! LOOK!
THAT BUNCH OVER THERE — THEY'RE... THEY'RE CHANGING!
GOSH, IT'S HUMAN—OR IS IT?—WHAT A KISSER!—JUST LIKE MY COUSIN BERT BACK IN ROCHDALE!
THEY'RE AS HUMAN AS YOU, DIG—THAT ROCK STUFF THEY WEAR MUST JUST BE PROTECTIVE ARMOUR.
KEEP STILL EVERYONE! LET'S SEE WHAT HE'LL DO.
AND HIS MATES, SIR—THERE'S A BIT OF A GATHERING GOING ON.
AND I DON'T LIKE T' WAY THEY'RE ALL EYEING US—HUNGRY LIKE.
SONDAR LOOK OUT!
DAN! WHERE ARE THEY TAKING HIM? — THAT CRATER WHERE THE LIGHT IS — THEY'RE NOT GOING TO...
I'M AFRAID THEY ARE, JOCELYN, AND WE'RE BOUND HAND AND FOOT!
LET HIM ALONE, YOU MURDERING COWARDS!
AAAAAAH!
A LIVE VOLCANO!
YES, JOCELYN—AND I'M AFRAID IT'S OUR TURN NEXT.
SORRY, URB LAD, WE SHAN'T BE ABLE TO MAKE A SPACEMAN OF YOU AFTER ALL!
CONTINUED...
FRANK HAMPSON

READ EAGLE INVESTIGATOR'S CANADIAN ADVENTURE – *p. 12*

FOURPENCE-HALFPENNY

EVERY FRIDAY

EAGLE

11 JULY 1952 Vol. 3 No. 14

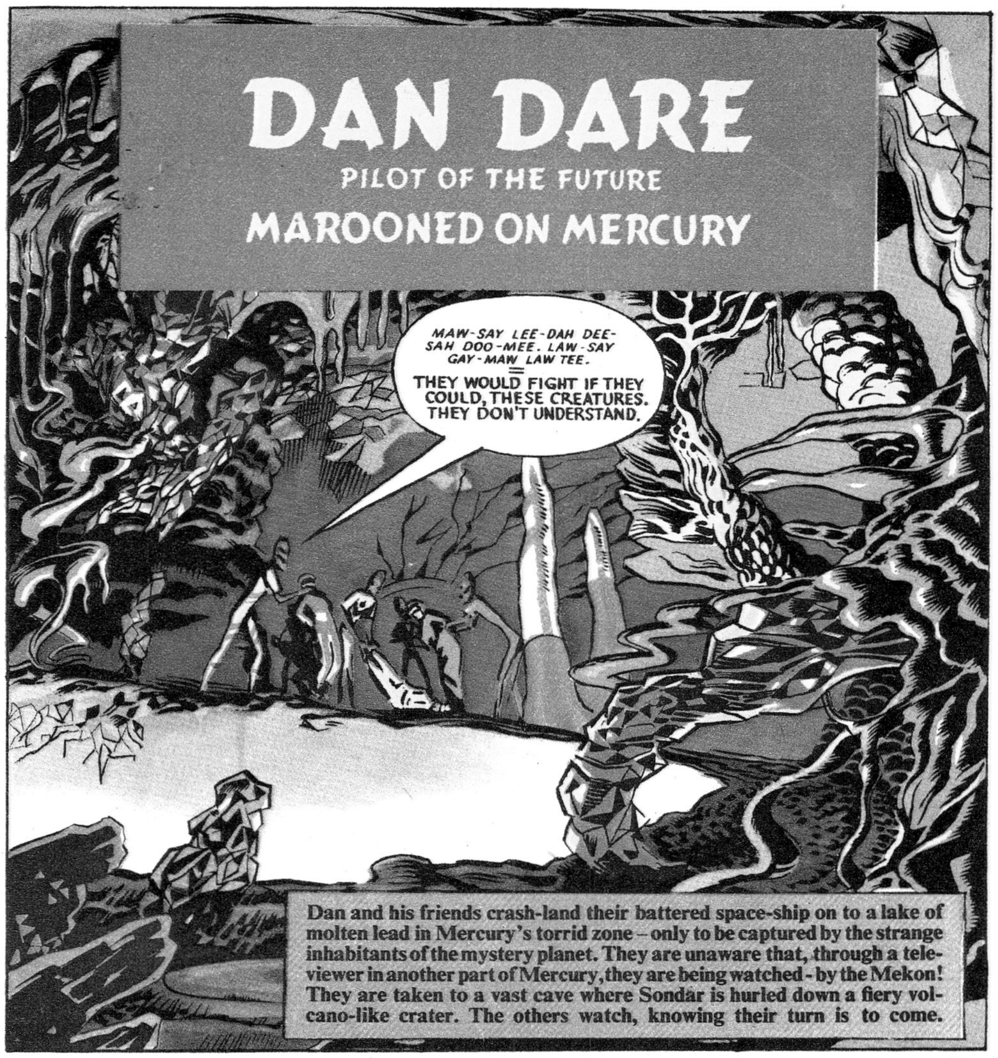
DAN DARE
PILOT OF THE FUTURE
MAROONED ON MERCURY
MAW-SAY LEE-DAH DEE-SAH DOO-MEE. LAW-SAY GAY-MAW LAW TEE. = THEY WOULD FIGHT IF THEY COULD, THESE CREATURES. THEY DON'T UNDERSTAND.
Dan and his friends crash-land their battered space-ship on to a lake of molten lead in Mercury's torrid zone – only to be captured by the strange inhabitants of the mystery planet. They are unaware that, through a tele-viewer in another part of Mercury, they are being watched - by the Mekon! They are taken to a vast cave where Sondar is hurled down a fiery volcano-like crater. The others watch, knowing their turn is to come.

SORRY, FOLKS — THEY'VE GOT US!
THEY'RE MUCH TOO STRONG.
REE-MAH LEE-DAH! THROW THEM OVER!
DAN! DAN!
SEE-DAH LAW-MEE = THERE'S ANOTHER OF THEM.
LAW-MEE SAW MEE-DAH FAW-MEE, LEE-DAH TEE-DAN MAW-TEE = HE'S DIFFERENT FROM THE LAST ONE —— SMALLER.
IT'S TAKING A LONG TIME. FUNNY, IT DOESN'T SEEM TO BE GETTING ANY HOTTER.

AS HE FALLS, DAN FINDS THAT THE CRATER HAS TURNED GRADUALLY INTO A SMOOTH, CURVING TUBE. INSTEAD OF MEETING CERTAIN DEATH HE IS SLIDING SWIFTLY INTO THE UNKNOWN.
DAYLIGHT!
WHOOSH
RAY SAW MAY SEE-DAH! FEE-MAH LEE-DAH. SEE-FAH LEE-DAH MEE-MAH LEE-SAH
TWO AND THREE ARRIVING! CUT THEM FREE. WE MUST GET THEM INDOORS AS SOON AS POSSIBLE.
COLONEL DARE—ARE YOU ALL RIGHT?
GOSH!
HELLO, SONDAR—I'VE LOST MY STOMACH I THINK, BUT OTHERWISE I'M ALL IN ONE PIECE.
TALK ABOUT BATTERSEA FUN-FAIR. WHAT'S THE BIG IDEA DO YOU THINK, SONDAR?
A MERCURIAN FORM OF TRANSPORT, I IMAGINE, PROFESSOR. PROBABLY FOR FREIGHT.
AND HERE'S URB—ONLY DIG AND THE DOG TO COME.
THAT'S STRANGE. THEY'RE CUTTING US LOOSE—I THOUGHT WE WERE PRISONERS!
WE'RE IN FOR A WALK I EXPECT... I SAY — WHAT'S HAPPENED TO DIGBY? HE'S A LONG TIME.
THEY WANT US TO MOVE, DAN.
BUT WHERE'S DIGBY? HE'S NOT ARRIVED AND I'M STAYING HERE TILL HE DOES.
ONE MORE! AND AN ANIMAL—WHERE ARE THEY? OH, CONFOUND IT! HOW CAN I MAKE THEM UNDERSTAND?
YOU CAN'T, SIR. AND IT LOOKS LIKE THEY'RE GOING TO MAKE US GO WITH THEM. BUT WE CAN'T LEAVE MR. DIGBY BEHIND.
I'LL SAY WE CAN'T. YOU LOT GO ON. I'M GOING TO GET BACK TO HIM SOMEHOW.
DAN! YOU CAN'T! YOU'LL NEVER GET BACK UP THERE!
MOO-LAW DEE-FAN MEE-DAH = GET HOLD OF THESE OTHERS
LEE-DAH GAY-MAW LAW-TEE! DEE SEE-FAN REE-FAN MEE DAH?... FOOLISH ONE! WHY SHOULD HE RUN? HE CANNOT ESCAPE!
THEY'LL CATCH HIM, I'M AFRAID, PROFESSOR. THEY CAN RUN LIKE THE WIND—AND CLIMB TOO, I EXPECT, IN THIS GRAVITY.
THEY'RE GAINING ON HIM, MISS.
BUT WHY SHOULD THEY HAVE KEPT DIGBY BEHIND? THEY SEEM FRIENDLY ENOUGH — SO FAR!
A FEW FEET MORE AND...
CONTINUED...

EAGLE'S OWN EXHIBITION IS AT THE SEASIDE - *see page 13*

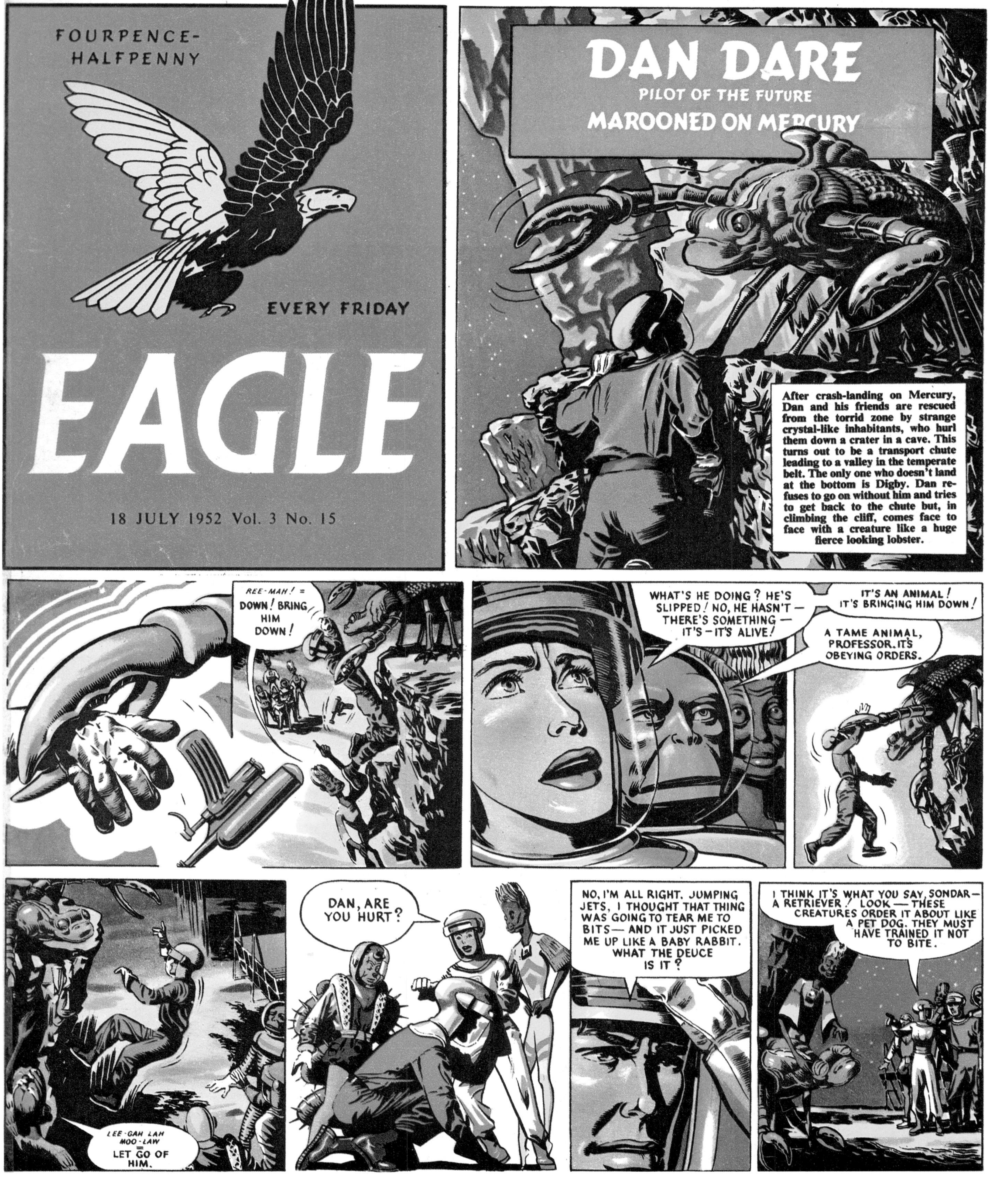
FOURPENCE-HALFPENNY
EVERY FRIDAY
EAGLE
18 JULY 1952 Vol. 3 No. 15
DAN DARE
PILOT OF THE FUTURE
MAROONED ON MERCURY
After crash-landing on Mercury, Dan and his friends are rescued from the torrid zone by strange crystal-like inhabitants, who hurl them down a crater in a cave. This turns out to be a transport chute leading to a valley in the temperate belt. The only one who doesn't land at the bottom is Digby. Dan refuses to go on without him and tries to get back to the chute but, in climbing the cliff, comes face to face with a creature like a huge fierce looking lobster.
REE-MAH! = DOWN! BRING HIM DOWN!
WHAT'S HE DOING? HE'S SLIPPED! NO, HE HASN'T — THERE'S SOMETHING — IT'S — IT'S ALIVE!
IT'S AN ANIMAL! IT'S BRINGING HIM DOWN!
A TAME ANIMAL, PROFESSOR. IT'S OBEYING ORDERS.
LEE-GAH LAH MOO-LAW = LET GO OF HIM.
DAN, ARE YOU HURT?
NO, I'M ALL RIGHT. JUMPING JETS, I THOUGHT THAT THING WAS GOING TO TEAR ME TO BITS — AND IT JUST PICKED ME UP LIKE A BABY RABBIT. WHAT THE DEUCE IS IT?
I THINK IT'S WHAT YOU SAY, SONDAR — A RETRIEVER! LOOK — THESE CREATURES ORDER IT ABOUT LIKE A PET DOG. THEY MUST HAVE TRAINED IT NOT TO BITE.

YOU'RE RIGHT, JOCELYN. MY WRIST'S ONLY BRUISED. THAT THING HAD A GRIP LIKE A VICE —— BUT IT'S NOT DONE ANY DAMAGE. IT'S DIG WE'VE GOT TO WORRY ABOUT.
WE MUST GO WITH THEM, COLONEL—AND MAKE THEM UNDERSTAND ABOUT SPACEMAN DIGBY. THEY CAN'T LIVE ALL THE TIME IN THIS ATMOSPHERE. IF THEY HAVE BREATHING CHAMBERS WE CAN TALK TO THEM.
AND LEAVE DIGBY IN THE LURCH WHILE WE LEARN THE LANGUAGE, I SUPPOSE! I'M NOT LEAVING HERE TILL...
NO, DAN! SONDAR'S RIGHT. IF IT WASN'T FOR THOSE CREATURES WE'D ALL BE DEAD BY NOW. I'M SURE THEY MEAN TO BE FRIENDLY.
AND THEY MEAN US TO GO WITH THEM, DAN O COLONEL. SEE—THEY ARRANGE A WAY FOR US.
YES, DAN. IF WE DON'T GO QUIETLY, THEY'LL TAKE US — BY FORCE. YOU CAN'T HELP DIG BY FIGHTING THEM. YOU'LL ONLY RESCUE HIM BY MAKING FRIENDS WITH THEM.
PERHAPS YOU'RE RIGHT, PROF. BUT IF THEY HURT OLD DIG ... I'LL ...
LEE-DAH RAH FOO-MEE...
TAKE THEM TO THE CAR. THEY MUSTN'T ESCAPE AGAIN—FOR THEIR OWN SAKE.
IT RESEMBLES ONE OF YOUR EARTH TRAINS, COLONEL DARE, WORKED BY A COMPRESSED SPRING IT SEEMS.
RIGHT AS USUAL, SONDAR, YOU SCIENTIFIC GENIUS. IT'LL GO PRETTY FAST TOO! HOLD ON TO YOUR HATS, EVERYONE.
NO NEED, COLONEL DARE. THERE ISN'T ENOUGH AIR TO MAKE A WIND.
TWANG
GOSH—I'VE LEFT MY INSIDE BEHIND.
DAN, O EXCELLENCY, WHERE DO THEY TAKE US?
I HAVEN'T A CLUE, URB, ME BOY—BUT WE'RE SLOWING DOWN. A SHORT TRIP AND A FAST ONE SEEMS TO BE THE MOTTO OF THIS CONTRAPTION.
WE'VE STOPPED!—SMASHING HAYSTACKS!—DID YOU EVER SEE ANYTHING LIKE IT?—LOOK!
NO, PROF.! WE'VE NEVER SEEN ANYTHING LIKE IT. A CITY OF MERCURY. WHAT DOES IT MEAN, DO YOU THINK? FOOD? AIR? A WAY BACK HOME? OR IS THAT JUST WISHFUL THINKING?
—HAROLD JOHNS

EAGLE'S SPECIAL INVESTIGATOR RIDES THE RANGE - *see page 12*

FOURPENCE-HALFPENNY

EVERY FRIDAY

EAGLE

25 JULY 1952 Vol. 3 No. 16

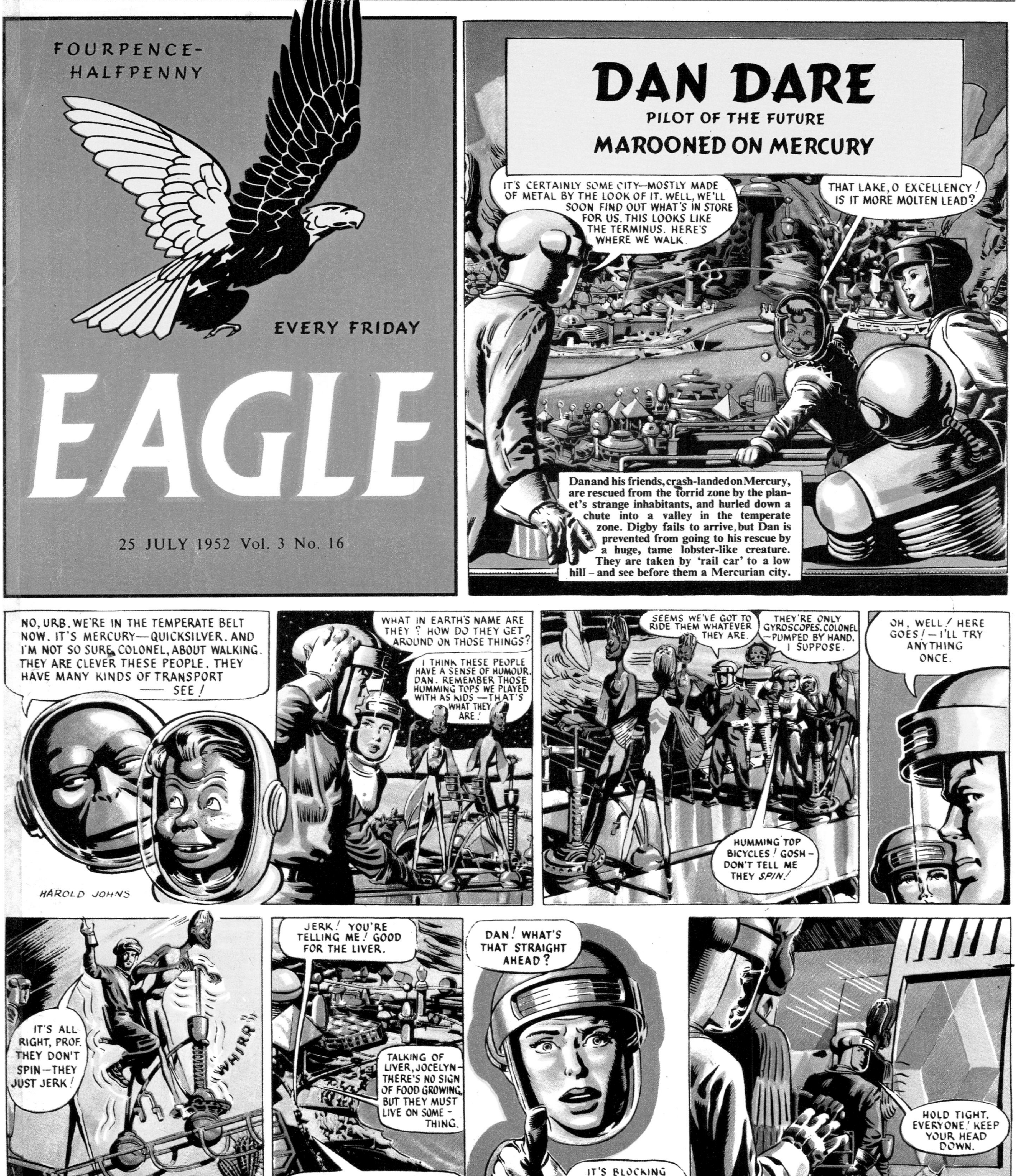
DAN DARE
PILOT OF THE FUTURE
MAROONED ON MERCURY
IT'S CERTAINLY SOME CITY—MOSTLY MADE OF METAL BY THE LOOK OF IT. WELL, WE'LL SOON FIND OUT WHAT'S IN STORE FOR US. THIS LOOKS LIKE THE TERMINUS. HERE'S WHERE WE WALK.
THAT LAKE, O EXCELLENCY! IS IT MORE MOLTEN LEAD?
Dan and his friends, crash-landed on Mercury, are rescued from the torrid zone by the planet's strange inhabitants, and hurled down a chute into a valley in the temperate zone. Digby fails to arrive, but Dan is prevented from going to his rescue by a huge, tame lobster-like creature. They are taken by 'rail car' to a low hill – and see before them a Mercurian city.
NO, URB. WE'RE IN THE TEMPERATE BELT NOW. IT'S MERCURY—QUICKSILVER. AND I'M NOT SO SURE, COLONEL, ABOUT WALKING. THEY ARE CLEVER THESE PEOPLE. THEY HAVE MANY KINDS OF TRANSPORT —— SEE!
HAROLD JOHNS
WHAT IN EARTH'S NAME ARE THEY? HOW DO THEY GET AROUND ON THOSE THINGS?
I THINK THESE PEOPLE HAVE A SENSE OF HUMOUR, DAN. REMEMBER THOSE HUMMING TOPS WE PLAYED WITH AS KIDS—THAT'S WHAT THEY ARE!
SEEMS WE'VE GOT TO RIDE THEM WHATEVER THEY ARE.
THEY'RE ONLY GYROSCOPES, COLONEL —PUMPED BY HAND, I SUPPOSE.
HUMMING TOP BICYCLES! GOSH - DON'T TELL ME THEY SPIN!
OH, WELL! HERE GOES! — I'LL TRY ANYTHING ONCE.
IT'S ALL RIGHT, PROF. THEY DON'T SPIN—THEY JUST JERK!
WHIRR
JERK! YOU'RE TELLING ME! GOOD FOR THE LIVER.
TALKING OF LIVER, JOCELYN—THERE'S NO SIGN OF FOOD GROWING, BUT THEY MUST LIVE ON SOME-THING.
AND IF THEY CAN BUILD MACHINES LIKE THIS, COLONEL, AND METAL HOUSES, THEY CAN BUILD US A SPACESHIP.
DAN! WHAT'S THAT STRAIGHT AHEAD?
IT'S BLOCKING THE RAIL — WE'RE GOING TO CRASH.
HOLD TIGHT, EVERYONE! KEEP YOUR HEAD DOWN.

CLICK
WHEE-E-E-W—I THOUGHT WE'D BE SCALPED THAT TIME!
WHOOSH
THEY RIDE THEIR BICYCLES RIGHT INDOORS IT SEEMS. WHAT'S THIS PLACE, SONDAR, DO YOU THINK?
CLICK
CLICK
AN AIRLOCK PERHAPS, COLONEL? I DON'T KNOW.
YES, SONDAR AND THEY'RE OPENING UP.
TWANG
COME ON, FOLKS. LET'S SEE WHAT THEY'VE GOT LAID ON FOR US.
LOOK—THEIR AIR SACS ARE DEFLATED! THE PRESSURE HAS INCREASED AND THEY'RE BREATHING THROUGH THEIR MOUTHS.
THEN SO CAN WE! ANYWAY, I'M GOING TO RISK IT—YOU OTHERS WAIT TILL I'VE TRIED IT.
CAREFUL, DAN! YOU DON'T KNOW.
COLONEL DARE! IT'S KILLING HIM.
DAN!
TAW GAY MAW-RAY = MORE OXYGEN. FOOL—YOU'LL SUFFOCATE HIM.
HELP ME GET HIS HELMET ON AGAIN.
IT'S ALL RIGHT, MISS.
OH, MOST HONOURED ALBERT FITZWILLIAM!
DIGBY!
WUFF WUFF
HE'LL BE O.K. IN A MINUTE, MISS. THESE CHAPS DON'T KNOW THE MIXTURE TO GIVE US YET—BUT THEY'RE LEARNING YOU CAN ALL TAKE YOUR HELMETS OFF.
DIG—YOU OLD SON OF A GUN. HOW DID YOU GET HERE?
WHATEVER ARE YOU DOING IN THAT RIGOUT, DIG?
WHAT DID THEY DO TO YOU, SIR DIGBY?
ONE AT A TIME, FOLKS, IF YOU PLEASE!—EE—IT'S GOOD TO SEE YOU, SIR—WILLY HERE KICKED UP SUCH A FUSS THAT THEY HAD TO PUT ON A SPECIAL TRAIN FOR US!
AND THAT'S NOT ALL. I'VE DISCOVERED SOMETHING, TOO—WE'RE NOT THE ONLY STRANGERS ON MERCURY!
THERE ARE SOME TREEN TYPES HERE ALREADY!
CONTINUED

EAGLE-BRITAIN'S NATIONAL STRIP CARTOON WEEKLY
FOURPENCE-HALFPENNY
EVERY FRIDAY
EAGLE
1 AUGUST 1952 Vol. 3 No. 17
DAN DARE
PILOT OF THE FUTURE
MAROONED ON MERCURY
TREENS ON MERCURY! WHAT DO YOU MEAN, DIG? HOW DO YOU KNOW ANYWAY? DON'T TELL US YOU'VE LEARNT THE LANGUAGE ALREADY!
Dan and his friends, crash-landed on Mercury, are rescued from the torrid zone by the planet's strange inhabitants and taken to a city in the temperate belt where an airlocked building enables them to remove their space-helmets. They find that Digby, whom they had left behind, has arrived before them – with the news that there are Treens already on Mercury.
OH! I DIDN'T TALK TO THEM, SIR! MIGHTY FUNNY SORT OF LINGO THEY'VE GOT! BUT LOOK WHAT ONE OF THEM GAVE ME.
LET ME SEE THAT, DIG!
SPACEMAN DIGBY IS RIGHT, COLONEL. THERE ARE TREENS HERE! THAT IS A TREEN HELMET BADGE.
WHEE-E-E-W!
AYE—AND IF I'M ANY JUDGE, THEY'RE AS ABOUT AS WELCOME AS A SWARM OF BEES AT A GARDEN PARTY.
THE MERCURIANS SEEMED RIGHT PLEASED TO SEE A REAL HUMAN BEING.
SPRAYED ME ALL OVER WITH SOME PLASTIC STUFF AND RIGGED ME UP WITH THEIR LATEST SPRING CREATION.
SPRAYED YOU? THAT'S TO TAKE THE PLACE OF A SPACE-SUIT, I IMAGINE.
ALL RIGHT, DIG, WE'LL HEAR ALL ABOUT YOUR ADVENTURES LATER. WHAT DO YOU MAKE OF THIS TREEN BUSINESS, SONDAR? MORE SURVIVORS OF THE RED MOON LIKE OURSELVES?
IT MAY BE SO, COLONEL DARE, OR IT MAY BE OUR OLD ENEMY.
WHIRR
WHIRR
OUR OLD ENEMY? WHAT ARE YOU GETTING AT, SONDAR?
YES, COLONEL DARE, THE MEKON! THERE WAS NO CERTAINTY HE WAS KILLED. PERHAPS HE ESCAPED! AND IF WE CAN REACH MERCURY—— SO COULD HE!
YOU CAN'T MEAN— NO, THAT'S RIDICULOUS!
IF THAT LITTLE LAD IS HERE HE'S NOT JUST HAVING A PLEASANT HOLIDAY, YOU CAN BET YOUR BOOTS.
YOU'RE RIGHT, DIG. WE'VE GOT TO FIND OUT PRETTY QUICK BEFORE HE FINDS US. COME ON. LET'S GET OUT OF HERE.
CLICK
SAY—WHERE'S EVERYONE GONE? THOSE MERCURIAN FELLOWS MUST HAVE SLIPPED OUT QUIETLY WHILE WE WERE TALKING.
AND THE DOOR IS LOCKED, DAN.

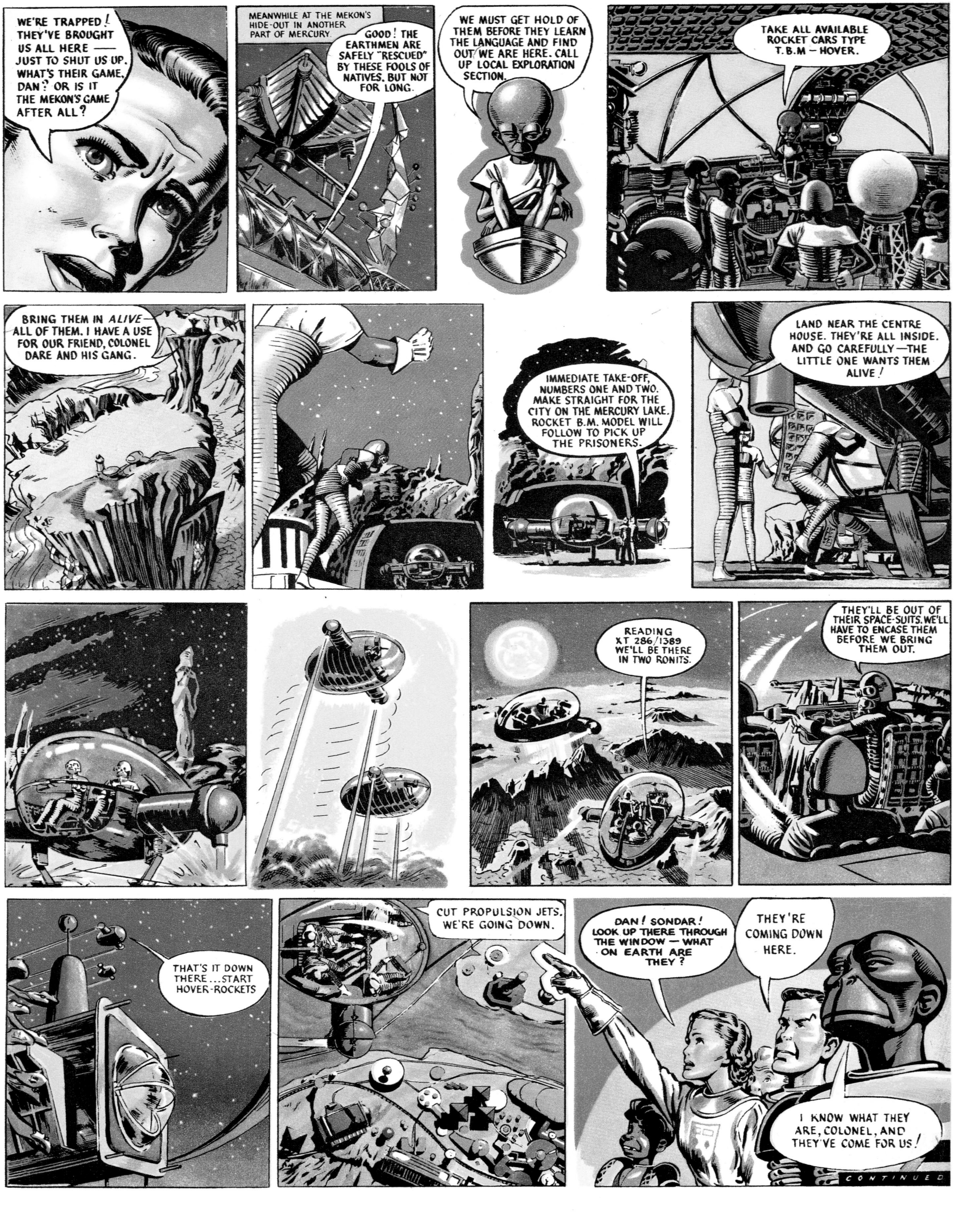
WE'RE TRAPPED! THEY'VE BROUGHT US ALL HERE — JUST TO SHUT US UP. WHAT'S THEIR GAME, DAN? OR IS IT THE MEKON'S GAME AFTER ALL?
MEANWHILE AT THE MEKON'S HIDE-OUT IN ANOTHER PART OF MERCURY.
GOOD! THE EARTHMEN ARE SAFELY "RESCUED" BY THESE FOOLS OF NATIVES, BUT NOT FOR LONG.
WE MUST GET HOLD OF THEM BEFORE THEY LEARN THE LANGUAGE AND FIND OUT WE ARE HERE. CALL UP LOCAL EXPLORATION SECTION.
TAKE ALL AVAILABLE ROCKET CARS TYPE T.B.M – HOVER.
BRING THEM IN ALIVE— ALL OF THEM. I HAVE A USE FOR OUR FRIEND, COLONEL DARE AND HIS GANG.
IMMEDIATE TAKE-OFF, NUMBERS ONE AND TWO. MAKE STRAIGHT FOR THE CITY ON THE MERCURY LAKE. ROCKET B.M. MODEL WILL FOLLOW TO PICK UP THE PRISONERS.
LAND NEAR THE CENTRE HOUSE. THEY'RE ALL INSIDE. AND GO CAREFULLY—THE LITTLE ONE WANTS THEM ALIVE!
READING XT 286/1389 WE'LL BE THERE IN TWO RONITS.
THEY'LL BE OUT OF THEIR SPACE-SUITS. WE'LL HAVE TO ENCASE THEM BEFORE WE BRING THEM OUT.
THAT'S IT DOWN THERE... START HOVER-ROCKETS
CUT PROPULSION JETS. WE'RE GOING DOWN.
DAN! SONDAR! LOOK UP THERE THROUGH THE WINDOW — WHAT ON EARTH ARE THEY?
THEY'RE COMING DOWN HERE.
I KNOW WHAT THEY ARE, COLONEL, AND THEY'VE COME FOR US!
CONTINUED

EAGLE-BRITAIN'S NATIONAL STRIP CARTOON WEEKLY

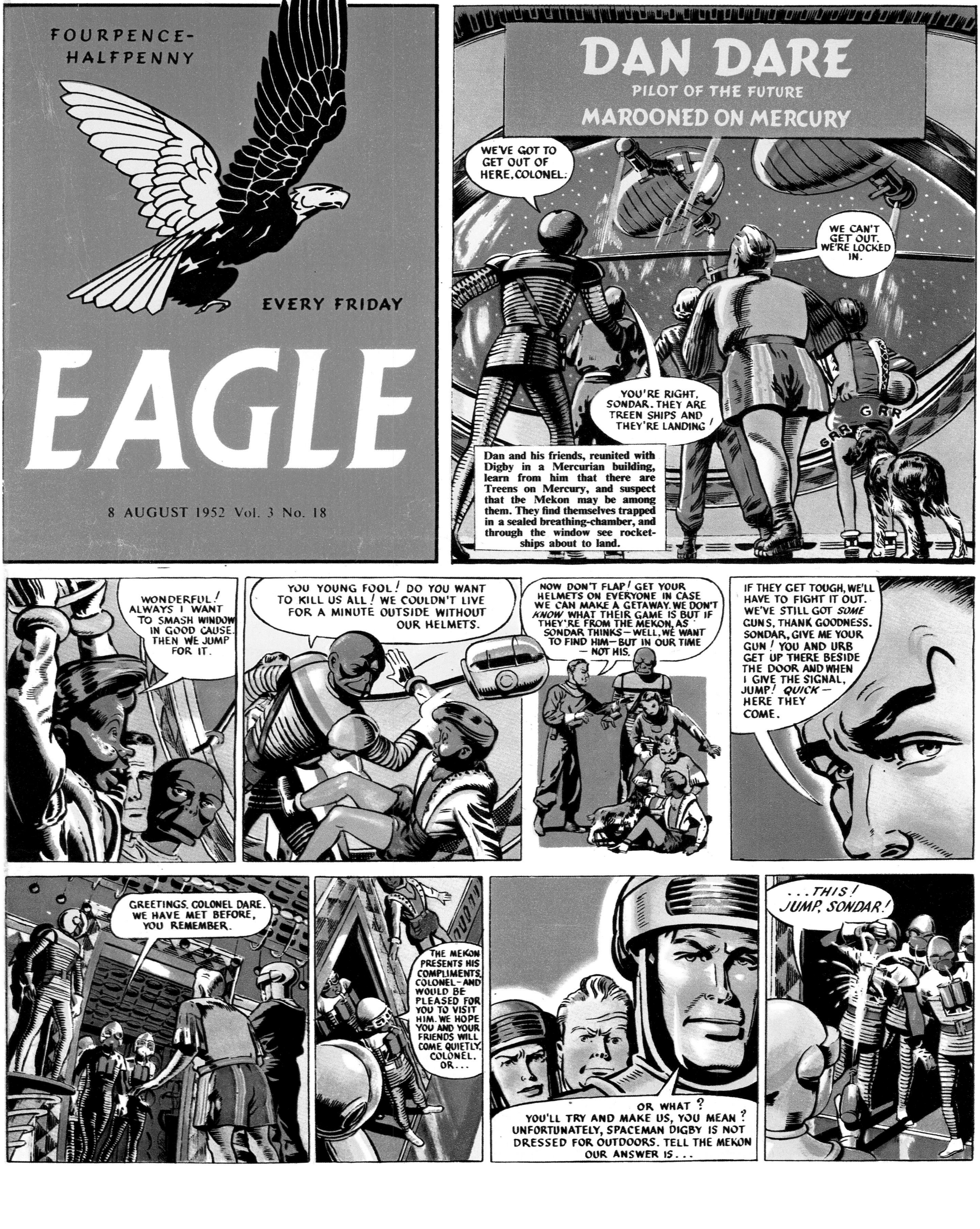
FOURPENCE-HALFPENNY
EVERY FRIDAY
EAGLE
8 AUGUST 1952 Vol. 3 No. 18
DAN DARE
PILOT OF THE FUTURE
MAROONED ON MERCURY
WE'VE GOT TO GET OUT OF HERE, COLONEL.
WE CAN'T GET OUT. WE'RE LOCKED IN.
YOU'RE RIGHT, SONDAR. THEY ARE TREEN SHIPS AND THEY'RE LANDING!
GRR
GRR
Dan and his friends, reunited with Digby in a Mercurian building, learn from him that there are Treens on Mercury, and suspect that the Mekon may be among them. They find themselves trapped in a sealed breathing-chamber, and through the window see rocket-ships about to land.
WONDERFUL! ALWAYS I WANT TO SMASH WINDOW IN GOOD CAUSE. THEN WE JUMP FOR IT.
YOU YOUNG FOOL! DO YOU WANT TO KILL US ALL! WE COULDN'T LIVE FOR A MINUTE OUTSIDE WITHOUT OUR HELMETS.
NOW DON'T FLAP! GET YOUR HELMETS ON EVERYONE IN CASE WE CAN MAKE A GETAWAY. WE DON'T KNOW WHAT THEIR GAME IS BUT IF THEY'RE FROM THE MEKON, AS SONDAR THINKS—WELL, WE WANT TO FIND HIM—BUT IN OUR TIME —NOT HIS.
IF THEY GET TOUGH, WE'LL HAVE TO FIGHT IT OUT. WE'VE STILL GOT SOME GUNS, THANK GOODNESS. SONDAR, GIVE ME YOUR GUN! YOU AND URB GET UP THERE BESIDE THE DOOR AND WHEN I GIVE THE SIGNAL, JUMP! QUICK—HERE THEY COME.
GREETINGS, COLONEL DARE. WE HAVE MET BEFORE, YOU REMEMBER.
THE MEKON PRESENTS HIS COMPLIMENTS, COLONEL—AND WOULD BE PLEASED FOR YOU TO VISIT HIM. WE HOPE YOU AND YOUR FRIENDS WILL COME QUIETLY, COLONEL, OR...
OR WHAT? YOU'LL TRY AND MAKE US, YOU MEAN? UNFORTUNATELY, SPACEMAN DIGBY IS NOT DRESSED FOR OUTDOORS. TELL THE MEKON OUR ANSWER IS...
...THIS! JUMP, SONDAR!

NICE WORK, FELLOWS.
KEEP AT IT — WE'VE GOT THEM GROGGY.
TAKE THAT, YOU GREEN HORROR.
EEK
GR-R-R
THEY'VE GOT DIGBY AND URB — LOOK OUT, DAN — BEHIND YOU!
OH HO — YOU'LL HAVE TO BE QUICKER THAN THAT TO CATCH ME, MY FRIEND.
WELL, THAT'S QUIETENED THEM FOR THE MOMENT. EVERYONE GET INTO THE AIRLOCK WHILE I KEEP MY EYES ON THESE CHAPS.
THAT'S THE TICKET. DRAG DIG AND URB INTO THE AIRLOCK! DON'T FORGET THAT DIG NEEDS A BREATHING MASK. I'M AFRAID WE'LL HAVE TO LEAVE WILLY BEHIND.
SIT UP, MY GREEN BEAUTY, WHILE I TAKE OFF YOUR MASK. WE NEED IT FOR DIGBY.
EVERYBODY IN, PROF. RIGHT — I'LL CLOSE THE DOOR.
YES. ALL O.K., DAN. I'LL HAVE DIG'S MASK FIXED IN A JIFFY.
BE READY FOR TROUBLE — THERE MAY BE MORE TREENS OUTSIDE.
NO SIGN OF ANYONE! QUICK- MAKE A DASH FOR THE ROCKET SHIPS.
WELL, THEY LOOK DESERTED ENOUGH. HOLD ON HERE A MINUTE WHILE I LOOK INSIDE THIS BIG JOB.
WE'RE IN LUCK. THERE'S NO ONE ABOARD. BRING URB AND DIG UP HERE. THE SOONER WE GET AWAY FROM HERE THE BETTER... WHAT THE DICKENS...
WHOOSH
DAN! DAN! COME BACK — WE'RE NOT ABOARD YET.
DAN! THIS IS NO TIME FOR FOOLING! COME BACK!
A NEAT LITTLE TRAP, COLONEL DARE. I DIDN'T UNDERESTIMATE YOU, MY FRIEND, BUT YOU UNDERESTIMATED ME!
CONTINUED

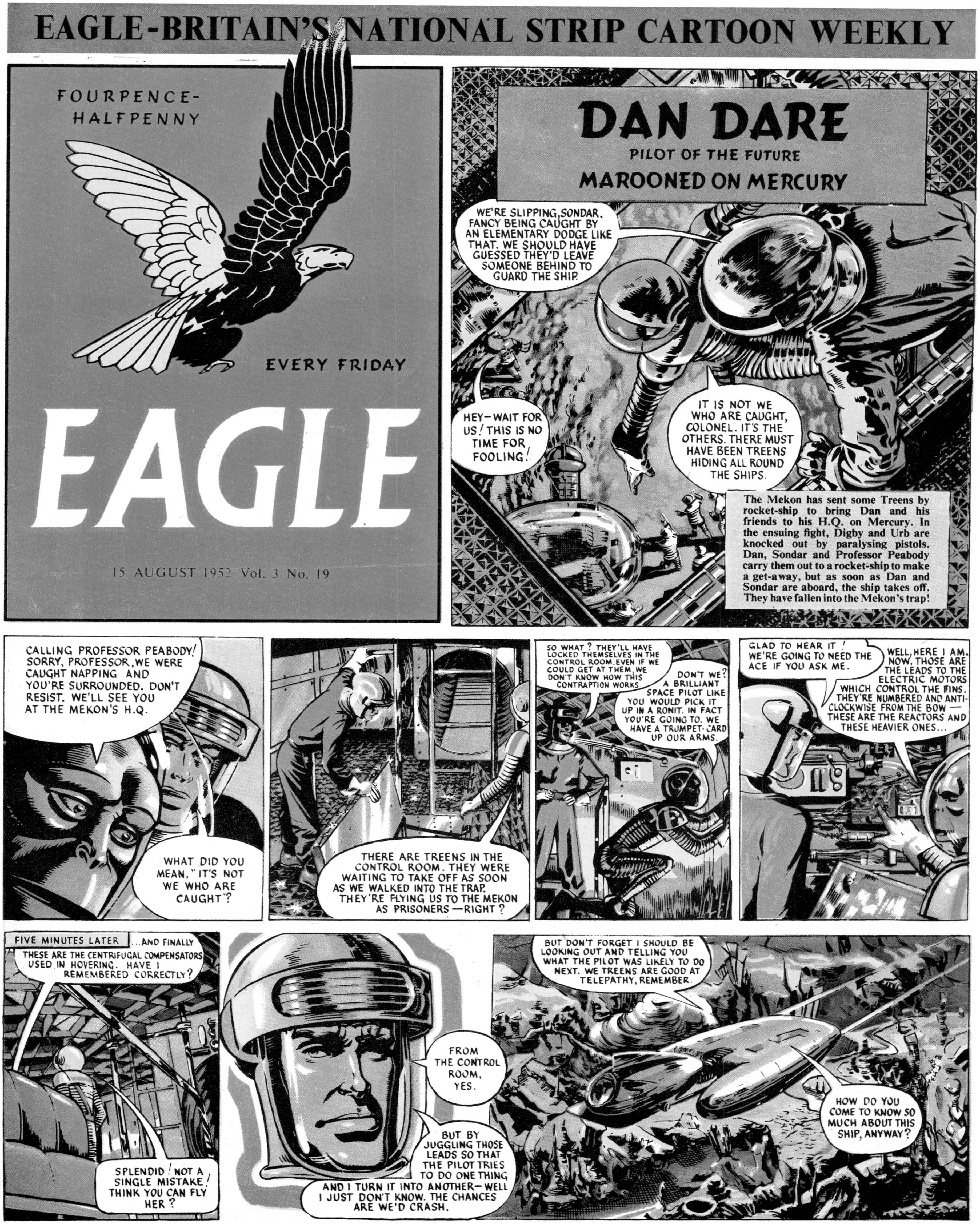

EAGLE-BRITAIN'S NATIONAL STRIP CARTOON WEEKLY
FOURPENCE-HALFPENNY
EVERY FRIDAY
EAGLE
15 AUGUST 1952 Vol. 3 No. 19
DAN DARE
PILOT OF THE FUTURE
MAROONED ON MERCURY
WE'RE SLIPPING, SONDAR. FANCY BEING CAUGHT BY AN ELEMENTARY DODGE LIKE THAT. WE SHOULD HAVE GUESSED THEY'D LEAVE SOMEONE BEHIND TO GUARD THE SHIP.
HEY—WAIT FOR US! THIS IS NO TIME FOR FOOLING!
IT IS NOT WE WHO ARE CAUGHT, COLONEL. IT'S THE OTHERS. THERE MUST HAVE BEEN TREENS HIDING ALL ROUND THE SHIPS.
The Mekon has sent some Treens by rocket-ship to bring Dan and his friends to his H.Q. on Mercury. In the ensuing fight, Digby and Urb are knocked out by paralysing pistols. Dan, Sondar and Professor Peabody carry them out to a rocket-ship to make a get-away, but as soon as Dan and Sondar are aboard, the ship takes off. They have fallen into the Mekon's trap!
CALLING PROFESSOR PEABODY! SORRY, PROFESSOR, WE WERE CAUGHT NAPPING AND YOU'RE SURROUNDED. DON'T RESIST. WE'LL SEE YOU AT THE MEKON'S H.Q.
WHAT DID YOU MEAN, "IT'S NOT WE WHO ARE CAUGHT"?
THERE ARE TREENS IN THE CONTROL ROOM. THEY WERE WAITING TO TAKE OFF AS SOON AS WE WALKED INTO THE TRAP. THEY'RE FLYING US TO THE MEKON AS PRISONERS—RIGHT?
SO WHAT? THEY'LL HAVE LOCKED THEMSELVES IN THE CONTROL ROOM. EVEN IF WE COULD GET AT THEM, WE DON'T KNOW HOW THIS CONTRAPTION WORKS.
DON'T WE? A BRILLIANT SPACE PILOT LIKE YOU WOULD PICK IT UP IN A RONIT. IN FACT YOU'RE GOING TO. WE HAVE A TRUMPET-CARD UP OUR ARMS.
GLAD TO HEAR IT! WE'RE GOING TO NEED THE ACE IF YOU ASK ME.
WELL, HERE I AM. NOW, THOSE ARE THE LEADS TO THE ELECTRIC MOTORS WHICH CONTROL THE FINS. THEY'RE NUMBERED AND ANTI-CLOCKWISE FROM THE BOW — THESE ARE THE REACTORS AND THESE HEAVIER ONES...
FIVE MINUTES LATER
...AND FINALLY THESE ARE THE CENTRIFUGAL COMPENSATORS USED IN HOVERING. HAVE I REMEMBERED CORRECTLY?
SPLENDID! NOT A SINGLE MISTAKE! THINK YOU CAN FLY HER?
FROM THE CONTROL ROOM, YES.
BUT BY JUGGLING THOSE LEADS SO THAT THE PILOT TRIES TO DO ONE THING
AND I TURN IT INTO ANOTHER—WELL I JUST DON'T KNOW. THE CHANCES ARE WE'D CRASH.
BUT DON'T FORGET I SHOULD BE LOOKING OUT AND TELLING YOU WHAT THE PILOT WAS LIKELY TO DO NEXT. WE TREENS ARE GOOD AT TELEPATHY, REMEMBER.
HOW DO YOU COME TO KNOW SO MUCH ABOUT THIS SHIP, ANYWAY?

I DESIGNED IT —— IT WAS LONG BEFORE THE WAR WITH VENUS AND EARTH.
THE MEKON ORDERED A DESIGN FOR ROCKET SHIPS FOR FLYING ROUND THE TEMPERATE BELT OF MERCURY. I NEVER SAW ONE BUILT BUT THIS IS IT.
SONDAR, YOU'RE INCREDIBLE. WELL, I'M GAME TO TRY IT, WITH YOU NAVIGATING! WE'LL WAIT TILL WE ARE NEAR THE MEKON'S HIDE-OUT AND THEN HI-JACK THE SHIP AND LAND HER WHERE THEY CAN'T GET AT US.
NO SIGN OF THE SMALL HOVER SHIPS, COLONEL. THEY'D NO SUN-SHIELDS LIKE THIS MODEL HAS, SO PERHAPS THEY CAN'T USE THEM FOR EARTHMEN. WE TREENS CAN STAND MORE HEAT THAN YOU.
I KNOW— YOU'RE LIKE SALAMANDERS; BUT IF THEY DON'T GET THIS BLACK MARIA BACK, I THINK THEY'LL RISK FLYING JOCELYN AND THE OTHERS IN THE SHADE OF THE MOUNTAINS.
MEANWHILE, BACK IN THE MERCURIAN CITY.
SHALL WE PARALYSE HER, TOO?
NO - SHE'LL GIVE NO TROUBLE AND THE MEKON WILL WANT TO QUESTION HER. GET THE OTHERS ON BOARD.
IF I CAN TRICK THEM AND GET THROUGH THE SPRING-DOOR OF THE AIR-LOCK WHERE WE FIRST WENT IN...
WHO'S SHE WAVING TO? DIDN'T WE GET ALL OF THEM?
EH? BETTER HAVE A LOOK.
IT WORKED! NOW FOR IT.
THE FEMALE EARTHLING IS ESCAPING —— AFTER HER.
CLICK
PARALYSE HER — SHE MUST NOT GET AWAY.
TOO LATE — THE DOOR HAS CLOSED.
SO FAR SO GOOD. THEY CAN'T FOLLOW ME TILL I'VE BEEN THROUGH THE AIRLOCK. BUT WHAT DO I DO NEXT?
THE MERCURIANS! I'D FORGOTTEN THEM! LEMME GO, YOU GORILLA!
AS THE ROCKET SHIP APPROACHES THE MEKON'S H.Q., DAN AND SONDAR PUT THEIR PLAN INTO OPERATION ...
AYE AYE, SIR. NUMBER THREE IT IS!
... COMPLETELY BAFFLING THE TREEN PILOT
NUMBER THREE ISN'T RESPONDING, SIR.
IT'S NO GOOD, SIR — THE FIN LEVER'S WORKING THE REACTOR JETS.
IT IS THE PRISONERS. THEY MUST BE TAMPERING WITH THE LEADS!
WHAT ARE WE GOING TO DO? GO INTO THE CABIN AND FIGHT THEM?
I HAVE A BETTER IDEA! CUT EVERYTHING. WITH THE POWER OFF THERE'LL BE NOTHING FOR THEM TO INTERFERE WITH, AND WHEN THEY SEE WE'RE GOING TO CRASH THEY'LL HAVE TO LET ME TAKE CONTROL AGAIN. EVEN COLONEL DARE'S NERVE WILL BREAK BEFORE IT'S TOO LATE TO PICK UP AGAIN. HOLD ON!
CONTINUED...

EAGLE-BRITAIN'S NATIONAL STRIP CARTOON WEEKLY
FOURPENCE-HALFPENNY
EVERY FRIDAY
EAGLE
22 AUGUST 1952 Vol. 3 No. 20
DAN DARE
PILOT OF THE FUTURE
MAROONED ON MERCURY
WE'RE GOING TO CRASH! SWITCH ON THE POWER AGAIN OR WE'RE DONE FOR.
NO! WAIT! COLONEL DARE'S NERVE WILL FAIL AT ANY MOMENT. HE'LL HAVE TO GIVE ME BACK CONTROL.
In their fight with the Mekon's Treens, Digby and Urb have been captured and Prof. Peabody has been seized by Mercurians. Dan and Sondar, tricked into entering a Treen rocket-ship, are being flown to the Mekon's H.Q. and try to divert the ship by tampering with the control leads. The Treen pilot cuts off the power, trusting that Dan's nerve will break before a crash.
WE'LL HAVE TO GIVE IN NOW, COLONEL, OR IT'LL BE TOO LATE.
THEY'LL GIVE IN FIRST. THEY'VE HAD ORDERS TO BRING US IN ALIVE TO THE MEKON.
THERE, I'VE SET HER SO THAT THE PILOT CAN PICK HER UP IF HE GIVES IN AND SWITCHES ON THE POWER AGAIN. IT'S UP TO HIM NOW WHETHER HE WANTS TO LIVE OR DIE.
YOU'VE LEFT IT TOO LATE! IF YOU LIVE TO FACE THE MEKON, YOU'LL WISH YOU HADN'T. HE WANTS COLONEL DARE ALIVE, AND HE WANTS TO WATCH SONDAR DIE.
ALL RIGHT, COLONEL DARE, YOU WIN — FOR THE MOMENT! BUT MY TURN WILL COME, I PROMISE YOU.
WITHIN A FEW INCHES OF IMPACT, THE SHIP BEGINS TO RISE.
SKREAK

PHEW! NARROWEST SQUEAK I'VE EVER HAD AND I'VE BEEN IN SOME TOUGH SPOTS IN MY TIME.
YOU WERE MAGNIFICENT, COLONEL. I SHOULD HAVE GIVEN IN AN INSTANT BEFORE THE PILOT DID. WE'D HAVE CRASHED IF THE SHIP HAD HAD ANOTHER COAT OF PAINT.
LOOK!
ONE OF THEIR ROCKET CARS LANDING –THAT'S WHAT I WAS WAITING FOR! WE'LL KEEP HOVERING TILL WE SEE WHERE THEY TAKE DIGBY AND THE OTHERS —IF THEY HAVEN'T FRIED THEM IN THOSE FLYING GREEN-HOUSES!
THEN WE'LL FIND SOMEWHERE TO LAND.
THEY'RE CARRYING OUT URB AND DIGBY NOW. THEY'RE STILL PARALYSED.
SONDAR! WHAT'S HAPPENED TO JOCELYN? SHE ISN'T WITH THE OTHERS.
YOU'RE RIGHT, COLONEL THAT MEANS SHE'S EITHER ESCAPED OR...
...OR BEEN KILLED! WE'VE GOT TO FIND OUT WHICH ENTRANCE THEY'RE TAKING DIG AND URB IN BY. THEN WE'LL JUGGLE WITH THE LEADS AND FORCE THESE TREENS TO LAND US WHERE WE WANT.
HERE ARE THE TWO PARALYSED PRISONERS, O MEKON. ONE OF THE PARTY HAS TEMPORARILY ESCAPED, BUT THE OTHER TWO ARE JUST ABOUT TO LAND.
YOU THINK SO? FOOLS! WE HAVE LOST COMMUNICATION WITH THE SHIP WHICH HOVERED OVER THE FIELD AND THEN TURNED AWAY. SOME-ONE WILL SUFFER FOR THIS.
WE COULD SHOOT THEM DOWN, O MEKON, BUT YOU WANTED COLONEL DARE ALIVE. IT'S NOT EASY WITH SUCH A MAN. HE IS CLEVER, THIS EARTHMAN.
HE'S NOT AS CLEVER AS I AM. FOLLOW HIM UNTIL YOU HAVE A CHANCE TO SEIZE HIM. YOU HALFWITS-YOU KNOW YOUR FATE IF YOU FAIL.
MEANWHILE, IN THE ROCKET SHIP
WELL DONE, COLONEL—— YOU'RE MAKING HIM DO WHAT YOU WANT. BUT THERE ARE NOT MANY PLACES TO LAND IN THESE MOUNTAINS. WE'LL HAVE TO TRY THAT LEDGE DOWN THERE AND HOPE FOR THE BEST. AND I THINK HE'LL TRY TO FOOL YOU BY CUTTING OUT THE CENTRIFUGAL COMPENSATORS!
SO I DO IT FIRST-AND SCARE HIM INTO PUTTING FULL POWER ON THE FINS.
THAT'S IT, YOU OLD MIND-READER! ATTA-BOY!
THIS IS STALEMATE THEY WON'T LET US LAND AT OUR H.Q. WE'LL HAVE TO LET THEM LAND WHERE THEY LIKE AND THEN FIGHT IT OUT.
THEY'RE TRYING TO GET US DOWN ON THE NARROW LEDGE THERE. RIGHT! THAT GIVES ME AN IDEA. LISTEN CAREFULLY.
OUT WITH YOU, SONDAR. QUICK– BEFORE THEY TIP US OVER THE EDGE. AT LEAST, THEY CAN'T FLY OFF — I'VE DISCONNECTED ALL THE LEADS.
HOW ABOUT TRYING TO TIP THEM OVER?
NO— WE NEED THE SHIP. BESIDES, THEY'RE OUT—THE CONTROL CABIN'S EMPTY.
THEY MUST BE ON THE OTHER SIDE. I'LL GO ROUND WHILE YOU GUARD THE CABIN.
QUICK! CONNECT UP THE LEADS AND THEN ATTRACT THE COLONEL'S ATTENTION WHILE I GET BACK TO THE CONTROLS.
NOT SO FAST, MY BEAUTY! WHAT HAVE YOU BEEN UP TO?
THE SHIP! IT'S MOVING!
LOOK OUT, SONDAR!
CONTINUED

EAGLE-BRITAIN'S NATIONAL STRIP CARTOON WEEKLY

FOURPENCE-HALFPENNY
EVERY FRIDAY
EAGLE
29 AUGUST 1952 Vol. 3 No. 21
DAN DARE
PILOT OF THE FUTURE
MAROONED ON MERCURY
Digby and Urb have been captured by the Treens and taken to the Mekon's H.Q. Prof. Peabody has escaped from them, only to fall into the hands of the Mercurians. Dan and Sondar have been pitting their wits against two Treens for control of a rocket-ship, and, after a fight on a cliff edge, Dan sees Sondar knocked over as the ship takes off. Dan makes a desperate leap at the moving ship.
MADE IT! NOW TO GET INTO THE CABIN AND FIGHT IT OUT.
STEADY DOES IT, DANNY BOY! ONE SLIP AND IT'S CURTAINS FOR YOURS TRULY.
NOW FOR IT! YOU'VE GOT A SURPRISE COMING, MY GREEN FRIEND! AH...
COME IN OUT OF THE COLD, COLONEL.
THAT JUMP OF YOURS WAS BADLY CALCULATED, COLONEL. I HAD TO SIDESLIP TO CATCH YOU. HAD YOU FORGOTTEN THAT GRAVITY HERE IS ONLY ONE FOURTH?
SONDAR!
HOW THE MEKON DID YOU GET HERE? I THOUGHT I SAW YOU FALL OFF THE EDGE!
THAT WAS THE PILOT. I BEAT HIM IN THE RACE FOR THE CONTROLS AFTER HIS FRIEND HAD RE-CONNECTED THE LEADS. WHERE DO YOU WANT TO GO NOW?
BACK TO THE MERCURIAN CITY. WE MUST FIND OUT WHAT HAPPENED TO THE PROFESSOR. THE MEKON WON'T DO ANYTHING TO URB AND DIGBY AS LONG AS THEY'RE UNCONSCIOUS
IN THE CITY-BY-THE-MERCURY-LAKE
I'M DOING FINE SO FAR! — YOUR LANGUAGE ISN'T SO DIFFICULT AFTER ALL — IF YOU'RE MUSICAL.
AH-OO EE-AH!
=
LOOK! A SPACE-SHIP.

HE'S RIGHT, WILLY, AND IT'S LANDING, TOO.
IT'S DAN AND SONDAR! THEY MUST HAVE GOT CONTROL OF THE TREEN SHIP AFTER ALL.
AND THEY'VE COME BACK TO RESCUE ME! THEY DON'T KNOW YOU MERCURIANS! THEY'LL BE SURPRISED TO FIND OUR GREEN FRIENDS HERE ALL TRUSSED UP.
WILLY! BEHAVE YOURSELF! DON'T BITE A MAN WHEN HE'S DOWN.
THANK HEAVEN YOU'RE SAFE, JOCELYN. WHEN YOU DIDN'T TURN UP AT THE MEKON'S H.Q WITH URB AND DIG, WE THOUGHT YOU'D BEEN KILLED.
NOT ME! I GOT INTO THE AIRLOCK BEFORE THE TREENS OUTSIDF COULD GRAB ME.
THEN SUDDENLY THE LOCALS HERE SPRANG AT ME, I THOUGHT THEY WERE GOING TO HAND ME BACK TO THE TREENS, BUT IT TURNED OUT THAT THEY'D TRUSSED UP THE ONES WE KNOCKED OUT IN THE FIGHT, AND THEY WERE AFRAID I'D COME BACK TO KILL THEM.
THEY THOUGHT YOU'D KILL HELPLESS PRISONERS? THEY MUST HAVE A LOW OPINION OF US. THE MEKON AND HIS GANG MUST HAVE GIVEN THEM A BAD IMPRESSION OF THE PEOPLE OF OTHER PLANETS.
YES THEY DISAPPROVE OF HIM STRONGLY — I'VE LEARNED THAT MUCH
HOW D'YOU KNOW? HAVE YOU MANAGED TO LEARN THE LANGUAGE?
A GOOD DEAL OF IT. IT'S TERRIBLY EASY REALLY — NO VERBS AND NO GRAMMAR. THE ONLY TROUBLE IS, IT'S SUNG!
I GUESSED IT WOULD BE. THEIR MOUTHS CAN ONLY FORM VOWELS, SO MUSICAL NOTES TAKE THE PLACE OF CONSONANTS.
THAT'S RIGHT, SONDAR. LOOK — I'VE BEEN JOTTING DOWN SOME OF THEIR WORDS ON THIS METAL PLATE THEY USE FOR WRITING. FOR THE NOTES THEY SING I'VE WRITTEN D.R.M.F.S.L.T.G. — REPRESENTING THE EIGHT NOTES OF SCALE.
THE TONIC SOL-FA ISN'T IT? A DIFFERENT NOTE TAGGED ON TO A VOWEL GIVES A DIFFERENT WORD. VERY INGENIOUS, JOCELYN.
ONCE YOU MAKE A START YOU GET ON LIKE A HOUSE ON FIRE. TRY ME! WHAT DO YOU WANT TO ASK THEM?
WHAT DEVILMENT IS THE MEKON PLANNING?
THAT BECOMES "WHAT BAD INSIDE BRAIN GREEN MAN BIG-HEAD". HERE GOES — MEE MAW-MEE LEE-RAH GAY-MAW FOO MAH-FAY DAW-TEE DOO-LAW?
DAN! HE SAYS THE MEKON IS CORNERING MOST OF THE SUPPLIES OF SOMETHING OR OTHER — BUT I DON'T UNDERSTAND WHAT! I THINK IT'S ...
SAY — WHAT'S THE MATTER WITH THAT FELLOW? HE'S EXCITED ABOUT SOMETHING!
FOO MAH-FAY REE-FAH.
WHAT!
HE SAYS THE TREENS HAVE GONE! BUT THEY CAN'T HAVE! THEY WERE ALL TIED UP OUT THERE A MINUTE AGO!
HE'S RIGHT, THEY'RE GONE, AND I BET OUR ROCKET SHIP'S GONE, TOO. WE WERE FOOLS TO LEAVE IT UNGUARDED!
AND THEY'RE PROBABLY WAITING FOR US OUTSIDE — READY TO POUNCE!
CONTINUED

EAGLE-BRITAIN'S NATIONAL STRIP CARTOON WEEKLY

FOURPENCE-
HALFPENNY
EVERY FRIDAY
EAGLE
5 SEPTEMBER 1952 Vol. 3 No. 22

DAN DARE
PILOT OF THE FUTURE
MAROONED ON MERCURY
WE CAN'T LET THEM GET AWAY! WE RISKED OUR LIVES TO GET THAT ROCKET SHIP, AND WE NEED IT TO RESCUE DIGBY AND URB.
YOU CAN'T RESCUE THEM IF YOU'RE PARALYSED, DAN! IF THEY HAVEN'T GOT THEIR GUNS TRAINED ON THE EXIT, THEY'RE NOT VERY CLEVER TREENS!
GRR
GRR
Digby and Urb have been captured and taken to the Mekon's H.Q. Dan and Sondar have seized a rocketship and returned to the Mercurian city to find Miss Peabody. She has made friends with the Mercurians and learnt their language. They say the Mekon is cornering supplies of some mysterious substance. Suddenly they discover that the Treens they had made prisoners have escaped.

BUT WE CAN'T JUST SIT HERE AND LET THEM GET AWAY WITH IT! BESIDES, WE'RE TRAPPED.
CALL THIS A TRAP IF YOU LIKE. I CALL IT A FORTRESS! NOW WE'VE MADE FRIENDS WITH THE MERCURIANS, WE CAN HOLD IT AGAINST ALL COMERS.

FRIENDS? HOW DO WE KNOW? I ADMIT THEY RESCUED US, BUT THEIR BEHAVIOUR'S VERY STRANGE.
WHAT DO YOU EXPECT? WE FIGHT TREENS ALL OVER THEIR HOUSES, AND GENERALLY MAKE A NUISANCE OF OURSELVES, BUT NOW THEY KNOW WE'RE AGAINST THE MEKON...
ALL RIGHT, JOCELYN, YOU WIN. ASK THEIR ADVICE.

WE'RE YOUR FRIENDS. WE'RE AGAINST THE TREENS. WILL YOU HELP US?
SAH!

HE DIDN'T SAY MUCH! WHAT'S "SAH" MEAN?
JUST "WITH!" IN OTHER WORDS, "COME ALONG WITH ME." LOOKS LIKE THEY'RE GOING TO HELP US.

WHAT'S THE BIG IDEA, JOCELYN? WHAT WERE THEY GABBLING ABOUT?
THEY'RE GOING TO TAKE US TO THE MEKON'S HIDE-OUT BY THE BACK-DOOR SO TO SPEAK. SEEMS THERE'S ANOTHER WAY OUT OF THIS PLACE — UNDERGROUND BY THE LOOK OF IT.
AND THE MEKON IS PLANNING SOME EVIL—WITH SOMETHING HE'S FOUND ON MERCURY? WE'VE GOT TO FIND OUT WHAT IT IS. IT MAY BE AGAINST VENUS
—TO OUST ME AND RECOVER HIS KINGDOM, OR AGAINST EARTH— AND REVENGE ON YOU, COLONEL.
ALL IN GOOD TIME, SONDAR. WE'VE GOT TO FIND HIS H.Q.— AND RESCUE DIG AND URB. THAT'S THE FIRST JOB — IF WE'RE NOT TOO LATE ALREADY.

AND THIS LOOKS LIKE THE START. IT'S LIKE A NEW VERSION OF THE LONDON UNDERGROUND WHEN I WAS A KID.

FROM THE LOOK OF IT, IT'S NOT GOING TO STAY UNDERGROUND LONG. I DON'T FANCY THAT TUNNEL VERY MUCH.
IT'S EITHER THIS OR THOSE TREEN GANGSTERS OUTSIDE. TAKE YOUR CHOICE! HERE WE GO!

WHOOSH!
NOW I KNOW WHAT IT FEELS LIKE TO BE SHOT OUT OF A GUN AT THE CIRCUS.
THESE MERCURIANS CERTAINLY HAVE SOME ODD IDEAS ABOUT GETTING AROUND.
LOOK! THEY'VE SPOTTED US! IT'S THE TREEN ROCKET-SHIP!
THE MEKON MUST HAVE SENT ANOTHER LOT OF HIS GANG AFTER US — AND THEY'VE RELEASED THE TREENS WE KNOCKED OUT. THEY'LL NOT LET US GET AWAY THIS TIME!
BUT DAN — THEY CAN'T GET US WHILE WE'RE IN THIS THING. THEY....
CAN'T THEY? JUST YOU WATCH...
LOOK OUT!
MEANWHILE, IN THE MEKON'S H.Q.
GOOD! GOOD! STOP THEM AT ALL COSTS! IF THEY ONCE GET AWAY TO.....
FOOLS! FOOLS! I WANT THEM ALIVE! BREAK THE RAILS- STOP THE CAR! BUT DON'T KILL THEM!
YES, O DIGBY - I WILL ACTION AS YOU SAY. YOUR PLAN HAS GOOD EXCELLENCE.
GOOD LAD!
NOW, YOU LITTLE GREEN HORROR! YOU'RE IN FOR A NASTY SHOCK.
STOP! THE MEKON'S ORDERS! CEASE FIRE! RETURN AT ONCE! RETURN TO BASE!
NOW I FIX THE TELEVIEW. PUT THAT TOGETHER IF YOU CAN!
A MILLION CURSES! TAKE THEM AWAY! DESTROY THEM!
CONTINUED

EAGLE-BRITAIN'S NATIONAL STRIP CARTOON WEEKLY

OUCH!
TOO TOO!
IT MEANS "BANG, CRASH". IT'S WHAT THEY SAY WHEN ANYTHING GOES WALLOP. THESE FELLOWS SEEM TO LOVE SMASHES.
THEY CERTAINLY FINISH THEIR JOURNEYS WITH A BANG! THEY MUST BE MUCH TOUGHER THAN WE ARE. GRAVITY HERE MAKES FALLING ONLY A QUARTER AS HARD, AND WHAT WAS HE SAYING "TOO TOO" FOR?
I WISH THEY'D REMEMBER WE DON'T BELONG TO MERCURY.
HE'S TRYING TO TELL US SOMETHING. I'VE GOT IT! HIS AIR SACS ARE DEFLATED. WE CAN TAKE OUR HELMETS OFF.
HE SAYS WE'RE RIGHT UNDERNEATH THE MEKON'S LAIR. HE'LL HAVE THE SHOCK OF HIS LIFE WHEN WE POP IN BY THE BACK DOOR.
DON'T BE TOO SURE, COLONEL. THE MEKON IS A CUNNING ONE. IT WOULD BE AS WELL NOT TO UNDERESTIMATE HIM.
HULLO, THERE'S SOME SORT OF MACHINERY IN THERE. MIGHT BE INTERESTING. HANG ON WHILE I INVESTIGATE.
YOU'LL HAVE TO WAIT A TIME FOR YOUR EYES TO BECOME ACCUSTOMED TO THE DIMNESS.
FAW LEE-RAH! LOO-MEE.
DAN! STOP! HE SAYS "DON'T GO IN". I DON'T KNOW WHAT THE OTHER WORD MEANS.
HE'S TOO LATE. WHY DOESN'T HE WANT US TO KNOW WHAT'S IN THERE? IT MAY BE A CLUE TO THE MEKON'S PLOT.
SAW-RAY RAH-FAY!
OH, NO YOU DON'T! THE COLONEL IS...
SONDAR! HE'S SAYING IT'S "HEAT DEATH." HE'S WARNING US! IT MEANS DAN'LL BE BURNT TO DEATH.
STAY WHERE YOU ARE, JOCELYN. YOU CAN'T HELP ME! I'M TRAPPED IN THIS MACHINE THING.
TELL HIM TO GET OUT AND SAVE HIMSELF – NO HUMAN BEING COULD BREAK THIS METAL.
SNAP
MEANWHILE – UNSEEN BY DAN AND PEABODY...
OH, DAN, I THOUGHT YOU WERE DONE FOR THAT TIME! AND I FELT SO HELPLESS!
QUICK – GET HIM UP ALOFT BEFORE THEY SEE US.
SEE THE IDEA? CONCENTRATED SUNRAYS. LENSES FOCUS THE SUN'S RAYS ON TO A BATTERY OF BI-METALLIC RODS, CAUSING THEM TO CURVE AND TURN THAT DRUM. THEN THE SHUTTERS CLOSE, THE RODS COOL AND STRAIGHTEN OUT, AND THE WHOLE PROCESS STARTS AGAIN.
I EXPECT THE DRUM RATCHETS UP A WEIGHT TO STORE THE POWER CREATED. MOST INGENIOUS – ALL AUTOMATIC, TOO.
WHICH MEANS YOU CAN'T BEG IT TO STOP SO – HEY! WHERE'S SONDAR?
GONE EXPLORING, PERHAPS.
NONSENSE! HE WAS KNOCKED COLD WHEN THE MERCURIAN THREW HIM. THERE'S SOMETHING FUNNY GOING ON HERE.
CONTINUED

EAGLE-BRITAIN'S NATIONAL STRIP CARTOON WEEKLY

FOURPENCE-HALFPENNY

EVERY FRIDAY

EAGLE

19 SEPTEMBER 1952 Vol. 3 No. 24

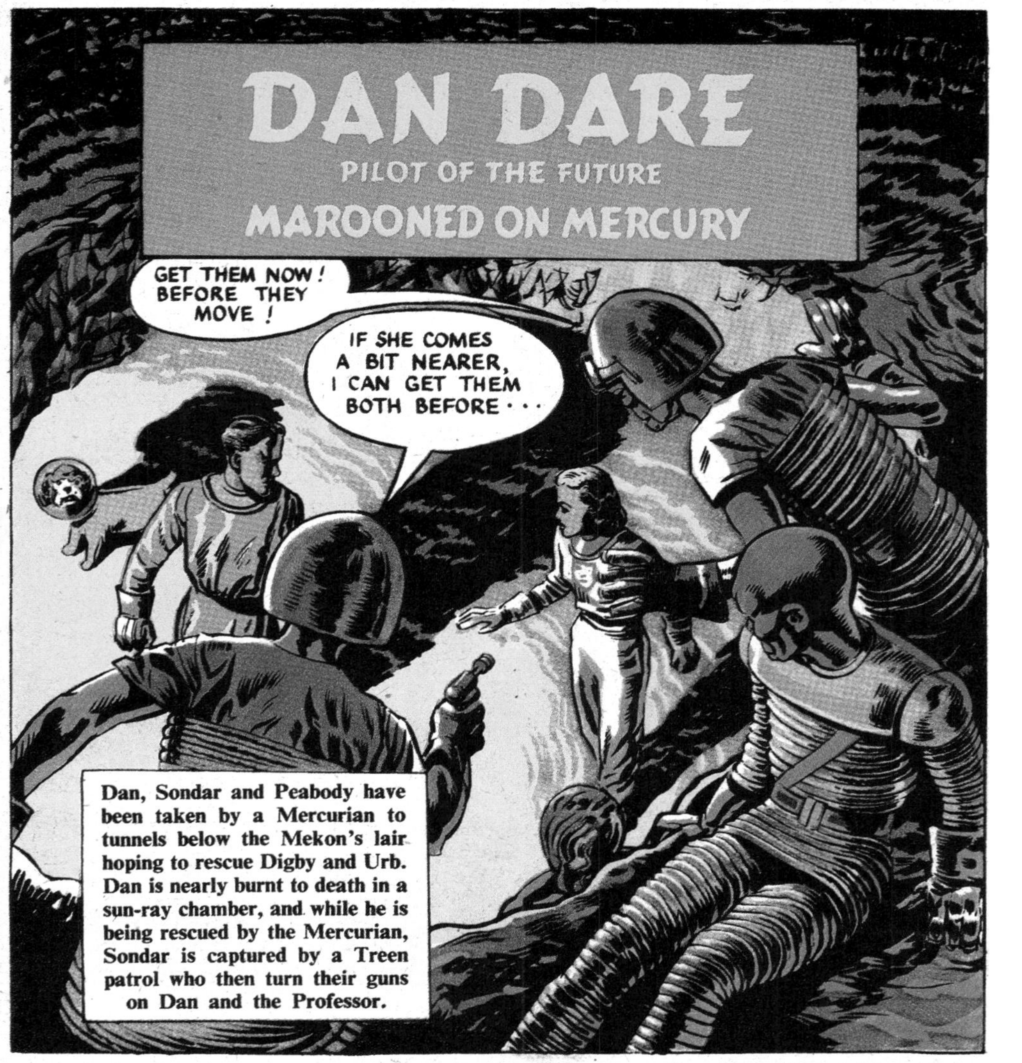
DAN DARE
PILOT OF THE FUTURE
MAROONED ON MERCURY
GET THEM NOW! BEFORE THEY MOVE!
IF SHE COMES A BIT NEARER, I CAN GET THEM BOTH BEFORE...
Dan, Sondar and Peabody have been taken by a Mercurian to tunnels below the Mekon's lair hoping to rescue Digby and Urb. Dan is nearly burnt to death in a sun-ray chamber, and while he is being rescued by the Mercurian, Sondar is captured by a Treen patrol who then turn their guns on Dan and the Professor.

LOOK OUT, COLONEL!
TREENS UP HERE!
COME ON, JOCELYN! SONDAR'S UP THERE! THE TREENS HAVE GOT HIM. HE NEEDS HELP.
WHAT DO YOU THINK I AM? A KANGAROO? LET'S FIND ANOTHER WAY UP AND TAKE THEM FROM THE REAR.
REE-MAH FOO MAH-FAY!
WHOOSH
HOLD ON A MOMENT, JOCELYN...
...TWO TREENS COMING DOWN! SEEMS OUR MERCURIAN FRIEND DOESN'T NEED ANY HELP.
TOO-TOO!
THEY DO LIKE THROWING THINGS. HOPE HE DOESN'T THROW SONDAR, TOO, FOR THE FUN OF IT!
WHAM
THESE CHAPS MUST BE A PATROL FROM THE MEKON'S H.Q. WELL, IF THERE'S A WAY DOWN THERE'S ALSO A WAY UP. LET'S FIND IT!
THE QUICKEST WAY WOULD BE TO BRING THESE TREENS ROUND AND MAKE THEM TALK.
FAW-FOO! THAT'S MERCURIAN FOR "TUT-TUT". YOU KNOW WE DON'T BELIEVE IN TORTURE, SONDAR! WE'LL HAVE TO FIND SOME OTHER WAY.

I WOULDN'T PUT MY WORST ENEMY IN THE SUN RAY CHAMBER I WAS TRAPPED IN. WE'LL LEAVE CRUELTY TO THE MEKON AND USE OUR BRAINS INSTEAD.
WE CAN EITHER TIE UP THE TREENS AND EXPLORE ON OUR OWN...
... OR WE CAN BRING THE TREENS ROUND... LET THEM 'ESCAPE', AND THEN FOLLOW THEM.
BETTER TRY BOTH PLANS. YOU AND I WILL SET OFF NOW, SONDAR. JOCELYN, YOU CONTINUE YOUR STUDY OF MERCURIAN WITH OUR FRIEND HERE, WHILE YOU WATCH THE TREENS. THEN FOLLOW THEM.
RIGHT. AND WE MAY 'BE IN SCOTLAND 'AFORE YE!'
IF WE KEEP ON GOING UPWARDS WE'RE BOUND TO BE GETTING NEARER OUR GAOL.
YOU MEAN 'GOAL' — I HOPE!
HOW FAR HAVE WE GONE NOW, WOULD YOU RECKON, SONDAR?
VERTICALLY? I ESTIMATE WE ARE ABOUT THREE QUARTERS OF THE WAY UP — WHETHER WE'VE ALWAYS TAKEN THE RIGHT TURNING IS ANOTHER MATTER.
WE MUST BE GETTING NEAR IT NOW. WHAT HAVE THEY BEEN MINING HERE IN THIS PIT, DO YOU THINK?
TITANIUM, BY THE LOOK OF THE ORE. A USEFUL METAL, COLONEL! THE MERCURIANS USE IT A LOT IN BUILDING — BUT A TREEN DESIGNED THIS BRIDGE. YOU'RE RIGHT, WE MUST BE GETTING NEAR.
LOOK — THERE'S SOME KIND OF MINER'S POWER-DRILL. SOMEONE'S BEEN WORKING HERE QUITE RECENTLY.
BUT WE'VE COME TO A DEAD END. THERE MUST BE A WAY UP. LET'S GO BACK AND EXAMINE THE ROOF ALL THE WAY.
JUMPING JETS! LOOK! THE BRIDGE!
AAAHH!
IT'S SWUNG ROUND! THEY MUST HAVE BEEN WATCHING US ALL THE TIME! WE'RE TRAPPED – TRAPPED BETWEEN A BLANK WALL AND A YAWNING CHASM.
MEANWHILE, IN THE MEKON'S CONTROL ROOM...
COLONEL DARE AND SONDAR HAVE BEEN ISOLATED, O MEKON, BUT THERE IS NO SIGN OF PROFESSOR PEABODY.
OUR PATROL HAS JUST APPEARED! THEY, TOO, HAVE BEEN CUT OFF BY THE MOVING BRIDGE. SHALL WE LET THEM ACROSS.
NO!
THE COLONEL MIGHT OVERCOME THEM AND ESCAPE. WE CAN TAKE NO CHANCES WITH HIM. OPEN THE ROCK DOOR IN THE TUNNEL WHERE HE'S TRAPPED, AND HE'LL WALK INTO THE CELL. THEN LET THE PATROL ACROSS THE BRIDGE.
CAN WE JUMP IT, SONDAR?
NOT EVEN ON MERCURY, COLONEL, UNLESS YOU CAN BEAT THE UNIVERSE-OLYMPICS RECORD! LET US GO BACK AND EXAMINE THE WALLS OF THE TUNNEL AGAIN. THOSE TWO TREENS THERE MUST BE THE ONES WE LEFT WITH THE PROFESSOR, BUT THEY CAN'T GET ACROSS EITHER.
WELL, I'LL BE... DO YOU SEE WHAT I SEE?
YES... IF YOU SEE A TRAP SET BY THE MEKON, COLONEL. DON'T GO IN!
DR. LIVINGSTONE, I PRESUME.
WHO IS IT, COLONEL? YOU LOOK AS IF YOU'D SEEN A GHOST.
I HAVE! THIS IS THE PILOT OF THE "KINGFISHER", THE SPACESHIP THAT WAS LOST WITH ALL HANDS WHEN WE WERE FIRST ATTEMPTING TO REACH VENUS THROUGH YOUR BARRIER-RAY! I SAW IT DISINTERGRATING WITH MY OWN EYES.
I'M NO GHOST, DAN! WE BALED OUT JUST BEFORE THE CRASH, AND WERE PICKED UP BY...
SLAM
COLONEL DARE! THE DOOR! YOUR 'FRIEND' HAS BEEN THE BAIT IN THE MOUSE-TRAP.
CONTINUED

EAGLE-BRITAIN'S NATIONAL STRIP CARTOON WEEKLY

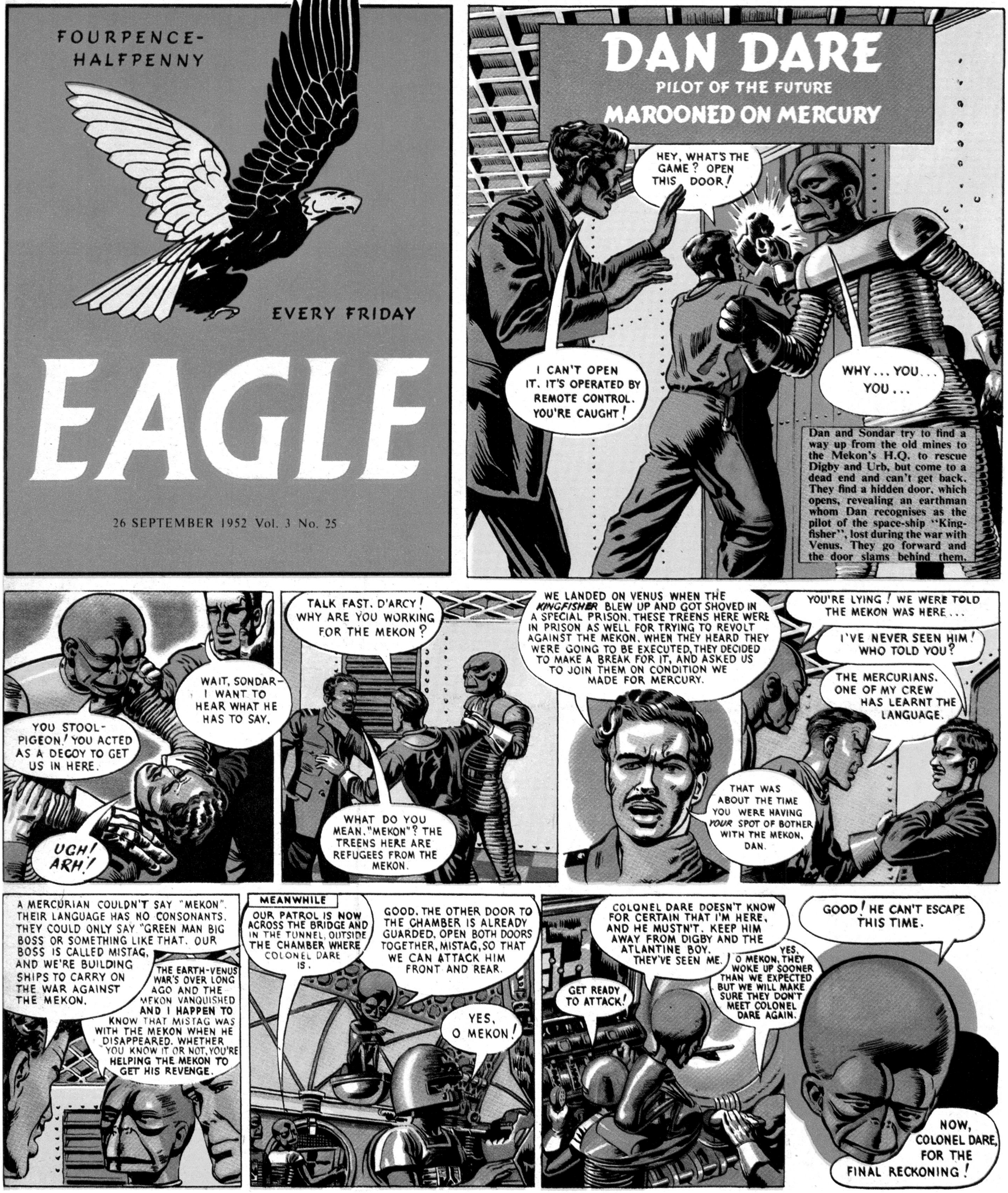
FOURPENCE-HALFPENNY
EVERY FRIDAY
EAGLE
26 SEPTEMBER 1952 Vol. 3 No. 25
DAN DARE
PILOT OF THE FUTURE
MAROONED ON MERCURY
HEY, WHAT'S THE GAME? OPEN THIS DOOR!
I CAN'T OPEN IT. IT'S OPERATED BY REMOTE CONTROL. YOU'RE CAUGHT!
WHY ... YOU... YOU ...
Dan and Sondar try to find a way up from the old mines to the Mekon's H.Q. to rescue Digby and Urb, but come to a dead end and can't get back. They find a hidden door, which opens, revealing an earthman whom Dan recognises as the pilot of the space-ship "Kingfisher", lost during the war with Venus. They go forward and the door slams behind them.
WAIT, SONDAR-I WANT TO HEAR WHAT HE HAS TO SAY.
YOU STOOL-PIGEON! YOU ACTED AS A DECOY TO GET US IN HERE.
UGH! ARH!
TALK FAST, D'ARCY! WHY ARE YOU WORKING FOR THE MEKON?
WHAT DO YOU MEAN, "MEKON"? THE TREENS HERE ARE REFUGEES FROM THE MEKON.
WE LANDED ON VENUS WHEN THE KINGFISHER BLEW UP AND GOT SHOVED IN A SPECIAL PRISON. THESE TREENS HERE WERE IN PRISON AS WELL FOR TRYING TO REVOLT AGAINST THE MEKON. WHEN THEY HEARD THEY WERE GOING TO BE EXECUTED, THEY DECIDED TO MAKE A BREAK FOR IT, AND ASKED US TO JOIN THEM ON CONDITION WE MADE FOR MERCURY.
THAT WAS ABOUT THE TIME YOU WERE HAVING YOUR SPOT OF BOTHER WITH THE MEKON, DAN.
YOU'RE LYING! WE WERE TOLD THE MEKON WAS HERE...
I'VE NEVER SEEN HIM! WHO TOLD YOU?
THE MERCURIANS. ONE OF MY CREW HAS LEARNT THE LANGUAGE.
A MERCURIAN COULDN'T SAY "MEKON". THEIR LANGUAGE HAS NO CONSONANTS. THEY COULD ONLY SAY "GREEN MAN BIG BOSS OR SOMETHING LIKE THAT. OUR BOSS IS CALLED MISTAG, AND WE'RE BUILDING SHIPS TO CARRY ON THE WAR AGAINST THE MEKON.
THE EARTH-VENUS WAR'S OVER LONG AGO AND THE MEKON VANQUISHED AND I HAPPEN TO KNOW THAT MISTAG WAS WITH THE MEKON WHEN HE DISAPPEARED. WHETHER YOU KNOW IT OR NOT, YOU'RE HELPING THE MEKON TO GET HIS REVENGE.
MEANWHILE
OUR PATROL IS NOW ACROSS THE BRIDGE AND IN THE TUNNEL OUTSIDE THE CHAMBER WHERE COLONEL DARE IS.
GOOD. THE OTHER DOOR TO THE CHAMBER IS ALREADY GUARDED. OPEN BOTH DOORS TOGETHER, MISTAG, SO THAT WE CAN ATTACK HIM FRONT AND REAR.
YES, O MEKON!
COLONEL DARE DOESN'T KNOW FOR CERTAIN THAT I'M HERE, AND HE MUSTN'T. KEEP HIM AWAY FROM DIGBY AND THE ATLANTINE BOY. THEY'VE SEEN ME.
YES, O MEKON, THEY WOKE UP SOONER THAN WE EXPECTED BUT WE WILL MAKE SURE THEY DON'T MEET COLONEL DARE AGAIN.
GET READY TO ATTACK!
GOOD! HE CAN'T ESCAPE THIS TIME.
NOW, COLONEL DARE, FOR THE FINAL RECKONING!

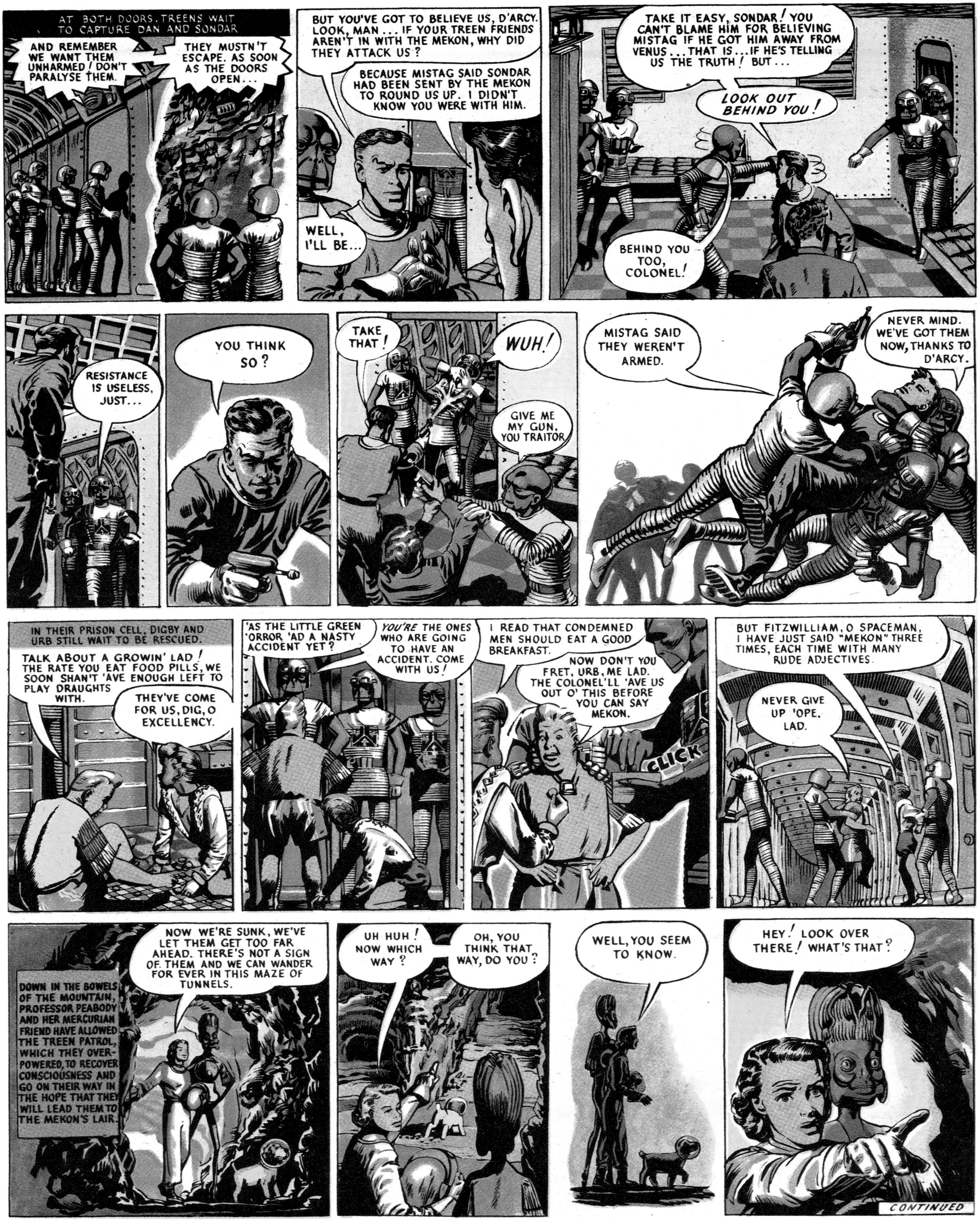

AT BOTH DOORS, TREENS WAIT TO CAPTURE DAN AND SONDAR
AND REMEMBER WE WANT THEM UNHARMED! DON'T PARALYSE THEM.
THEY MUSTN'T ESCAPE. AS SOON AS THE DOORS OPEN...
BUT YOU'VE GOT TO BELIEVE US, D'ARCY. LOOK, MAN... IF YOUR TREEN FRIENDS AREN'T IN WITH THE MEKON, WHY DID THEY ATTACK US?
BECAUSE MISTAG SAID SONDAR HAD BEEN SENT BY THE MEKON TO ROUND US UP. I DIDN'T KNOW YOU WERE WITH HIM.
WELL, I'LL BE...
TAKE IT EASY, SONDAR! YOU CAN'T BLAME HIM FOR BELIEVING MISTAG IF HE GOT HIM AWAY FROM VENUS... THAT IS... IF HE'S TELLING US THE TRUTH! BUT...
LOOK OUT BEHIND YOU!
BEHIND YOU TOO, COLONEL!
RESISTANCE IS USELESS, JUST...
YOU THINK SO?
TAKE THAT!
WUH!
GIVE ME MY GUN, YOU TRAITOR
MISTAG SAID THEY WEREN'T ARMED.
NEVER MIND. WE'VE GOT THEM NOW, THANKS TO D'ARCY.
IN THEIR PRISON CELL, DIGBY AND URB STILL WAIT TO BE RESCUED.
TALK ABOUT A GROWIN' LAD! THE RATE YOU EAT FOOD PILLS, WE SOON SHAN'T 'AVE ENOUGH LEFT TO PLAY DRAUGHTS WITH.
THEY'VE COME FOR US, DIG, O EXCELLENCY.
'AS THE LITTLE GREEN 'ORROR 'AD A NASTY ACCIDENT YET?
YOU'RE THE ONES WHO ARE GOING TO HAVE AN ACCIDENT. COME WITH US!
I READ THAT CONDEMNED MEN SHOULD EAT A GOOD BREAKFAST.
NOW DON'T YOU FRET, URB, ME LAD. THE COLONEL'LL 'AVE US OUT O' THIS BEFORE YOU CAN SAY MEKON.
CLICK
BUT FITZWILLIAM, O SPACEMAN, I HAVE JUST SAID "MEKON" THREE TIMES, EACH TIME WITH MANY RUDE ADJECTIVES.
NEVER GIVE UP 'OPE, LAD.
DOWN IN THE BOWELS OF THE MOUNTAIN, PROFESSOR PEABODY AND HER MERCURIAN FRIEND HAVE ALLOWED THE TREEN PATROL, WHICH THEY OVERPOWERED, TO RECOVER CONSCIOUSNESS AND GO ON THEIR WAY IN THE HOPE THAT THEY WILL LEAD THEM TO THE MEKON'S LAIR.
NOW WE'RE SUNK, WE'VE LET THEM GET TOO FAR AHEAD. THERE'S NOT A SIGN OF THEM AND WE CAN WANDER FOR EVER IN THIS MAZE OF TUNNELS.
UH HUH! NOW WHICH WAY?
OH, YOU THINK THAT WAY, DO YOU?
WELL, YOU SEEM TO KNOW.
HEY! LOOK OVER THERE! WHAT'S THAT?
CONTINUED

EAGLE - BRITAIN'S NATIONAL STRIP CARTOON WEEKLY

FOURPENCE-HALFPENNY

EVERY FRIDAY

EAGLE

3 OCTOBER 1952 Vol. 3 No. 26

DAN DARE
PILOT OF THE FUTURE
MAROONED ON MERCURY
WHY, IT'S A SWING BRIDGE . . . AND IT'S TURNED AGAINST US. WE MUST BE GETTING WARM, BECAUSE THOSE TREENS CERTAINLY CAME THIS WAY. WE SHOULDN'T HAVE LET THEM GET SO FAR AHEAD.
THEY'D HAVE SEEN US IF WE'D FOLLOWED ANY CLOSER.
Dan and Sondar, trying to rescue Digby and Urb from the Mekon's H.Q., are shut in an underground cell with an earthman, D'Arcy. D'Arcy denies that the Mekon is on Mercury and claims to be working against him under Mistag. Meanwhile Prof. Peabody and the Mercurian have been following two Treens in the hope of being led to the Mekon's hide-out.

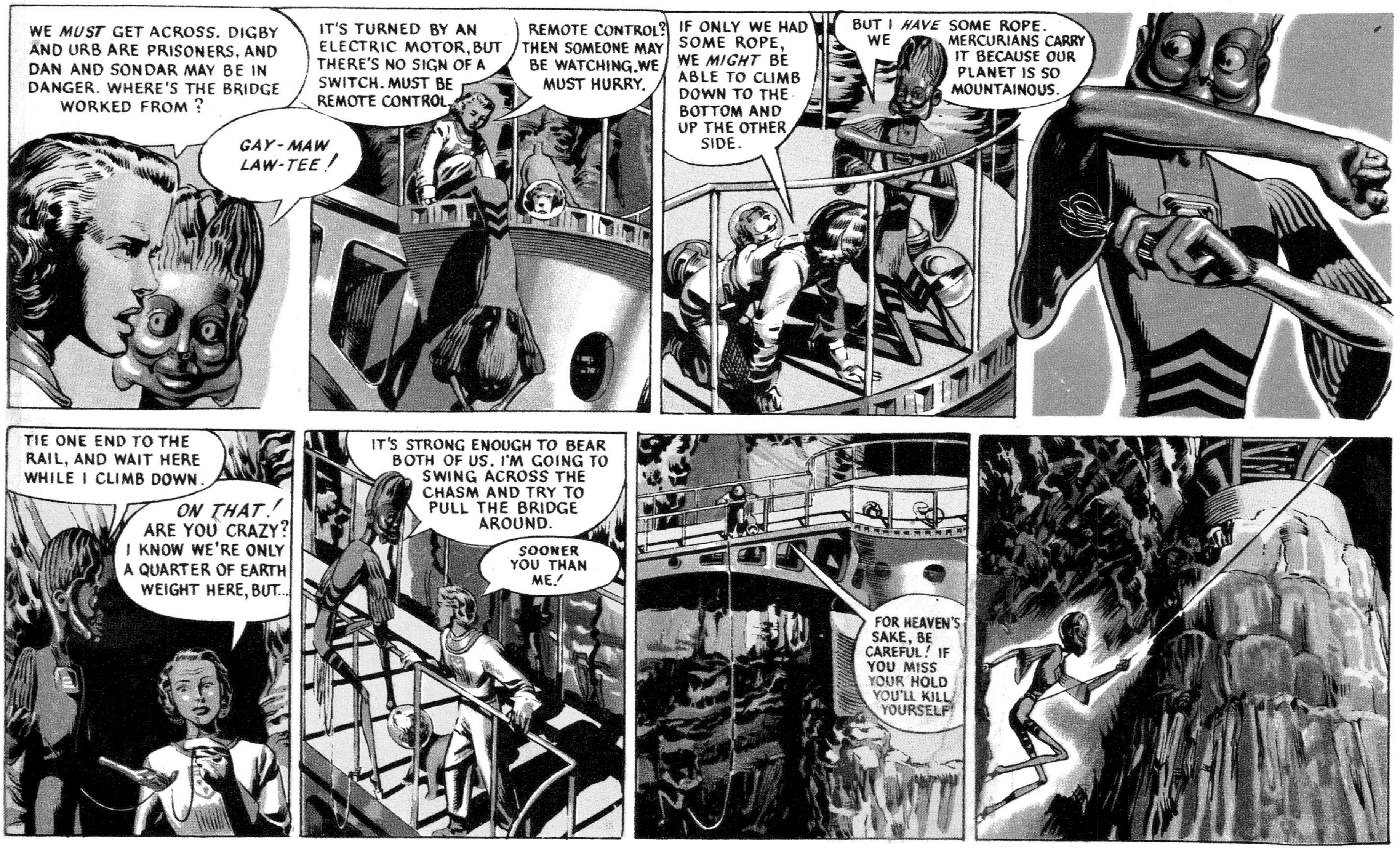
WE MUST GET ACROSS. DIGBY AND URB ARE PRISONERS, AND DAN AND SONDAR MAY BE IN DANGER. WHERE'S THE BRIDGE WORKED FROM ?
GAY-MAW LAW-TEE !
IT'S TURNED BY AN ELECTRIC MOTOR, BUT THERE'S NO SIGN OF A SWITCH. MUST BE REMOTE CONTROL.
REMOTE CONTROL? THEN SOMEONE MAY BE WATCHING, WE MUST HURRY.
IF ONLY WE HAD SOME ROPE, WE MIGHT BE ABLE TO CLIMB DOWN TO THE BOTTOM AND UP THE OTHER SIDE.
BUT I HAVE SOME ROPE. WE MERCURIANS CARRY IT BECAUSE OUR PLANET IS SO MOUNTAINOUS.
TIE ONE END TO THE RAIL, AND WAIT HERE WHILE I CLIMB DOWN.
ON THAT! ARE YOU CRAZY? I KNOW WE'RE ONLY A QUARTER OF EARTH WEIGHT HERE, BUT...
IT'S STRONG ENOUGH TO BEAR BOTH OF US. I'M GOING TO SWING ACROSS THE CHASM AND TRY TO PULL THE BRIDGE AROUND.
SOONER YOU THAN ME!
FOR HEAVEN'S SAKE, BE CAREFUL! IF YOU MISS YOUR HOLD YOU'LL KILL YOURSELF!

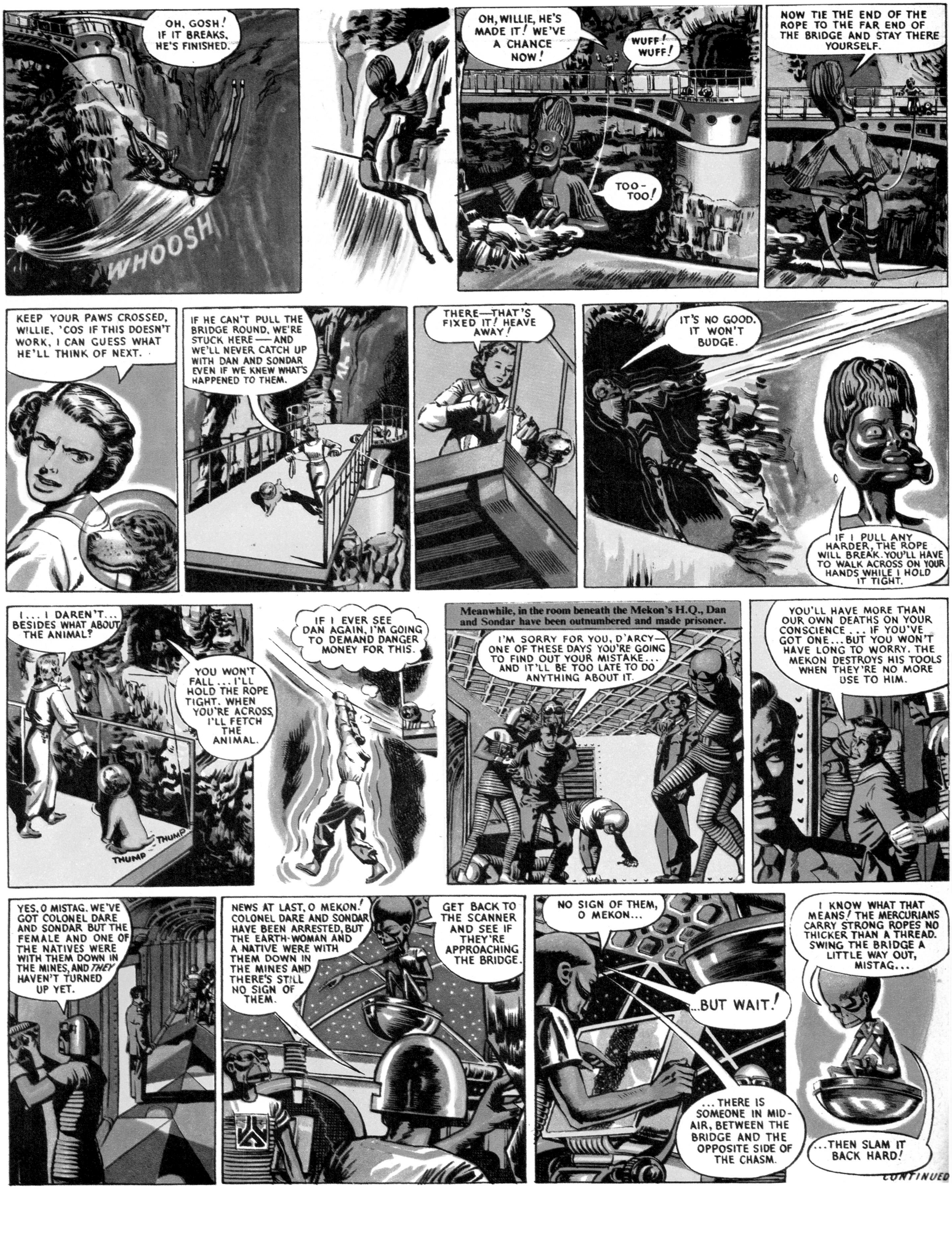
OH, GOSH! IF IT BREAKS, HE'S FINISHED.
WHOOSH
OH, WILLIE, HE'S MADE IT! WE'VE A CHANCE NOW!
WUFF! WUFF!
TOO-TOO!
NOW TIE THE END OF THE ROPE TO THE FAR END OF THE BRIDGE AND STAY THERE YOURSELF.
KEEP YOUR PAWS CROSSED, WILLIE, 'COS IF THIS DOESN'T WORK, I CAN GUESS WHAT HE'LL THINK OF NEXT.
IF HE CAN'T PULL THE BRIDGE ROUND, WE'RE STUCK HERE — AND WE'LL NEVER CATCH UP WITH DAN AND SONDAR EVEN IF WE KNEW WHAT'S HAPPENED TO THEM.
THERE — THAT'S FIXED IT! HEAVE AWAY!
IT'S NO GOOD. IT WON'T BUDGE.
IF I PULL ANY HARDER, THE ROPE WILL BREAK. YOU'LL HAVE TO WALK ACROSS ON YOUR HANDS WHILE I HOLD IT TIGHT.
I... I DAREN'T... BESIDES WHAT ABOUT THE ANIMAL?
YOU WON'T FALL... I'LL HOLD THE ROPE TIGHT. WHEN YOU'RE ACROSS, I'LL FETCH THE ANIMAL.
THUMP THUMP
IF I EVER SEE DAN AGAIN, I'M GOING TO DEMAND DANGER MONEY FOR THIS.
Meanwhile, in the room beneath the Mekon's H.Q., Dan and Sondar have been outnumbered and made prisoner.
I'M SORRY FOR YOU, D'ARCY — ONE OF THESE DAYS YOU'RE GOING TO FIND OUT YOUR MISTAKE... AND IT'LL BE TOO LATE TO DO ANYTHING ABOUT IT.
YOU'LL HAVE MORE THAN OUR OWN DEATHS ON YOUR CONSCIENCE... IF YOU'VE GOT ONE... BUT YOU WON'T HAVE LONG TO WORRY. THE MEKON DESTROYS HIS TOOLS WHEN THEY'RE NO MORE USE TO HIM.
YES, O MISTAG. WE'VE GOT COLONEL DARE AND SONDAR BUT THE FEMALE AND ONE OF THE NATIVES WERE WITH THEM DOWN IN THE MINES, AND THEY HAVEN'T TURNED UP YET.
NEWS AT LAST, O MEKON! COLONEL DARE AND SONDAR HAVE BEEN ARRESTED, BUT THE EARTH-WOMAN AND A NATIVE WERE WITH THEM DOWN IN THE MINES AND THERE'S STILL NO SIGN OF THEM.
GET BACK TO THE SCANNER AND SEE IF THEY'RE APPROACHING THE BRIDGE.
NO SIGN OF THEM, O MEKON...
...BUT WAIT!
...THERE IS SOMEONE IN MID-AIR, BETWEEN THE BRIDGE AND THE OPPOSITE SIDE OF THE CHASM.
I KNOW WHAT THAT MEANS! THE MERCURIANS CARRY STRONG ROPES NO THICKER THAN A THREAD. SWING THE BRIDGE A LITTLE WAY OUT, MISTAG...
...THEN SLAM IT BACK HARD!
CONTINUED

YOU CAN WIN A FLIGHT TO A RANCH IN THE U.S.A.! – *see p. 11*

FOURPENCE-
HALFPENNY
EVERY FRIDAY
EAGLE
10 OCTOBER 1952 Vol. 3 No. 27

DAN DARE
PILOT OF THE FUTURE
MAROONED ON MERCURY
LOOK OUT! THE BRIDGE IS MOVING! THE ROPE'S GOING SLACK!
HAUL ON IT THEN! KEEP THE ROPE TIGHT!
Digby and Urb have been captured by the Mekon. With the help of earthman D'Arcy, Dan and Sondar have been lured into a cell in the Mekon's H.Q. and overpowered. Prof Peabody and her Mercurian friend, coming to the rescue, are crossing an underground chasm on a thin 'rope' when the Treens spot them. The Mekon gives orders to break the rope by jerking the swing-bridge to which it is tied.

FUNNY! THE BRIDGE HAS STOPPED MOVING NOW. PERHAPS IT'S JAMMED. I'D BETTER LET THE ROCK TAKE THE STRAIN SO AS TO HAVE A HAND FREE FOR WILLIE.

THE MERCURIAN IS HALF WAY ACROSS WHEN THE TREENS SUDDENLY SWING THE BRIDGE BACK.
SNAP

TOO TOO!
YEEOW!
WHAM

OH YOU DROPPED POOR WILLIE! I'M THANKFUL YOU'RE SAFE, BUT...
I NEEDED BOTH HANDS TO CLIMB THE ROPE

YOU SAVED HIM! GOSH, YOU'RE AS QUICK AS YOU ARE STRONG. THEY NEARLY GOT YOU THEN.
YES, IT WAS A CLEVER TRICK, MOST AMUSING

YOU DON'T EARN YOUR KEEP, WILLIE, BUT WE COULDN'T BEAR TO LOSE YOU. NOW STOP LICKING, WILLIE, AND I'LL TAKE OFF THAT BROKEN HELMET
QUICK – THIS WAY! I SEE A DOOR.

THERE'S BEEN A FIGHT. THAT PROVES WE'VE COME THE RIGHT WAY.
QUICK! THE FAR DOOR! IT'S CLOSING.
BUT DID DAN AND SONDAR WIN? WE MUST FIND THEM.
GRR
WOW

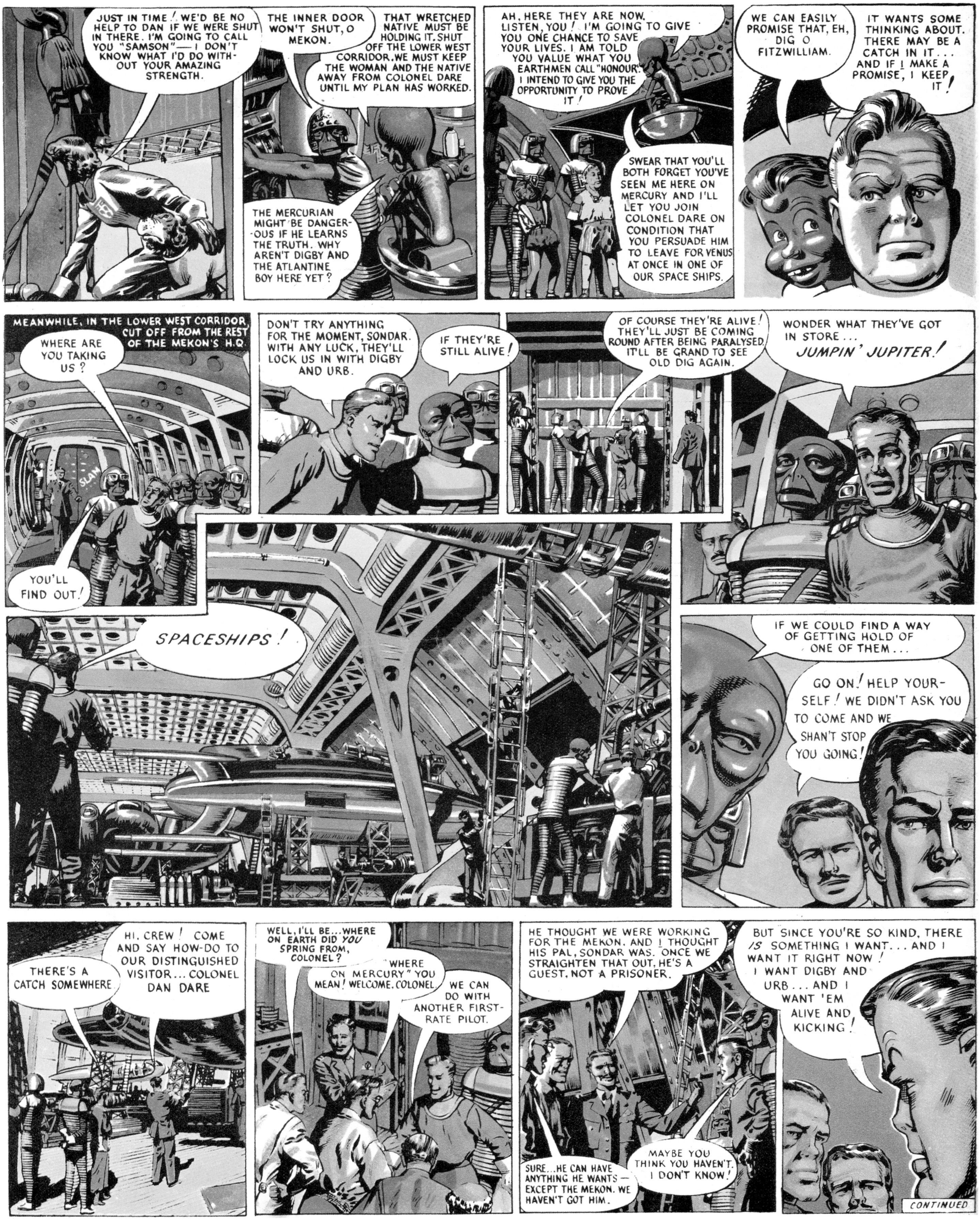

JUST IN TIME! WE'D BE NO HELP TO DAN IF WE WERE SHUT IN THERE. I'M GOING TO CALL YOU "SAMSON"— I DON'T KNOW WHAT I'D DO WITHOUT YOUR AMAZING STRENGTH.
THE INNER DOOR WON'T SHUT, O MEKON.
THAT WRETCHED NATIVE MUST BE HOLDING IT. SHUT OFF THE LOWER WEST CORRIDOR. WE MUST KEEP THE WOMAN AND THE NATIVE AWAY FROM COLONEL DARE UNTIL MY PLAN HAS WORKED.
THE MERCURIAN MIGHT BE DANGEROUS IF HE LEARNS THE TRUTH. WHY AREN'T DIGBY AND THE ATLANTINE BOY HERE YET?
AH, HERE THEY ARE NOW. LISTEN, YOU! I'M GOING TO GIVE YOU ONE CHANCE TO SAVE YOUR LIVES. I AM TOLD YOU VALUE WHAT YOU EARTHMEN CALL "HONOUR". I INTEND TO GIVE YOU THE OPPORTUNITY TO PROVE IT!
SWEAR THAT YOU'LL BOTH FORGET YOU'VE SEEN ME HERE ON MERCURY AND I'LL LET YOU JOIN COLONEL DARE ON CONDITION THAT YOU PERSUADE HIM TO LEAVE FOR VENUS AT ONCE IN ONE OF OUR SPACE SHIPS.
WE CAN EASILY PROMISE THAT, EH, DIG O FITZWILLIAM.
IT WANTS SOME THINKING ABOUT. THERE MAY BE A CATCH IN IT... AND IF I MAKE A PROMISE, I KEEP IT!
MEANWHILE, IN THE LOWER WEST CORRIDOR, CUT OFF FROM THE REST OF THE MEKON'S H.Q.
WHERE ARE YOU TAKING US?
SLAM
YOU'LL FIND OUT!
DON'T TRY ANYTHING FOR THE MOMENT, SONDAR. WITH ANY LUCK, THEY'LL LOCK US IN WITH DIGBY AND URB.
IF THEY'RE STILL ALIVE!
OF COURSE THEY'RE ALIVE! THEY'LL JUST BE COMING ROUND AFTER BEING PARALYSED. IT'LL BE GRAND TO SEE OLD DIG AGAIN.
WONDER WHAT THEY'VE GOT IN STORE... JUMPIN' JUPITER!
SPACESHIPS!
IF WE COULD FIND A WAY OF GETTING HOLD OF ONE OF THEM...
GO ON! HELP YOURSELF! WE DIDN'T ASK YOU TO COME AND WE SHAN'T STOP YOU GOING!
THERE'S A CATCH SOMEWHERE
HI, CREW! COME AND SAY HOW-DO TO OUR DISTINGUISHED VISITOR... COLONEL DAN DARE
WELL, I'LL BE... WHERE ON EARTH DID YOU SPRING FROM, COLONEL?
"WHERE ON MERCURY" YOU MEAN! WELCOME, COLONEL.
WE CAN DO WITH ANOTHER FIRST-RATE PILOT.
HE THOUGHT WE WERE WORKING FOR THE MEKON. AND I THOUGHT HIS PAL, SONDAR WAS. ONCE WE STRAIGHTEN THAT OUT, HE'S A GUEST, NOT A PRISONER.
SURE... HE CAN HAVE ANYTHING HE WANTS — EXCEPT THE MEKON. WE HAVEN'T GOT HIM.
MAYBE YOU THINK YOU HAVEN'T. I DON'T KNOW!
BUT SINCE YOU'RE SO KIND, THERE IS SOMETHING I WANT... AND I WANT IT RIGHT NOW! I WANT DIGBY AND URB... AND I WANT 'EM ALIVE AND KICKING!
CONTINUED

READ THE ADVENTURES OF REX MILLIGAN ON PAGE 12

FOURPENCE-HALFPENNY

EVERY FRIDAY

EAGLE

17 OCTOBER 1952 Vol. 3 No. 28

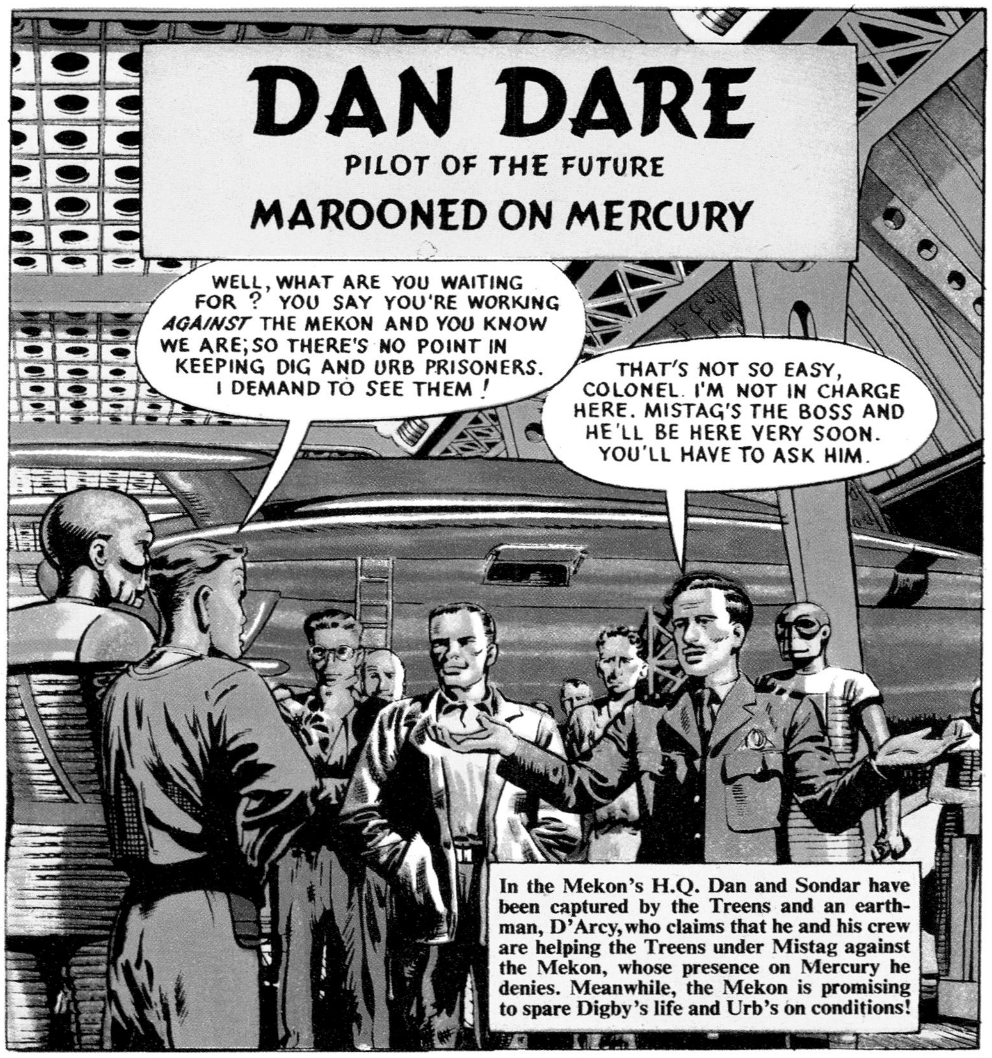
DAN DARE
PILOT OF THE FUTURE
MAROONED ON MERCURY
WELL, WHAT ARE YOU WAITING FOR ? YOU SAY YOU'RE WORKING *AGAINST* THE MEKON AND YOU KNOW WE ARE; SO THERE'S NO POINT IN KEEPING DIG AND URB PRISONERS. I DEMAND TO SEE THEM !
THAT'S NOT SO EASY, COLONEL. I'M NOT IN CHARGE HERE. MISTAG'S THE BOSS AND HE'LL BE HERE VERY SOON. YOU'LL HAVE TO ASK HIM.
In the Mekon's H.Q. Dan and Sondar have been captured by the Treens and an earthman, D'Arcy, who claims that he and his crew are helping the Treens under Mistag against the Mekon, whose presence on Mercury he denies. Meanwhile, the Mekon is promising to spare Digby's life and Urb's on conditions!

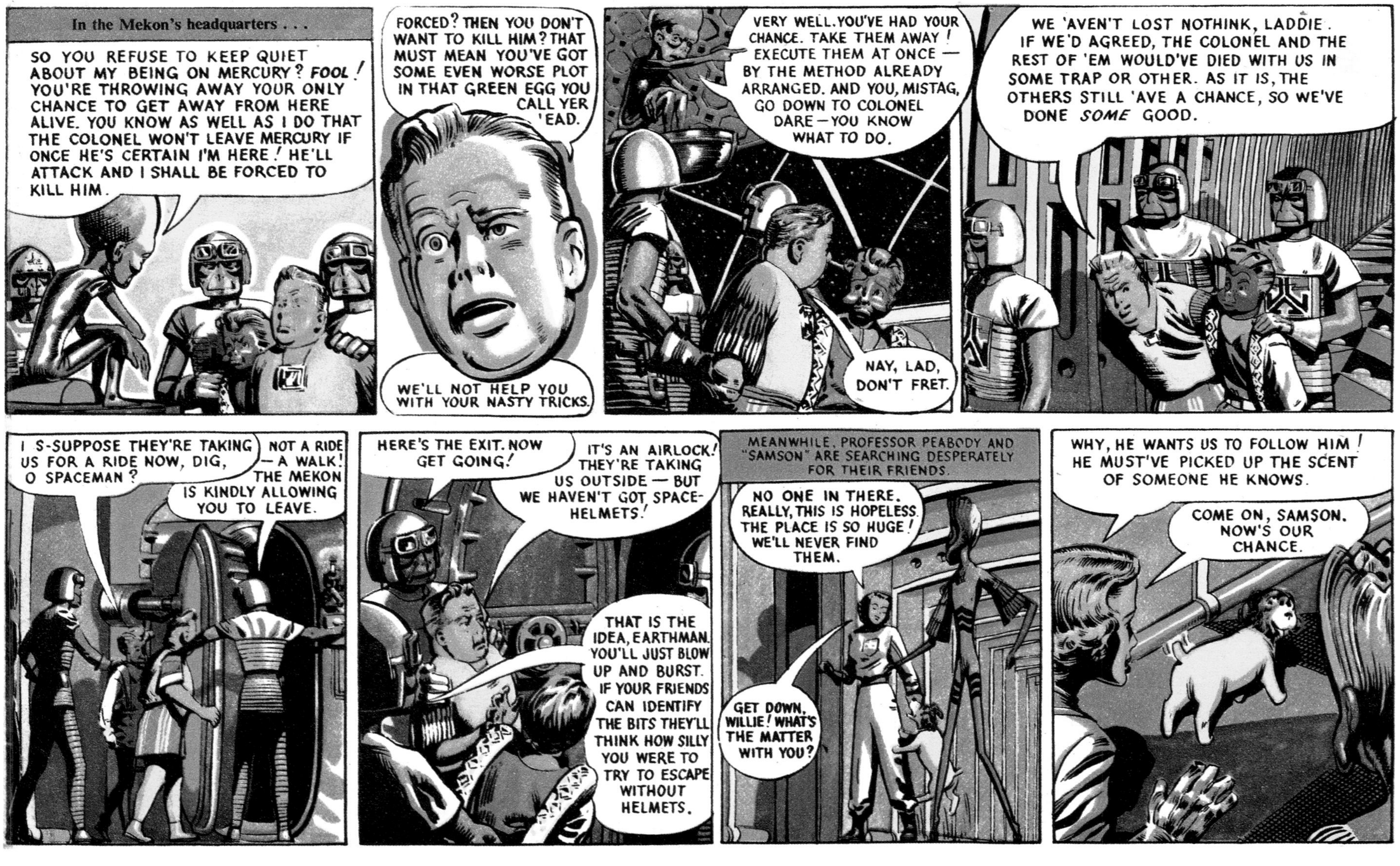
In the Mekon's headquarters . . .
SO YOU REFUSE TO KEEP QUIET ABOUT MY BEING ON MERCURY? *FOOL* ! YOU'RE THROWING AWAY YOUR ONLY CHANCE TO GET AWAY FROM HERE ALIVE. YOU KNOW AS WELL AS I DO THAT THE COLONEL WON'T LEAVE MERCURY IF ONCE HE'S CERTAIN I'M HERE ! HE'LL ATTACK AND I SHALL BE FORCED TO KILL HIM.
FORCED? THEN YOU DON'T WANT TO KILL HIM? THAT MUST MEAN YOU'VE GOT SOME EVEN WORSE PLOT IN THAT GREEN EGG YOU CALL YER 'EAD.
WE'LL NOT HELP YOU WITH YOUR NASTY TRICKS.
VERY WELL. YOU'VE HAD YOUR CHANCE. TAKE THEM AWAY ! EXECUTE THEM AT ONCE — BY THE METHOD ALREADY ARRANGED. AND YOU, MISTAG, GO DOWN TO COLONEL DARE — YOU KNOW WHAT TO DO.
NAY, LAD, DON'T FRET.
WE 'AVEN'T LOST NOTHINK, LADDIE . IF WE'D AGREED, THE COLONEL AND THE REST OF 'EM WOULD'VE DIED WITH US IN SOME TRAP OR OTHER. AS IT IS, THE OTHERS STILL 'AVE A CHANCE, SO WE'VE DONE *SOME* GOOD.
I S-SUPPOSE THEY'RE TAKING US FOR A RIDE NOW, DIG, O SPACEMAN ?
NOT A RIDE — A WALK! THE MEKON IS KINDLY ALLOWING YOU TO LEAVE.
HERE'S THE EXIT. NOW GET GOING!
IT'S AN AIRLOCK! THEY'RE TAKING US OUTSIDE — BUT WE HAVEN'T GOT SPACE-HELMETS!
THAT IS THE IDEA, EARTHMAN. YOU'LL JUST BLOW UP AND BURST. IF YOUR FRIENDS CAN IDENTIFY THE BITS THEY'LL THINK HOW SILLY YOU WERE TO TRY TO ESCAPE WITHOUT HELMETS.
MEANWHILE, PROFESSOR PEABODY AND "SAMSON" ARE SEARCHING DESPERATELY FOR THEIR FRIENDS.
NO ONE IN THERE. REALLY, THIS IS HOPELESS. THE PLACE IS SO HUGE! WE'LL NEVER FIND THEM.
GET DOWN, WILLIE! WHAT'S THE MATTER WITH YOU?
WHY, HE WANTS US TO FOLLOW HIM ! HE MUST'VE PICKED UP THE SCENT OF SOMEONE HE KNOWS.
COME ON, SAMSON. NOW'S OUR CHANCE.

GOOD DOG! IF YOU FIND THEM, I'LL TAKE BACK WHAT I SAID ABOUT YOU NOT EARNING YOUR KEEP.
SNUFF
SHUFFLE
MEANWHILE, IN THE HANGAR...
IF YOU'RE ON THE LEVEL, D'ARCY, TAKE ME TO MISTAG AT ONCE.
AH, HERE HE IS NOW. COLONEL DARE WAS GETTING IMPATIENT, MISTAG.
WE WERE WRONG ABOUT THE NEW ARRIVALS, MISTAG. THEY, TOO, ARE THE MEKON'S ENEMIES. I CAN VOUCH FOR COLONEL DARE.
REALLY? I'M GLAD TO HEAR THAT, D'ARCY. WE WERE LED ASTRAY BY SONDAR BEING WITH HIM.
I AM HAPPY THAT WE HAVE SUCH USEFUL ALLIES IN OUR STRUGGLE AGAINST THE MEKON.
NOT SO FAST, MISTAG! BEFORE WE CAN TALK OF BEING ALLIES, I WANT TO DISCUSS THE MATTER WITH MY CREW. YOUR MEN CAPTURED SPACEMAN DIGBY AND THE ATLANTINE BOY CALLED URB. WHERE ARE THEY?
IT GRIEVES ME TO BE THE BEARER OF BAD NEWS, COLONEL. THEY FOOLISHLY ATTEMPTED TO ESCAPE...
AND YOUR MEN HAD TO SHOOT, I SUPPOSE? DO YOU EXPECT US TO BELIEVE THAT?
UNFORTUNATELY, THEIR ESCAPE WAS NOT DISCOVERED UNTIL THEY HAD LEFT THE BUILDING — WITHOUT SPACE HELMETS! I CAN ONLY SUPPOSE THEY FORGOT THAT THIS PLANET HAS PRACTICALLY NO ATMOSPHERE; OR PERHAPS THEY DIDN'T REALISE THE DOOR LED STRAIGHT OUTSIDE, AND...
YOU MEAN... THEY'RE DEAD! TAKE ME TO THEM.
I WANT TO SEE THEIR REMAINS!
CERTAINLY, IF YOU WISH IT. IT WON'T BE A VERY PLEASANT SIGHT BUT...
IT WON'T BE THE ONLY UNPLEASANT SIGHT WE'VE SEEN TODAY.
WILLIE CONTINUES TO FOLLOW THE SCENT ALONG THE CORRIDOR
HE'S MOVING QUICKER NOW — THE SCENT MUST BE FRESH!
SNIFF SNIFF
HE'S DONE IT! WILLIE'S DONE IT.
WUFF WUFF
THERE THEY ARE! QUICK, SAMSON! IT'S DIG AND URB.
STOP THEM!
STOP THEM, SAMSON!
SLAM
SSS
WOW WOW WOW
IN SPITE OF THE TREENS TRYING TO DRAG HIM AWAY, SAMSON TURNS OFF THE EXHAUST,.. CONTROLLING THE AIR IN THE AIRLOCK...
...AND BREAKS THE LEVER SO THAT IT CAN'T BE TURNED ON AGAIN
SNAP
DAN! THANK HEAVEN YOU'VE COME, DAN. WE MUST GET THOSE DOORS OPEN! DIG AND URB ARE IN THE AIRLOCK WITHOUT HELMETS. THE EXHAUST WAS WORKING — I'M AFRAID WE MAY BE TOO LATE!
CONTINUED

NEW *LUCK OF THE LEGION* ADVENTURE STARTS TODAY!

FOURPENCE-
HALFPENNY
EVERY FRIDAY
EAGLE
24 OCTOBER 1952 Vol. 3 No. 29

DAN DARE
PILOT OF THE FUTURE
MAROONED ON MERCURY
DAN! QUICK! HURRY!
COME ON, SONDAR! LOOKS AS IF WE'RE JUST IN TIME! WHAT ABOUT YOUR NOBLE FRIENDS NOW, D'ARCY?
WAIT, COLONEL DARE. THIS IS ALL A MISTAKE, I ASSURE YOU.
Dan and Sondar have been captured by Treens and an earthman D'Arcy who claims, however, to be fighting under Mistag against the Mekon. Mistag pretends that Digby and Urb are dead but on the Mekon's orders they are being forced without spacesuits into an airlock and the exhaust is turned on. In the nick of time, Peabody and her Mercurian friend, Dan, Sondar and Mistag arrive at the airlock.

PROVE IT THEN, MISTAG. CALL OFF YOUR MEN AND OPEN THAT AIRLOCK.
WILLINGLY...
GUARDS! STAND BACK! THE EARTHMEN ARE OUR ALLIES NOW AGAINST THE MEKON. RELEASE YOUR PRISONERS!

WHAT DOES HE MEAN, "MISTAKE"? THESE ARE THE MEKON'S MEN, DAN, AND THEY'VE JUST THROWN DIG AND URB OUT THROUGH THAT AIRLOCK. THERE'S NO MISTAKE ABOUT THAT!
IMPOSSIBLE, O EARTH-WOMAN. THE MEKON IS NOT HERE ON MERCURY!
THAT'S WHAT ALL THE TREENS SAY, JOCELYN, AND WE'VE ONLY GOT THE MERCURIANS' WORD FOR IT, SO WE'RE GIVING THEM THE BENEFIT OF THE DOUBT.

BUT THERE ISN'T ANY DOUBT AND IT ISN'T ONLY THE MERCURIANS WHO SAY THE MEKON'S HERE. DON'T YOU REMEMBER, DAN? WHEN THE TREENS FIRST TRIED TO CAPTURE US, THEIR LEADER SAID, "THE MEKON PRESENTS HIS COMPLIMENTS, COLONEL."
THE BLUNDERING FOOL!
GOSH, YES. YOU'RE QUITE RIGHT. WELL DONE, JOCELYN! THAT SETTLES IT. ACTION, SONDAR!

OPEN THE DOORS, JOCELYN, WHILE WE KEEP THE TREENS OFF... AND LOOK OUT FOR D'ARCY—HE'S WORKING FOR THE MEKON.
NOT ANY MORE I'M NOT... GIVE ME THAT PISTOL, YOU BRUTE.
I'VE BEEN WAITING FOR A LONG TIME TO GET MY HANDS ON YOU, MISTAG.
RIGHT, DAN.
UGH! UGH! PULL HIM OFF.

DAN! SAMSON! HURRY!
THIS LEVER'S BROKEN.
I CAN'T SHIFT IT AND DIGBY WILL BE...

HALLO, PROF. HAVING A SPOT OF BOTHER?
DIGBY! HOW ON EARTH...? THANK HEAVENS YOU'RE SAFE.

BY GUM! IT'S A PROPER SET-TO. COME ON, URB LAD. LET'S GET STUCK IN.
I AM EAGER TO BE STICKING. LEAD ON, O NOBLE SPACEWARRIOR FITZALBERT, INTO BATTLE!

WELL, THAT'S THAT. HULLO, DIG, SORRY YOU'RE TOO LATE FOR THE SCRAP. HOW DID YOU GET OUT OF THERE ?
WE JUST PUSHED THE DOOR OPEN AND WALKED. IT WAS A PIECE OF PARKIN. BUT DON'T ASK ME HOW IT HAPPENED.
YOU HAVE OUR MERCURIAN FRIEND TO THANK FOR THAT... HE SHUT OFF THE EXHAUST JUST IN TIME.
THE DOORS ARE OPERATED BY AIR PRESSURE, URB. WHEN THERE IS AIR IN THE LOCK, THEY CAN BE OPENED FROM EITHER SIDE. WHEN THE AIR IS DRAWN OUT OF THE LOCK BY THE EXHAUST, THE DOORS ARE AUTOMATICALLY SEALED BY THE PRESSURE FROM THIS SIDE. THE MECHANISM IS WORKED BY...
JUST A MINUTE, SONDAR! SORRY TO INTERRUPT THE LECTURE, URB, BUT WE OUGHT TO BE WORKING OUT OUR NEXT MOVE NOW—AND QUICKLY—BEFORE THE MEKON FINDS OUT WHAT'S GOING ON.
YOU'RE RIGHT, JOCELYN, BUT THERE'S NOTHING TO WORK OUT.
MAKE FOR THAT HANGAR, EVERYBODY, AT THE DOUBLE...I'LL EXPLAIN AS WE GO.
COLONEL DARE, I WANT TO APOLOGISE. I'VE BEEN A COMPLETE FOOL.
ALL RIGHT, D'ARCY, SAVE ALL THAT TILL LATER. I SHALL NEED YOUR HELP NOW... LISTEN, EVERYBODY. WHEN WE GET TO THE HANGAR, THIS IS WHAT I WANT YOU TO DO...
REPORT FROM POST 7, O MEKON. COLONEL DARE AND HIS PARTY ARE APPROACHING NUMBER TWO HANGAR FROM NUMBER THREE CORRIDOR.
MISTAG HAS BLUNDERED. HE SHALL PAY FOR THIS!
CALL NUMBER TWO HANGAR!
ALL MECHANICS TO STAND BY FOR EMERGENCY OPERATION ORDER FROM MEKON PERSONALLY.
OUTSIDE THE ENTRANCE OF Nº 2 HANGAR.
ATTENTION ALL MECHANICS, NUMBER TWO HANGAR! STAND BY FOR PERSONAL ORDER FROM THE MEKON.
...AND THAT'S THE PLAN. IS IT ALL CLEAR?
AYE, AYE, SIR, CLEAR AS MUD.
QUICK, DAN! THERE'S NO TIME TO LOSE. THEY'RE BROADCASTING AN ORDER FROM THE MEKON IN THERE.
RIGHT!...
...ALL READY?
ACTION!
ATTENTION ALL MECHANICS, NUMBER TWO HANGAR! EMERGENCY ORDERS FROM THE ALL-WISE ONE. SPACECRAFT HERMES TO TAKE OFF IMMEDIATELY. EMERGENCY OPERATION!
TOO TOO!
GOOD OLD SAMSON. HE'S PUT THE LOUD SPEAKER OUT OF ACTION.
THAT'S THE HERMES, DAN. GET YOUR PARTY FITTED UP WITH SPACE SUITS AND GET ABOARD.
DAKIN! MAKE FINAL CHECK OF MAGNETIC MOTORS FOR IMMEDIATE TAKE OFF.
GARROD! REMOVE THE CHOCKS AND PREPARE TO MOVE HERMES INTO THE AIRLOCK.
EVERYONE GOT A SPACE SUIT? THEN WE'RE READY TO GO!
GOOD! IF WE DON'T GET GOING SOON THESE TREENS WILL SMELL A RAT.
WITH DAN AND CO. ABOARD, THE HERMES GLIDES SMOOTHLY INTO THE AIRLOCK...
I DO NOT UNDERSTAND THIS ORDER AT ALL.
CLOSE AIRTIGHT DOOR! OPEN EXHAUST VALVE!
SWING BOOSTER JET INTO TAKE-OFF POSITION.
VACUUM IN AIRLOCK COMPLETE.
CONTACT—FIRE ALL!
OPEN ROOF READY FOR TAKE-OFF
COME ON, WILLIE LAD, TIME TO WAKE UP. WE'RE SPACE-BORNE AGAIN, THANK HEAVENS.
AND THAT'S ANOTHER ONE IN THE EYE FOR THE LITTLE GREEN MONSTER.
MISTAG REPORTING FROM NUMBER TWO HANGAR, WISEST OF THE WISE. COLONEL DARE HAS SEIZED THE HERMES AND ESCAPED WITH ALL HIS PARTY. D'ARCY AND THE OTHER EARTHMEN ARE WITH HIM.
INCOMPETENT IMBECILE. YOU'VE LET HIM TRICK YOU!
BUT YOU NEEDN'T THINK YOU'LL GET FAR IN THE HERMES, MY CLEVER COLONEL. SHE'S MAGNETIC POWERED.
PLOT COURSE OF HERMES. WHEN SHE REACHES VELOCITY/ALTITUDE RATIO XLQ/42, FIRE DEMAGNETIZING RAY... THAT'LL PUT A STOP TO DARE'S LITTLE TRICKS.
CONTINUED

FOURPENCE-HALFPEN'NY

EVERY FRIDAY

EAGLE

31 OCTOBER 1952 Vol. 3 No. 30

DO NOT IMAGINE YOU CAN PROVOKE ME WITH VAIN TAUNTS, EARTHLING. YOU AND YOUR FRIENDS ARE PRISONERS IN SPACE — COMPLETELY AT MY MERCY. I DEMAND YOUR UNCONDITIONAL SURRENDER.
THINK AGAIN, MY LITTLE GREEN TREEN! WE'RE NOT SURRENDERING TO YOU UNCONDITIONALLY OR ON ANY TERMS.
WE'LL SEE ABOUT THAT... SWITCH OFF!
CALL HANGAR No. 7! ALERT ELECTRO-FIGHTERS EL/43 AND EL/44... EMERGENCY MISSION.
ELECTRO-FIGHTERS, EL/43 AND EL/44 ... TAKE OFF IMMEDIATELY ... SPECIAL MISSION. INTERCEPT SPACE SHIP HERMES NOW ORBITING TEMPERATE BELT.
NUMBER 3 AIRLOCK CLEAR! ALL READY TO TAKE OFF.
MEANWHILE, IN "HERMES", D'ARCY SHOWS PEABODY THE "TELEGEOSCOPE," A NEW DIRECT SIGHT BOMB AIMER, WHICH THE MEKON HAS HAD FITTED TO HIS SHIP.
... IT'D BE HANDY FOR A SURVEY JOB, TOO. YOU SEE, IT CAN BE ADJUSTED FOR ANY ALTITUDE AND SPEED, AND THE VIEW CAN BE MAGNIFIED TO ANY DEGREE YOU LIKE.
DAN! DO COME AND LOOK AT THIS.
JUST THE JOB! I WANTED TO MAKE A RECCE. OF THE SURFACE WHILE WE ORBITED. THAT'S WHY I SET HER ON A COURSE ROUND THE TEMPERATE BELT.
KEEP YOUR EYES GLUED TO THAT SCREEN, PROF. GET YOUR MERCURIAN FRIEND TO EXPLAIN ANYTHING YOU DON'T UNDERSTAND.
WE SHALL NEED ALL THE INFORMATION WE CAN COLLECT ABOUT THIS PLANET BEFORE WE'RE THROUGH.
NOW THEN, D'ARCY! LET'S HAVE YOUR STORY. HOW DO YOU AND THE REST OF YOUR CREW FIT INTO THE PICTURE? IF WE KNEW THAT WE MIGHT GET A CLUE ABOUT WHAT THE MEKON'S UP TO.
AND MAKE IT SNAPPY! IF I KNOW THE LITTLE GREEN NIGHTMARE, HE'S NOT GOING TO LEAVE US IN PEACE MUCH LONGER.
RIGHT! YOU KNOW ALREADY HOW WE WERE CAPTURED ON VENUS AND THROWN INTO PRISON
ONE DAY, MISTAG APPEARED IN OUR CELL. HE TOLD US THE WAR WAS OVER AND THE MEKON HAD WON. HE SAID HE AND HIS FRIENDS HAD ALWAYS BEEN AGAINST THE MEKON AND NOW THEY WERE PLANNING AN ESCAPE TO MERCURY. THEY ASKED US TO JOIN THEM, AND OF COURSE WE JUMPED AT IT.
AS SOON AS THE POWER WAS RESTORED ON VENUS, WE WENT BY TELESENDER TO A SECRET SPACE DEPOT AT THE POLE. THE PLACE WAS SWARMING WITH TREENS, AND THERE WAS A WHOLE FLEET OF SPACE SHIPS WAITING TO TAKE OFF
HOW WE GOT AWAY WITHOUT GETTING SPOTTED, I DON'T KNOW, BUT WE DID. ON THE JOURNEY, MISTAG TOLD US HE WAS PLANNING TO BUILD UP A STRIKING FORCE STRONG ENOUGH TO RETURN AND OVERTHROW THE MEKON.
WHEN WE ARRIVED, WE WERE ENLISTED IN MISTAG'S SPACE FLEET — AT LEAST WE THOUGHT IT WAS MISTAG'S THEN — THE OTHERS WENT TO WORK AS MECHANICS, AND I BECAME A TEST PILOT. THEN YOU ARRIVED, COLONEL, WITH SONDAR, AND MISTAG TOLD US...
ALL RIGHT, D'ARCY. I KNOW THE REST.
IT'S CLEAR NOW HOW THE MEKON TRICKED YOU, BUT WHY DID HE DO IT? THAT'S WHAT I WANT TO KNOW. WHY BRING EARTHMEN TO MERCURY AT ALL?
COLONEL!
COLONEL DARE!
COME QUICKLY PLEASE, O ILLUSTRIOUS SPACE COLONEL. HERE IS A SIGHT FOR TO SEE.
TREEN FIGHTERS, COLONEL! COMING IN FAST ON THE PORT BOW.
IT'S A SIGHT I COULD HAVE DONE WITHOUT SEEING, URB
SO THE MEKON DOESN'T WANT US ALIVE AFTER ALL. I GUESSED WRONG. SORRY, CHAPS.
HOLD TIGHT! HERE THEY COME!
CONTINUED

EAGLE-BRITAIN'S NATIONAL STRIP CARTOON WEEKLY

FOURPENCE-HALFPENNY
EVERY FRIDAY
EAGLE
7 NOVEMBER 1952 Vol. 3 No. 31
DAN DARE
PILOT OF THE FUTURE
MAROONED ON MERCURY
SHALL WE STAND TO THE GUNS, SIR?
NO GOOD, DIG. WITH THE SHIP'S POWER CUT, THE GUNS ARE OUT OF ACTION, TOO.
DAN, LOOK! THEY'RE FLATTENING OUT OF THEIR DIVE... ON TO THE SAME COURSE AS US!
Dan and his friends are orbiting Mercury in the 'Hermes'. The power cut, they are 'prisoners in space' of the Mekon, who demands their 'unconditional surrender'. They reject this demand. D'Arcy tells how he was tricked into working for the Mekon. Suddenly, two Treen fighters appear and dive to attack.
NOW WHAT ARE THEY PLAYING AT? I DON'T LIKE THE LOOK OF THIS.
THE YELLOW ONE'S TURNED. THEY'RE FACING EACH OTHER.
MEKON ON SET AGAIN, COLONEL.
YOUR FRIENDS' LIVES ARE IN YOUR HANDS, COLONEL DARE. DO YOU PUT YOURSELF AT MY DISPOSAL ... OR DO I ORDER MY FIGHTERS TO ATTACK?
WELL, CHAPS? YOU ALL HEARD THAT. DO WE SURRENDER OR NOT?
NO!
NEVER!
TELL HIM TO GO AND BOIL HIS HEAD.
SURRENDER? NEVER!
THERE'S YOUR ANSWER, MEKON. CLEAR ENOUGH FOR YOU?
ON YOUR OWN HEADS BE IT THEN.
MEKON CALLING EL/43 AND 44! ATTACK AS ORDERED!
LOOKS LIKE SOME SORT OF GAS.
PUMPKIN-HEAD MUST BE SLIPPING. YOU CAN'T ATTACK SPACE-SHIPS WITH GAS. AT LEAST...
NOW WHAT'S THE GAME?
UGH!... OUCH! WH-WH-WHAT'S HAPP-P-PENING?

CRACKLE

TOO TOO TOO!

I-IT'S AN EL-ELECTRIC CH-CH-CHARGE. THE SH-SH-SHIP'S ALIVE

THOSE G-G-GAS J-JETS W-WERE AIR ST-STREAMS, F-FIRED TO MAKE A CH-CHANNEL AND C-CIRCUIT F-FOR THE C-CURRENT.

EE-EE-EEK!

SUSPEND ATTACK.

HERMES HAS BEEN 'LIVE' FOR 3 RONITS, O MEKON!

STAND BY TO RECEIVE CALL FROM HERMES.

I SUSPECT THEY WILL HAVE A DIFFERENT ANSWER FOR ME THIS TIME.

OH! THANK HEAVENS THEY'VE STOPPED!

PHEW! I KNOW THEY USED TO SEND CHAPS TO THE "ELECTRIC CHAIR", BUT I NEVER THOUGHT TO END MY DAYS IN AN ELECTRIC SPACE-SHIP.

YOU'RE NOT GOING TO END YOUR DAYS ANYWHERE YET, DIG... I WAS RIGHT. THE MEKON DOES WANT US ALIVE. HE'S ONLY TRYING TO WEAKEN OUR RESISTANCE.

HAVE WE GOT ANY HEAVY DUTY TREEN SPACE SUITS ON BOARD, D'ARCY?

YES, DAN. WE'RE FULLY EQUIPPED FOR...

GOOD! NOW LISTEN!

EVERYONE GET INTO TREEN SPACE SUITS! AND MAKE IT SNAPPY!

IT WAS A GOOD IDEA, LITTLE TREEN, BUT IT WON'T WORK AGAIN, SO YOU CAN CALL OFF YOUR ELECTRO-FIGHTERS. DIDN'T THEY TELL YOU WE WERE CARRYING SPACE SUITS? AND, OF COURSE, THEY'RE INSULATED.

SPACE SUITS? ALL RIGHT, COLONEL! FIRST ROUND TO YOU, BUT I HAVEN'T FINISHED WITH YOU YET. NOT BY A LONG WAY.

SONDAR! CALL UP THE MEKON'S H.Q. I WANT ANOTHER WORD WITH THE LITTLE GREEN HORROR.

I DIDN'T IMAGINE YOU HAD. BUT TAKE YOUR TIME, WON'T YOU? WE'RE BUSY UP HERE... GOOD BYE FOR NOW!

GET BACK TO THAT TELEGEOSCOPE, PROF, BEFORE HE THINKS UP SOME NEW NASTINESS.

SONDAR! I WANT A WORD WITH YOU.

COME ON, SAMSON! MORE GEOGRAPHY LESSONS!

YOU HEARD D'ARCY'S STORY, AND YOU KNOW HOW THE TREEN MIND WORKS. WHAT WAS THE MEKON PLAYING AT? WHY DID HE WANT TO BRING EARTH-MEN TO MERCURY? GOT ANY IDEAS?

YES, COLONEL, I HAVE. IT IS FOR THE SAME REASON AS HE WANTS TO KEEP YOU ALIVE. AS HE TOLD DIGBY, HE NEEDS SOMEONE TO FLY A SPECIAL MISSION TO VENUS.

AND, AS THE TREEN FIGHTERS RETURN TO BASE, SONDAR EXPLAINS HIS IDEAS ABOUT THE MEKON'S PLANS.

SO LONG AS HE LIVES, THE MEKON WILL NEVER ABANDON HIS PLAN TO CONQUER THE UNIVERSE. BUT, WHEN HE FLED TO MERCURY, HE MUST HAVE KNOWN IT WOULD TAKE HIM MANY YEARS BEFORE HE COULD EXPECT TO BE STRONG ENOUGH TO CONQUER VENUS AND EARTH COMBINED, WITH EXISTING WEAPONS, THEREFORE HE KNEW...

HE MUST CONCENTRATE ON DEVISING SOME NEW AND MORE FRIGHTFUL WEAPON, TO FORCE THE OTHER PLANETS INTO SUBMISSION WITH ONE QUICK STROKE, BEFORE THEY COULD MUSTER THEIR STRENGTH. SUCH A WEAPON WOULD BE SMALL BUT IRRE-SISTIBLE. IT WOULD BE CARRIED IN ONE SPACE-SHIP AND RELEASED AUTOMATICALLY BY MAGNETO-RADAR WHEN THE SHIP APPROACHED ITS TARGET. BUT NONE OF THE MEKON'S OWN MEN COULD SAFELY FLY SUCH A SHIP TO VENUS. THEY WOULD BE CHALLENGED AND SHOT DOWN BEFORE THEY GOT WITHIN RANGE...

ONLY A THERON OR EARTHMAN COULD FLY THIS MISSION. THAT WAS WHY D'ARCY WAS BROUGHT TO MERCURY, AND THAT IS WHY THE MEKON WANTS YOU ALIVE, COLONEL, AND TRIES TO FORCE YOU TO DO HIS WILL. D'ARCY COULD HAVE FLOWN A SHIP TO VENUS... BUT HE HAD BEEN MISSING SO LONG, SOMEONE MIGHT HAVE SUSPECTED....

...BUT NOBODY WOULD EVER CHALLENGE COLONEL DARE.

I WONDER IF YOU'RE RIGHT?

HE IS, DAN! I'M SURE OF IT. THERE WAS A SPECIAL MISSION I WAS BOOKED FOR, AND THERE IS A SECRET WEAPON BEING MADE SOME-WHERE ON MERCURY. I'VE HEARD THE TREENS MENTION IT, THOUGH I DON'T KNOW WHAT IT IS.

BUT I DO!...

...AT LEAST, I THINK I DO. THE MERCURIANS ONCE TOLD US THE MEKON WAS CORNERING THEIR SUPPLIES OF SOMETHING. I KNOW WHAT THAT IS NOW. SAMSON'S EXPLAINED. IT'S... SEE-DAH TEE-DAH DAH-GOO!

WHAT IS IT, SAMSON? WHAT'S THE MATTER?

RAY-LAW!

DAN! SONDAR! COME OVER HERE. QUICK! LOOK AT THIS!

CONTINUED

EXCITING NEW SERIES – THE ADVENTURE CLUB – see page 4

FOURPENCE-HALFPENNY

EVERY FRIDAY

EAGLE

14 NOVEMBER 1952 Vol. 3 No. 32

I WAS IN THE FIRST FLIGHT TO LAND. AS SOON AS WE TOUCHED DOWN, A CROWD OF MERCURIANS HURRIED UP. THEY SEEMED FRIENDLY ENOUGH, AND THE TREENS DIDN'T WANT ANY TROUBLE, TILL WE'D ESTABLISHED OURSELVES...

THEY LED US TO ONE OF THEIR BUILDINGS AND WE TOOK OUR HELMETS OFF. THEN THEY OFFERED US SOME OF THIS STUFF. IT SEEMED A FRIENDLY GESTURE, SO SOME OF THE TREENS TOOK SOME AND ATE IT...

WITHIN HALF A MINUTE, THEY WERE SEIZED WITH TERRIBLE PAINS, AND BEFORE WE COULD DO ANYTHING, THEY WERE LYING DEAD AT OUR FEET, COVERED WITH THE MOST AWFUL BROWN RASH. OF COURSE, THE TREENS THOUGHT IT WAS DELIBERATE...

AAHHHH-H-H

UGH

THEY ATTACKED AT ONCE WITH THEIR SUPERIOR WEAPONS. THE NATIVES HADN'T A HOPE. AFTER THAT, THE MERCURIANS GAVE UP TRYING TO BE FRIENDLY. THE TREENS FORCED THEM TO PROVIDE WORKING PARTIES WHEN THEY NEEDED THEM; OTHERWISE THE TWO RACES IGNORED EACH OTHER.

SO THIS IS THE SECRET WEAPON THE MEKON WANTS ME TO FLY TO VENUS!

OF COURSE, WE WERE FORBIDDEN TO EAT LOCAL VEGETATION. WE'VE LIVED ON FOOD BATHS EVER SINCE. I'VE NEVER SEEN ANY OF THIS FAY-SAW STUFF AGAIN UNTIL THIS MINUTE.

I DON'T GET IT, SIR? IT'S ONE THING TO DROP POISONED VEGETABLES ON A PLANET; IT'S ANOTHER THING TO MAKE PEOPLE EAT 'EM.

BESIDES, HOW COULD YOU CARRY ENOUGH IN ONE SPACE-SHIP TO HAVE ANY SERIOUS EFFECT?

AND WHY ARE THEY COLLECTING THE STUFF DOWN THERE? WHAT ARE THEIR SCIENTISTS DOING WITH IT?

TAKE IT EASY! ONE AT A TIME!

WE SHALL KNOW THE ANSWERS TO ALL THOSE QUESTIONS WHEN WE BREAK INTO VILGOTH AND SEE FOR OURSELVES.

BREAK INTO THAT PLACE? OH, WELL! I SUPPOSE IT'S ALL IN THE DAY'S WORK! BUT WE'VE GOT TO GET OUT OF THIS 'ERE SPACESHIP FIRST, AND I DON'T SEE...

THAT'S UP TO THE MEKON, DIG. HE WANTS US ALIVE, SO HE'LL HAVE TO GIVE US BACK OUR POWER SOMETIME AND WHEN HE DOES, WE'LL BE READY FOR HIM.

MEANWHILE, IN THE MEKON'S HEADQUARTERS ON THE OTHER SIDE OF THE PLANET.

HERMES REPORTED OVER VILGOTH, O MEKON... SHALL I ORDER ANY ACTION?

NO! NO FURTHER ACTION. I PROPOSE TO USE THE SIMPLEST AND MOST EFFICIENT OF ALL WEAPONS — TIME!

HERMES WAS NOT STOCKED WITH PROVISIONS, AND EARTH-LINGS DO NOT SURVIVE LONG WITHOUT FOOD OR WATER... WE WILL IGNORE THEM TILL THEIR WILL-POWER IS BROKEN BY STARVATION AND EXHAUSTION.

THEN THEY WILL BE ONLY TOO HAPPY TO OBEY MY SIMPLE INSTRUCTIONS... REPORT AGAIN IN 60 TAMITS!

UNAWARE OF THE MEKON'S PLAN TO STARVE THEM INTO SURRENDER, DAN & Co. ROLL ON, HOUR AFTER HOUR, IN AN ENDLESS JOURNEY ROUND MERCURY.

I DON'T KNOW WHAT THE MEKON'S GAME IS, BUT HE'S CERTAINLY GIVING US PLENTY OF TIME TO STUDY THE GEOGRAPHY OF THIS PLANET.

AYE — AND THE LINGO — I CAN SING IT LIKE A NATIVE NOW, EXCEPT WHEN I GO FLAT — AND THAT'S MOST OF THE TIME!

...UNTIL, MANY DAYS LATER...

STEADY, PROF!

VILGOTH COMING ROUND AGAIN!... I'M SICK OF THE SIGHT OF IT. I SHALL SCREAM IF I HAVE TO LOOK AT IT AGAIN

I'M WORRIED COLONEL. YOU EARTHMEN CANNOT STAND SUCH A PRO-LONGED PERIOD OF STARVATION.

THAT'S WHAT THE MEKON'S COUNTING ON, BUT WE'VE GOT TO HOLD OUT AND FORCE HIM TO GIVE BACK OUR POWER... HOWEVER LONG THIS LASTS, THERE MUST BE NO QUESTION OF SURRENDER!

...AND DAYS LATER STILL...

SONDAR, O NOBLEST OF TREENS. IF THESE EARTHMEN DO NOT EATING AND DRINKING SOON, THEY WILL DIE WITH STARVING. EVEN I BEGIN TO FEEL HUNGER.

YOU ARE RIGHT, URB. I HAVE WAITED AS LONG AS I DARED, BUT I CANNOT LET MY FRIENDS DIE LIKE THIS. THE TIME HAS COME TO ACT.

WHAT ACTION, O SONDAR?

WHAT CAN WE DO TO HELP THEM?

I SHALL CALL THE MEKON AND AGREE TO SURRENDER ON HIS TERMS...

HULLO, TREEN CONTROL... TREEN CONTROL! SONDAR CALLING MEKON!

CONTINUED

EAGLE-BRITAIN'S NATIONAL STRIP CARTOON WEEKLY
FOURPENCE-HALFPENNY
EVERY FRIDAY
EAGLE
21 NOVEMBER 1952 Vol. 3 No. 33
DAN DARE
PILOT OF THE FUTURE
MAROONED ON MERCURY
... SONDAR CALLING MEK...
WAIT! THERE'S SOMETHING HAPPENING OUT THERE.
The Mekon is trying to starve Dan and his friends into surrender. After many days without food and water, they lie, sleeping and exhausted, in the space ship Hermes. Sondar decides that he cannot let his Earth friends die in this way, and starts to call up Treen H.Q. to accept the Mekon's terms.
HE IS RIGHT, O EXCELLENT SONDAR. A SPACE BOAT APPROACHES!
A TREEN HOVER-CAR!... WAKE UP, COLONEL... WAKE THEM ALL, URB!
AWAKE, AWAKE, O SLEEPING EARTHMEN! PLEASE TO RISE AND SHINE!
COLONEL DARE, PLEASE COME QUICKLY. THE MEKON IS PLANNING SOMETHING NEW.
M'M?... WHAT'S UP? REVEILLE ALREADY?
ALTITUDE/VELOCITY RATIO XLQ/42, SIR.
CUT ALL JETS!... PROCEED IN FREE ORBIT.
NOW WHAT'S HIS GAME?...
...HE CAN'T BE PLANNING TO ATTACK US WITH THAT LITTLE BUS?
JETS CUT, SIR. TRAVELLING IN FREE ORBIT.
ROCKET CAR TBM/17 CALLING HERMES... TBM/17 TO HERMES! MESSAGE FOR COLONEL DARE FROM THE MEKON!
GREETINGS, O COLONEL, FROM THE ALL-WISE ONE! HE HAS SENT ME TO DELIVER A LOAD OF FOOD AND DRINK TO YOU...
... HE FEARED THAT YOU AND YOUR FRIENDS MIGHT BE A LITTLE HUNGRY.
HE DIDN'T HAVE TO BE ALL-WISE TO GUESS THAT!... WHAT DO WE HAVE TO DO TO GET THIS FOOD?
ONLY SURRENDER, O COLONEL, AND ACCEPT THE MEKON'S TERMS.
SWITCH OFF, SONDAR!
...HULLO! SOMEONE'S MISSING! WHERE'S SAMSON?
LISTEN, CHAPS! I DON'T KNOW HOW MUCH LONGER WE CAN HOLD OUT WITHOUT...

HE'S JUST GONE INTO THE AIRLOCK!
THE EXHAUST'S WORKING, TOO. HE MUST BE GOING OUTSIDE.
EE! FANCY GOING OUT FOR A STROLL AT A TIME LIKE THIS!
?
THE IDIOT! HE'LL DRIFT OFF INTO SPACE.
NO! HE'LL BE ALL RIGHT, COLONEL. THERE ARE INSET HAND GRIPS ON THE OUTER HULL.
... WHAT'S HE THINK HE'S PLAYING AT?
IF THOSE TREENS SPOT HIM, HE'S HAD IT!
DIG! MY HELMET, QUICK! I'M GOING AFTER HIM.
D'ARCY! GET THAT OUTER DOOR SHUT! FILL THE AIR-LOCK AGAIN! EMERGENCY PRESSURE!
AYE, AYE, SIR.
I'M GOING WITH YOU, DAN. I BROUGHT SAMSON. HE'S MY RESPONSIBILITY.
PLEASE HURRY, O EXCELLENT SPACE COLONEL, SIR! SAMSON IS ABOUT TO JUMP ON THE HOVERBOAT.
THE FOOL! IF HE MISSES, HE WILL GO HURTLING OUT INTO SPACE AND...
TOO TOO!
PHEW!... HE'S MADE IT!
BUT WHAT'S HE GOING TO DO. NOW HE'S GOT THERE?
I DON'T KNOW! THAT'S WHAT I'M GOING TO FIND OUT. BUT I DON'T LIKE THE LOOK OF IT.
AIRLOCK CLEAR, SIR! YOU'LL BE QUITE SAFE WITH THOSE MAGNETIC BOOT CLIPS.
YOU'LL FIND A MAGNETIC GRAPNEL INSIDE THE AIRLOCK!
WATCH YOUR STEP, PROF.
TAH-GOO!
HE'S TRYING TO OPEN THAT DOOR. THE CRAZY...! SAMSON, STO-OP!
NO GOOD, DAN! HE CAN'T HEAR YOU THROUGH SPACE. HE HAS NO HELMET.
BESIDES, WHY SHOULD HE STOP? THERE'S NO AIRLOCK IN THOSE LITTLE TUBS... IF SAMSON CAN BREAK OPEN THAT DOOR AND LET THE AIR OUT, IT'LL PUT PAID TO THE TREEN CREW. AND THEN...
IF HE BREAKS THE DOOR, THE FORCE OF AIR RUSHING OUT WILL ACT AS A JET.
GOSH-YES! OF COURSE!
IT'LL BLOW THE HOVER-CAR AND ANYTHING ELSE THAT'S ATTACHED TO IT, TO THE OTHER SIDE OF SPACE, IF I DON'T GET OUT THERE AND...
DAN! LOOK OUT! THE DOOR! IT'S BREAKING!
DAN!
CONTINUED

SIX SUPER PRIZES TO BE WON THIS WEEK – see page 11
FOURPENCE-HALFPENNY
EVERY FRIDAY
EAGLE
28 NOVEMBER 1952 Vol. 3 No. 34
DAN DARE
PILOT OF THE FUTURE
MAROONED ON MERCURY
DAN!
THE FOOL! HE'S BLOWN THE HOVERCAR OFF ITS COURSE!
THAT'S TORN IT! NOW HE IS IN A RIGHT MESS!
A Treen hovercar, loaded with food, flies parallel with Hermes. Samson goes out to the surface of Hermes and leaps on to the hovercar. Dan and Peabody follow and see him wrenching off the hovercar's door. Dan throws a magnetic grapnel to the hovercar, but at that moment the door comes off, and the air rushing out acts as a jet. Dan is dragged off into space.
CURTAINS FOR COLONEL!
IF THOSE TREENS CAN GET THEIR HELMETS ON BEFORE THEY PERISH FROM ASPHYXIATION, THEN I FEAR WE HAVE LOOKED OUR LAST ON COLONEL DARE.
DON'T YOU BELIEVE IT, URB.
YOU OUGHT TO KNOW THE COLONEL BETTER THAN THAT, SONDAR.
HE'LL BE BACK! YOU'LL SEE.
MEANWHILE, AS THE HOVERCAR RACES ON ITS NEW COURSE AWAY FROM HERMES, DAN PULLS HIMSELF IN BY THE GRAPNEL ROPE.
... WHILE INSIDE THE HOVERCAR ...
AAH! MY HELMET, QUICK!... NO OXYGEN... UUUH!
HURRY! THIS WAS NO ACCIDENT. THERE IS SOMEONE OUTSIDE ON THE SURFACE OF THE SHIP.
SAMSON! WAIT! DON'T GO IN! IF THEY HAVE HELMETS ON...
WHAT'S THE USE? HE CAN'T HEAR A WORD!

NOW!
THUD
GOT YOU, YOU BRUTE!
HANG ON, SAMSON!... WITH YOU IN A SECOND!
LUCKILY IT'S ALL TURNED OUT FOR THE BEST, BUT NEXT TIME YOU WANT TO GO JOY RIDING IN SPACE, YOU...
?
...OH, NEVER MIND! TELL YOU WHEN WE GET BACK TO *HERMES*.
ALREADY THEY HAVE BEEN GONE MORE THAN 10 RONITS.
AND NOTHING TO DO BUT SIT AND WAIT. THAT SAMSON'S GOT A LOT TO ANSWER FOR!
IT'S NO USE BLAMING HIM. YOU KNOW HOW IMPULSIVE THESE MERCURIANS ARE... HE WAS ONLY TRYING TO HELP.
FOR PLUTO'S SAKE STOP MOANING, ALL OF YOU, AND LOOK AT THIS. SOMEONE'S IN THE AIRLOCK!
HULLO, CHAPS! HOPE YOU HAVEN'T BEEN WORRYING.
ANYONE HUNGRY?... I'VE GOT THAT HOVERCAR MOORED ALONGSIDE THE AIRLOCK.
DAN! THANK HEAVEN! HOW DID...
GOSH, SIR! AM I GLAD TO SEE YOU AGAIN?
HEAR WHAT HE SAYS, WILLIE? GRUB UP! COME AND GET IT!
EE! DROP O' GOOD STUFF THAT WAS! I WONDER WHERE IT CAME FROM.
ARTIFICIALLY CULTIVATED IN VILGOTH, I PRESUME.
YES, VILGOTH! WHERE THE MEKON'S SECRET WEAPON IS BEING MADE! WHERE THE FAY-SAW IS BEING COLLECTED AND WHERE WE'RE GOING RIGHT NOW.
GOING THERE, SIR? BUT HOW?
YOU'LL SEE! PUT YOUR HELMET ON AND COME OUTSIDE!
SONDAR! D'ARCY! ALL OF YOU! LET'S GET CRACKING... BEFORE THE MEKON FINDS OUT WHAT'S HAPPENING.
HERMES
GET THE IDEA NOW, DIG? WE ATTACH *HERMES* TO THE HOVERCAR BY HER SPACE-MOORING-HAWSERS...
...THEN I USE THE HOVERCAR TO TOW *HERMES* OFF HER ORBIT, CHECK HER SPEED AND LOWER HER TO THE SURFACE OF THE PLANET.
AH! LOOKS AS IF THEY'RE NEARLY READY. WE'LL GO ABOARD, DIG.
NUMBER FOUR HAWSER CORRECT, DAN!
MOORING COMPLETE, COLONEL!
RIGHT! GET BELOW, ALL! STAND BY TO BE TAKEN IN TOW!
I DON'T WANT TO BE AWKWARD, SIR, BUT IS THIS LITTLE TUB EVER GOING TO HOLD A GREAT SHIP LIKE THAT AGAINST THE PULL OF MERCURY'S GRAVITY?
YOUR GUESS IS AS GOOD AS MINE, DIG. IT ALL DEPENDS ON THE POWER OF THESE JETS. BUT WE'LL SOON FIND OUT.
ALL CLEAR ABOVE?
ALL CLEAR, SIR!
RIGHT! HERE WE GO!
CONTINUED

EAGLE-BRITAIN'S NATIONAL STRIP CARTOON WEEKLY

THEN WE MANOEUVRE TILL THE HERMES IS RESTING ON OUR TOP-SIDE, AND GRADUALLY REDUCE THE RATE OF FALL WITH OUR JETS.
WE HOPE!
SUFFERING SATURN! TALK ABOUT T' LAST STRAW! WE'RE TAKING T'WHOLE BLOOMIN' HAYSTACK ON OUR BACK!
SPEED DECREASES AGAIN, O SONDAR!
YES, IT WAS A BEAUTIFUL PIECE OF PILOTING. STUDY THE PANEL CAREFULLY NOW, O URB URTOS . . .
HERMES
. . AND YOU WILL UNDERSTAND THE COLONEL'S INTENTION. HE IS TRYING TO MANOEUVRE SO THAT WE LAND NEAR THE BASE OF VILGOTH.
GOSH, YES! THERE'S THE MERCURIAN CITY OF RAY-LAW STRAIGHT AHEAD OF US.
GRADUALLY DAN CHECKS THE SPEED OF FALL AND EASES THE GREAT SHIP TOWARDS THE SURFACE OF MERCURY, UNTIL . .
CHECK THRUST READING, DIGBY.
AND ALTITUDE?
POINT 97, SIR.
4,000 FEET.
HUH! IF WE'RE LUCKY, WE SHALL JUST MAKE IT.
WE SHOULD TOUCH DOWN ABOUT A COUPLE OF MILES THIS SIDE OF RAY-LAW, AND THEN . . .
HULLO! WHAT'S THAT DOWN THERE?
WHAT IS IT?
IT LOOKS LIKE FLAK.
BUT IT CAN'T BE.
THERE'S ANOTHER OF 'EM . . . AND ANOTHER . . . . WHAT THE HECK . . . ?
AIRBURST BOMBS! DROPPING FROM THE STERN OF THE HERMES. THERE MUST BE A HIDDEN BOMB RACK THERE SOMEWHERE, WITH AUTOMATIC RADAR RELEASE, AND BOMBS SET TO EXPLODE AT A GIVEN HEIGHT.
AYE! THAT'S ABOUT THE SIZE OF IT, SIR! THEY'RE ALL GOING OFF ABOUT 1,000 FEET UP, I'D GUESS . . . EE! WHAT'S UP, SIR? SUMMAT WRONG?
THAT DEPENDS ON HOW MANY BOMBS THE HERMES IS CARRYING, BUT IF THEY'RE STILL DROPPING WHEN WE GET DOWN TO 1,000 FEET . . . !
AN EXPLOSION OF THAT SIZE WOULDN'T DAMAGE THE HERMES, BUT FOR ANYONE SITTING IN THIS LITTLE TUB – WITH ITS DOOR MISSING, TOO . . .
BY GUM, YES! BUT WHY DON'T YOU KEEP US ABOVE 1,000 FEET, SIR, TILL THE BOMBS RUN OUT?
BECAUSE I CAN'T! IF WE'RE LUCKY, WE'LL HAVE JUST ENOUGH POWER TO GET US DOWN WITHOUT A CRASH LANDING. BUT THAT'S ALL! . . . WHAT'S THE ALTIMETER READING NOW?
2,000 FEET, SIR . . . 1,800 . . . 1,500 . . . 1,200.
HOW'S IT GOING, SIR?
THEY'RE STILL DROPPING!

CONTINUED

NEW RIDERS OF THE RANGE ADVENTURE STARTS TODAY!

FOURPENCE-HALFPENNY

EVERY FRIDAY

EAGLE

12 DECEMBER 1952 Vol. 3 No. 36

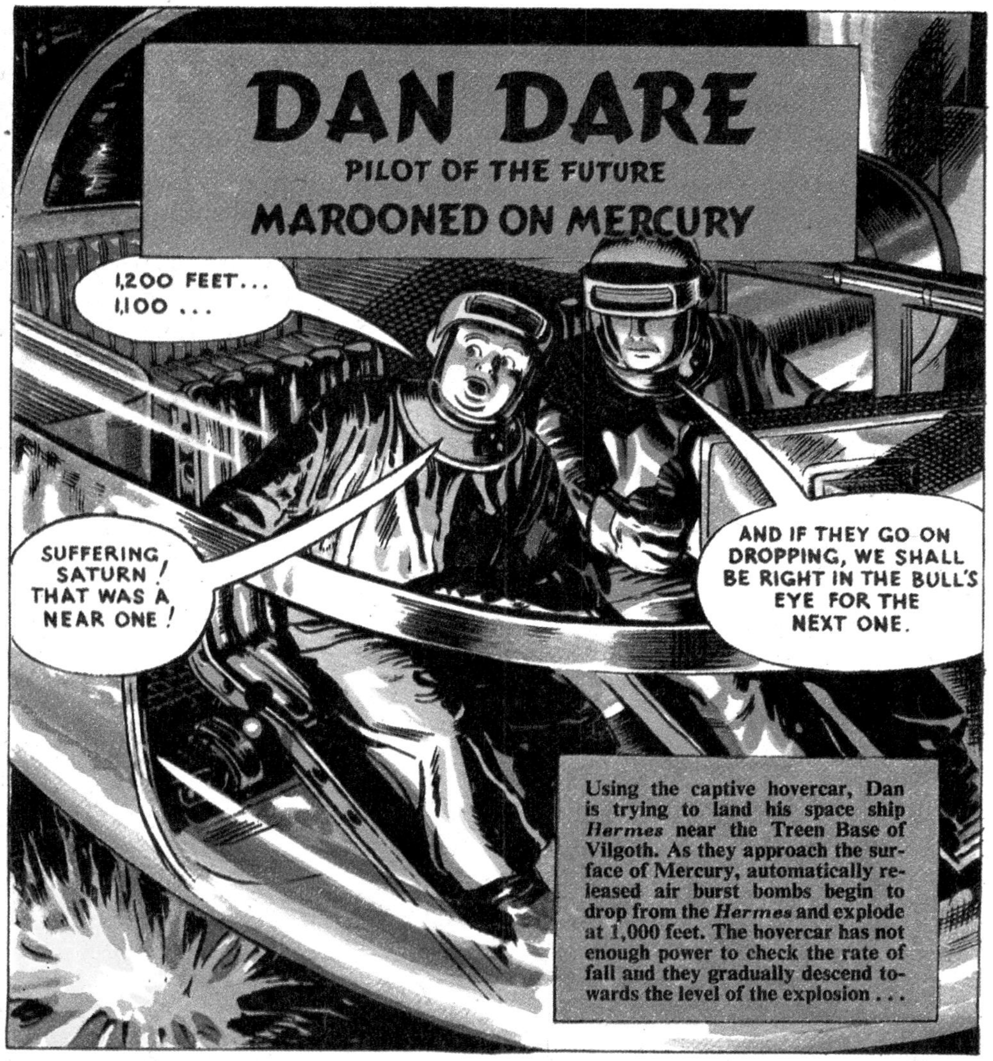

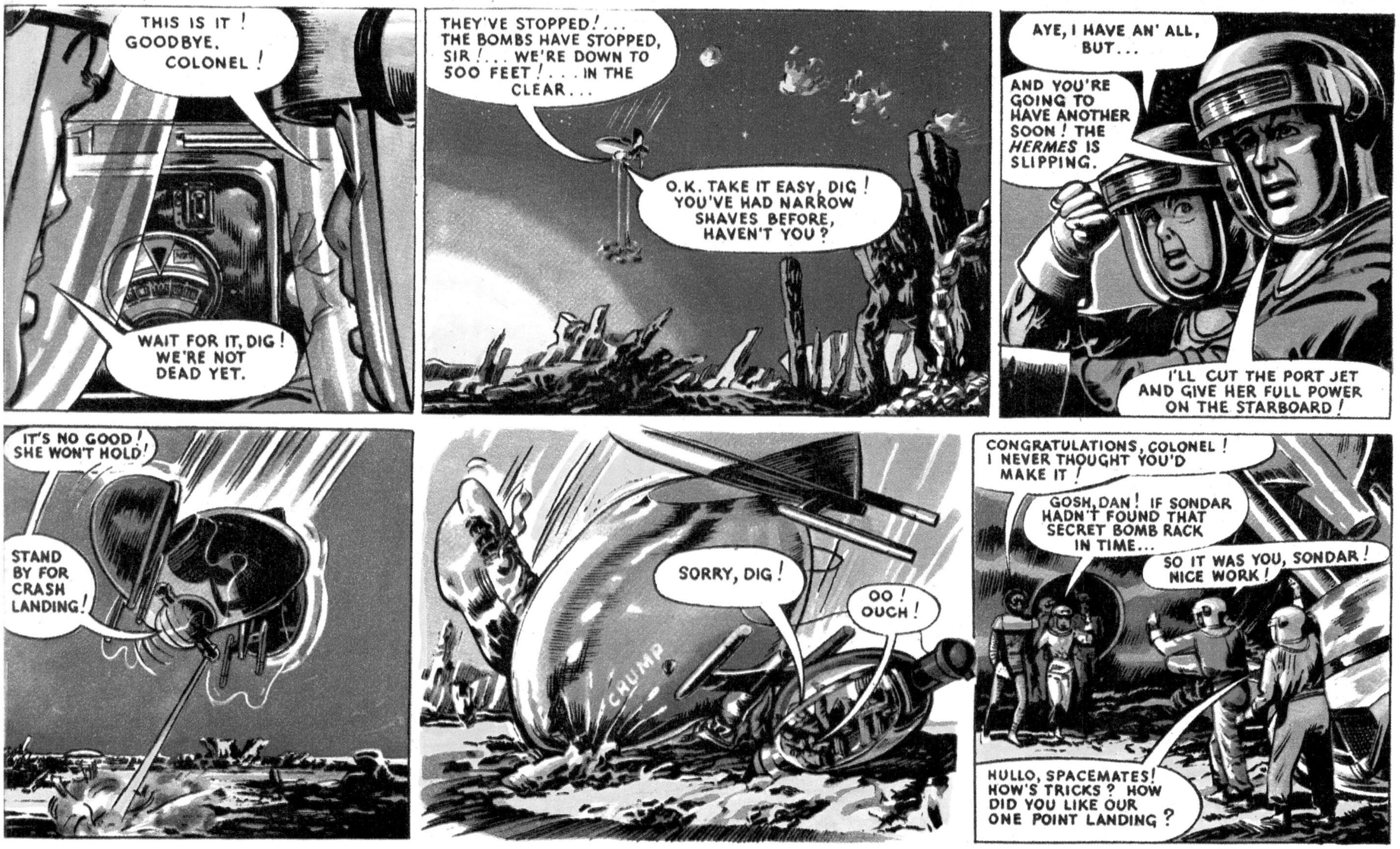

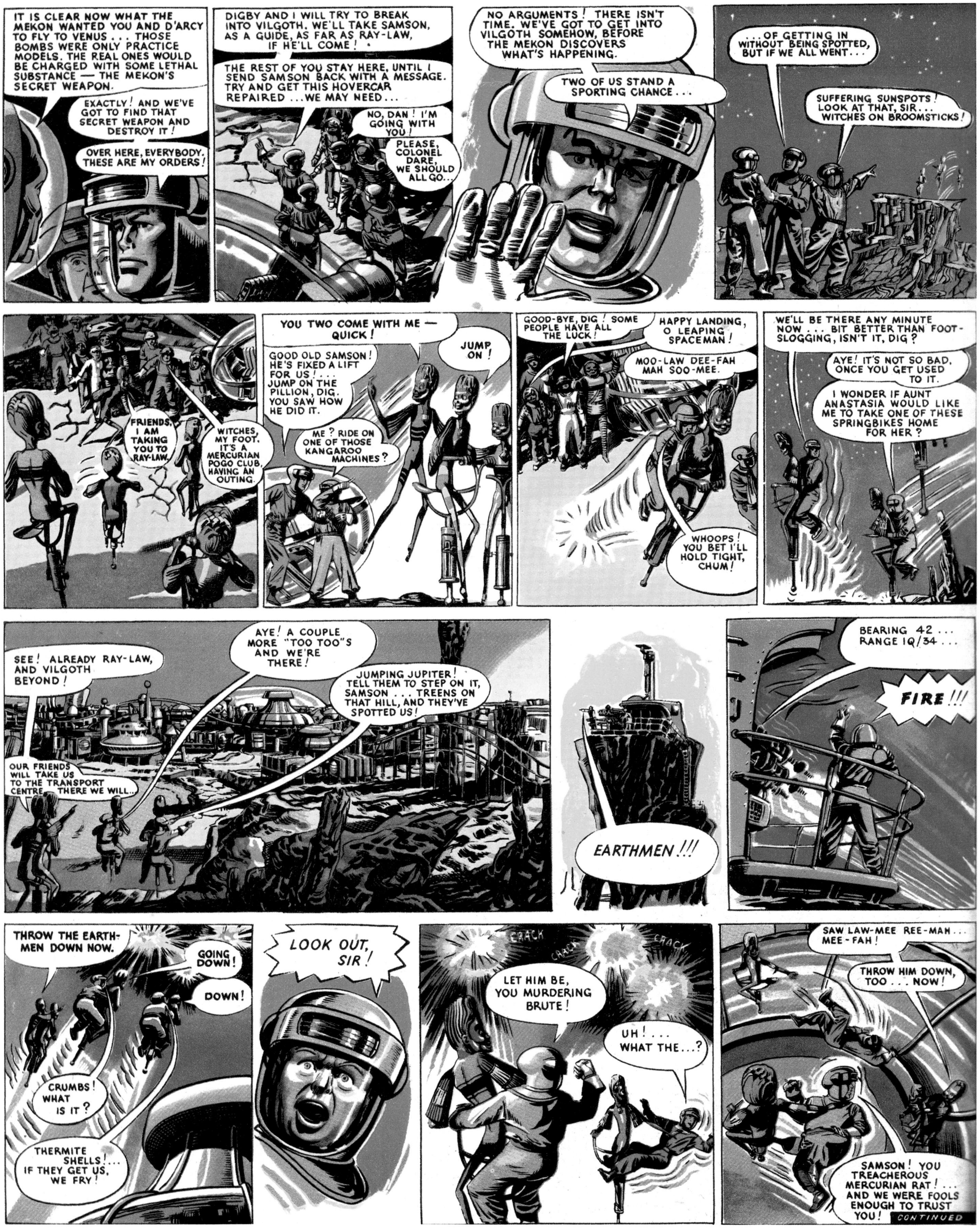
IT IS CLEAR NOW WHAT THE MEKON WANTED YOU AND D'ARCY TO FLY TO VENUS . . . THOSE BOMBS WERE ONLY PRACTICE MODELS. THE REAL ONES WOULD BE CHARGED WITH SOME LETHAL SUBSTANCE — THE MEKON'S SECRET WEAPON.
EXACTLY! AND WE'VE GOT TO FIND THAT SECRET WEAPON AND DESTROY IT!
OVER HERE, EVERYBODY. THESE ARE MY ORDERS!
DIGBY AND I WILL TRY TO BREAK INTO VILGOTH. WE'LL TAKE SAMSON, AS A GUIDE, AS FAR AS RAY-LAW, IF HE'LL COME!
THE REST OF YOU STAY HERE, UNTIL I SEND SAMSON BACK WITH A MESSAGE. TRY AND GET THIS HOVERCAR REPAIRED ...WE MAY NEED...
NO, DAN! I'M GOING WITH YOU!
PLEASE, COLONEL DARE, WE SHOULD ALL GO...
NO ARGUMENTS! THERE ISN'T TIME. WE'VE GOT TO GET INTO VILGOTH SOMEHOW, BEFORE THE MEKON DISCOVERS WHAT'S HAPPENING.
TWO OF US STAND A SPORTING CHANCE . . .
. . . OF GETTING IN WITHOUT BEING SPOTTED, BUT IF WE ALL WENT . . .
SUFFERING SUNSPOTS! LOOK AT THAT, SIR . . . WITCHES ON BROOMSTICKS!
FRIENDS, I AM TAKING YOU TO RAY-LAW.
WITCHES, MY FOOT. IT'S A MERCURIAN POGO CLUB, HAVING AN OUTING.
YOU TWO COME WITH ME — QUICK!
JUMP ON!
GOOD OLD SAMSON! HE'S FIXED A LIFT FOR US! . . . JUMP ON THE PILLION, DIG. YOU SAW HOW HE DID IT.
ME? RIDE ON ONE OF THOSE KANGAROO MACHINES?
GOOD-BYE, DIG! SOME PEOPLE HAVE ALL THE LUCK!
HAPPY LANDING, O LEAPING SPACEMAN!
MOO-LAW DEE-FAH MAH SOO-MEE.
WHOOPS! YOU BET I'LL HOLD TIGHT, CHUM!
WE'LL BE THERE ANY MINUTE NOW . . . BIT BETTER THAN FOOT-SLOGGING, ISN'T IT, DIG?
AYE! IT'S NOT SO BAD, ONCE YOU GET USED TO IT.
I WONDER IF AUNT ANASTASIA WOULD LIKE ME TO TAKE ONE OF THESE SPRINGBIKES HOME FOR HER?
SEE! ALREADY RAY-LAW, AND VILGOTH BEYOND!
AYE! A COUPLE MORE "TOO TOO"S AND WE'RE THERE!
JUMPING JUPITER! TELL THEM TO STEP ON IT, SAMSON . . . TREENS ON THAT HILL, AND THEY'VE SPOTTED US!
OUR FRIENDS WILL TAKE US TO THE TRANSPORT CENTRE... THERE WE WILL...
EARTHMEN!!!
BEARING 42 . . . RANGE 1Q/34 . . .
FIRE!!!
THROW THE EARTH-MEN DOWN NOW.
GOING DOWN!
DOWN!
CRUMBS! WHAT IS IT?
THERMITE SHELLS! . . . IF THEY GET US, WE FRY!
LOOK OUT, SIR!
CRACK
CRACK
CRACK
LET HIM BE, YOU MURDERING BRUTE!
UH! . . . WHAT THE . . .?
SAW LAW-MEE REE-MAH . . . MEE-FAH!
THROW HIM DOWN, TOO . . . NOW!
SAMSON! YOU TREACHEROUS MERCURIAN RAT! . . . AND WE WERE FOOLS ENOUGH TO TRUST YOU!
CONTINUED

1,000 CIRCUS SEATS FOR PRIZES – SEE PAGE 11

FOURPENCE-HALFPENNY

EVERY FRIDAY

EAGLE

19 DECEMBER 1952 Vol. 3 No. 37

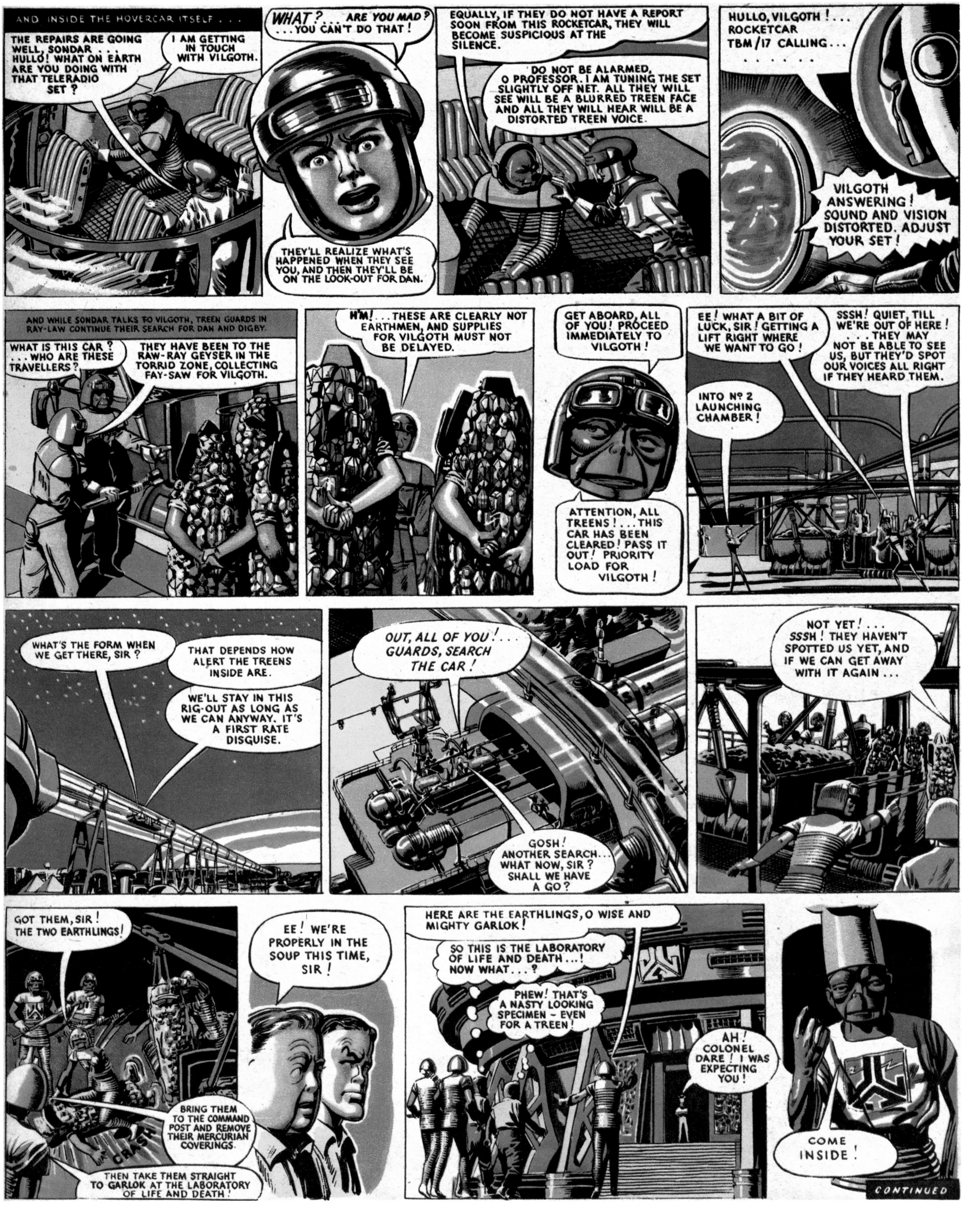

AND INSIDE THE HOVERCAR ITSELF . . .
THE REPAIRS ARE GOING WELL, SONDAR . . . HULLO! WHAT ON EARTH ARE YOU DOING WITH THAT TELERADIO SET ?
I AM GETTING IN TOUCH WITH VILGOTH.
WHAT? . . . ARE YOU MAD? . . . YOU CAN'T DO THAT!
THEY'LL REALIZE WHAT'S HAPPENED WHEN THEY SEE YOU, AND THEN THEY'LL BE ON THE LOOK-OUT FOR DAN.
EQUALLY, IF THEY DO NOT HAVE A REPORT SOON FROM THIS ROCKETCAR, THEY WILL BECOME SUSPICIOUS AT THE SILENCE.
DO NOT BE ALARMED, O PROFESSOR. I AM TUNING THE SET SLIGHTLY OFF NET. ALL THEY WILL SEE WILL BE A BLURRED TREEN FACE AND ALL THEY WILL HEAR WILL BE A DISTORTED TREEN VOICE.
HULLO, VILGOTH! . . . ROCKETCAR TBM/17 CALLING . . . .
VILGOTH ANSWERING! SOUND AND VISION DISTORTED. ADJUST YOUR SET!
AND WHILE SONDAR TALKS TO VILGOTH, TREEN GUARDS IN RAY-LAW CONTINUE THEIR SEARCH FOR DAN AND DIGBY.
WHAT IS THIS CAR? . . . WHO ARE THESE TRAVELLERS?
THEY HAVE BEEN TO THE RAW-RAY GEYSER IN THE TORRID ZONE, COLLECTING FAY-SAW FOR VILGOTH.
H'M! . . . THESE ARE CLEARLY NOT EARTHMEN, AND SUPPLIES FOR VILGOTH MUST NOT BE DELAYED.
GET ABOARD, ALL OF YOU! PROCEED IMMEDIATELY TO VILGOTH!
ATTENTION, ALL TREENS! . . . THIS CAR HAS BEEN CLEARED! PASS IT OUT! PRIORITY LOAD FOR VILGOTH!
EE! WHAT A BIT OF LUCK, SIR! GETTING A LIFT RIGHT WHERE WE WANT TO GO!
SSSH! QUIET, TILL WE'RE OUT OF HERE! . . . THEY MAY NOT BE ABLE TO SEE US, BUT THEY'D SPOT OUR VOICES ALL RIGHT IF THEY HEARD THEM.
INTO Nº 2 LAUNCHING CHAMBER!
WHAT'S THE FORM WHEN WE GET THERE, SIR?
THAT DEPENDS HOW ALERT THE TREENS INSIDE ARE.
WE'LL STAY IN THIS RIG-OUT AS LONG AS WE CAN ANYWAY. IT'S A FIRST RATE DISGUISE.
OUT, ALL OF YOU! . . . GUARDS, SEARCH THE CAR!
GOSH! ANOTHER SEARCH . . . WHAT NOW, SIR? SHALL WE HAVE A GO?
NOT YET! . . . SSSH! THEY HAVEN'T SPOTTED US YET, AND IF WE CAN GET AWAY WITH IT AGAIN . . .
GOT THEM, SIR! THE TWO EARTHLINGS!
CRASH
BRING THEM TO THE COMMAND POST AND REMOVE THEIR MERCURIAN COVERINGS.
THEN TAKE THEM STRAIGHT TO GARLOK AT THE LABORATORY OF LIFE AND DEATH!
EE! WE'RE PROPERLY IN THE SOUP THIS TIME, SIR!
HERE ARE THE EARTHLINGS, O WISE AND MIGHTY GARLOK!
SO THIS IS THE LABORATORY OF LIFE AND DEATH . . .! NOW WHAT . . .?
PHEW! THAT'S A NASTY LOOKING SPECIMEN – EVEN FOR A TREEN!
AH! COLONEL DARE! I WAS EXPECTING YOU!
COME INSIDE!
CONTINUED

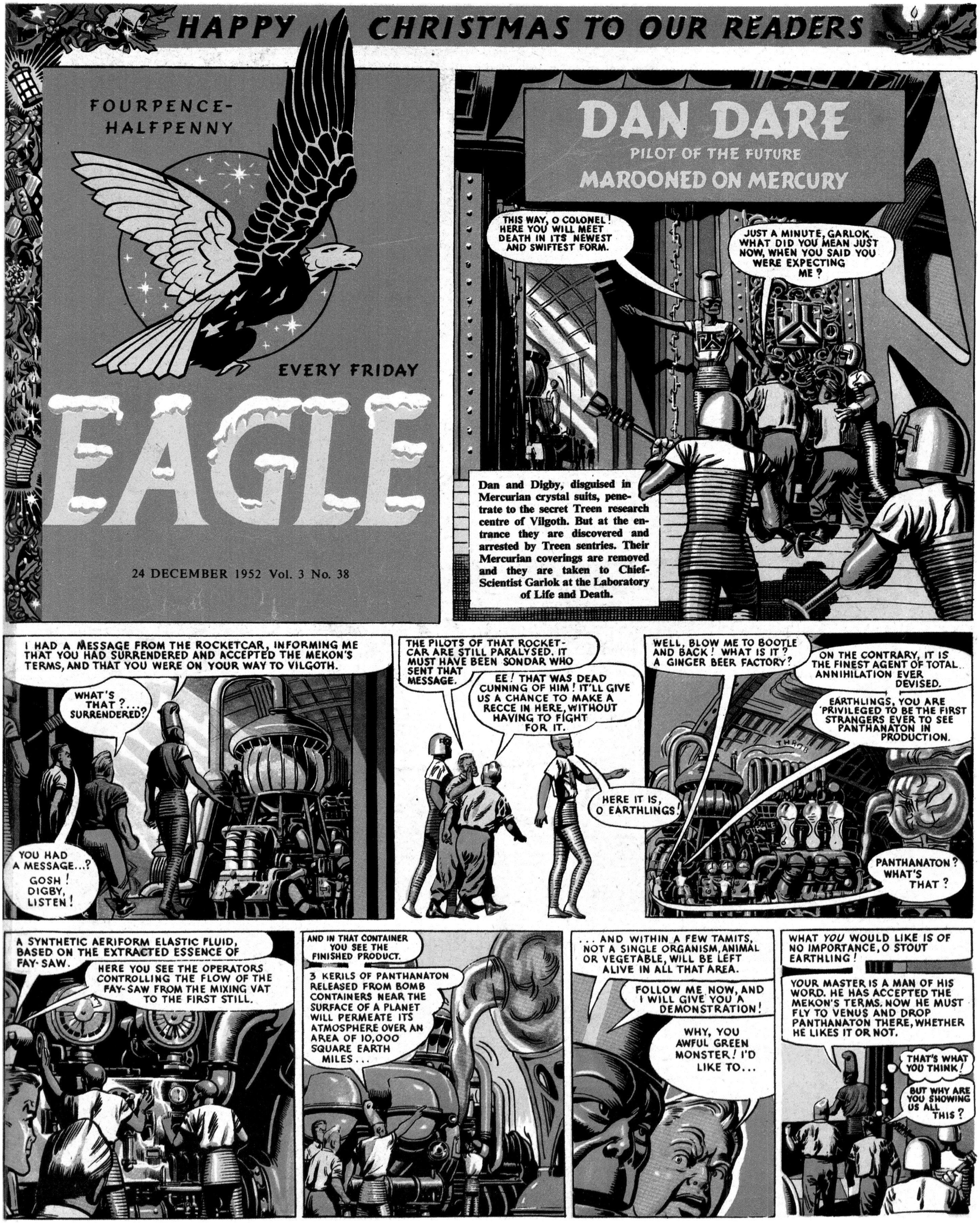
HAPPY CHRISTMAS TO OUR READERS
FOURPENCE-HALFPENNY
EVERY FRIDAY
EAGLE
24 DECEMBER 1952 Vol. 3 No. 38
DAN DARE
PILOT OF THE FUTURE
MAROONED ON MERCURY
THIS WAY, O COLONEL! HERE YOU WILL MEET DEATH IN ITS NEWEST AND SWIFTEST FORM.
JUST A MINUTE, GARLOK. WHAT DID YOU MEAN JUST NOW, WHEN YOU SAID YOU WERE EXPECTING ME?
Dan and Digby, disguised in Mercurian crystal suits, penetrate to the secret Treen research centre of Vilgoth. But at the entrance they are discovered and arrested by Treen sentries. Their Mercurian coverings are removed and they are taken to Chief-Scientist Garlok at the Laboratory of Life and Death.
I HAD A MESSAGE FROM THE ROCKETCAR, INFORMING ME THAT YOU HAD SURRENDERED AND ACCEPTED THE MEKON'S TERMS, AND THAT YOU WERE ON YOUR WAY TO VILGOTH.
WHAT'S THAT?.... SURRENDERED?
YOU HAD A MESSAGE...? GOSH! DIGBY, LISTEN!
THE PILOTS OF THAT ROCKET-CAR ARE STILL PARALYSED. IT MUST HAVE BEEN SONDAR WHO SENT THAT MESSAGE.
EE! THAT WAS DEAD CUNNING OF HIM! IT'LL GIVE US A CHANCE TO MAKE A RECCE IN HERE, WITHOUT HAVING TO FIGHT FOR IT.
HERE IT IS, O EARTHLINGS!
WELL, BLOW ME TO BOOTLE AND BACK! WHAT IS IT? A GINGER BEER FACTORY?
ON THE CONTRARY, IT IS THE FINEST AGENT OF TOTAL ANNIHILATION EVER DEVISED.
EARTHLINGS, YOU ARE PRIVILEGED TO BE THE FIRST STRANGERS EVER TO SEE PANTHANATON IN PRODUCTION.
PANTHANATON? WHAT'S THAT?
A SYNTHETIC AERIFORM ELASTIC FLUID, BASED ON THE EXTRACTED ESSENCE OF FAY-SAW.
HERE YOU SEE THE OPERATORS CONTROLLING THE FLOW OF THE FAY-SAW FROM THE MIXING VAT TO THE FIRST STILL.
AND IN THAT CONTAINER YOU SEE THE FINISHED PRODUCT.
3 KERILS OF PANTHANATON RELEASED FROM BOMB CONTAINERS NEAR THE SURFACE OF A PLANET WILL PERMEATE ITS ATMOSPHERE OVER AN AREA OF 10,000 SQUARE EARTH MILES...
... AND WITHIN A FEW TAMITS, NOT A SINGLE ORGANISM, ANIMAL OR VEGETABLE, WILL BE LEFT ALIVE IN ALL THAT AREA.
FOLLOW ME NOW, AND I WILL GIVE YOU A DEMONSTRATION!
WHY, YOU AWFUL GREEN MONSTER! I'D LIKE TO...
WHAT YOU WOULD LIKE IS OF NO IMPORTANCE, O STOUT EARTHLING!
YOUR MASTER IS A MAN OF HIS WORD. HE HAS ACCEPTED THE MEKON'S TERMS. NOW HE MUST FLY TO VENUS AND DROP PANTHANATON THERE, WHETHER HE LIKES IT OR NOT.
THAT'S WHAT YOU THINK!
BUT WHY ARE YOU SHOWING US ALL THIS?

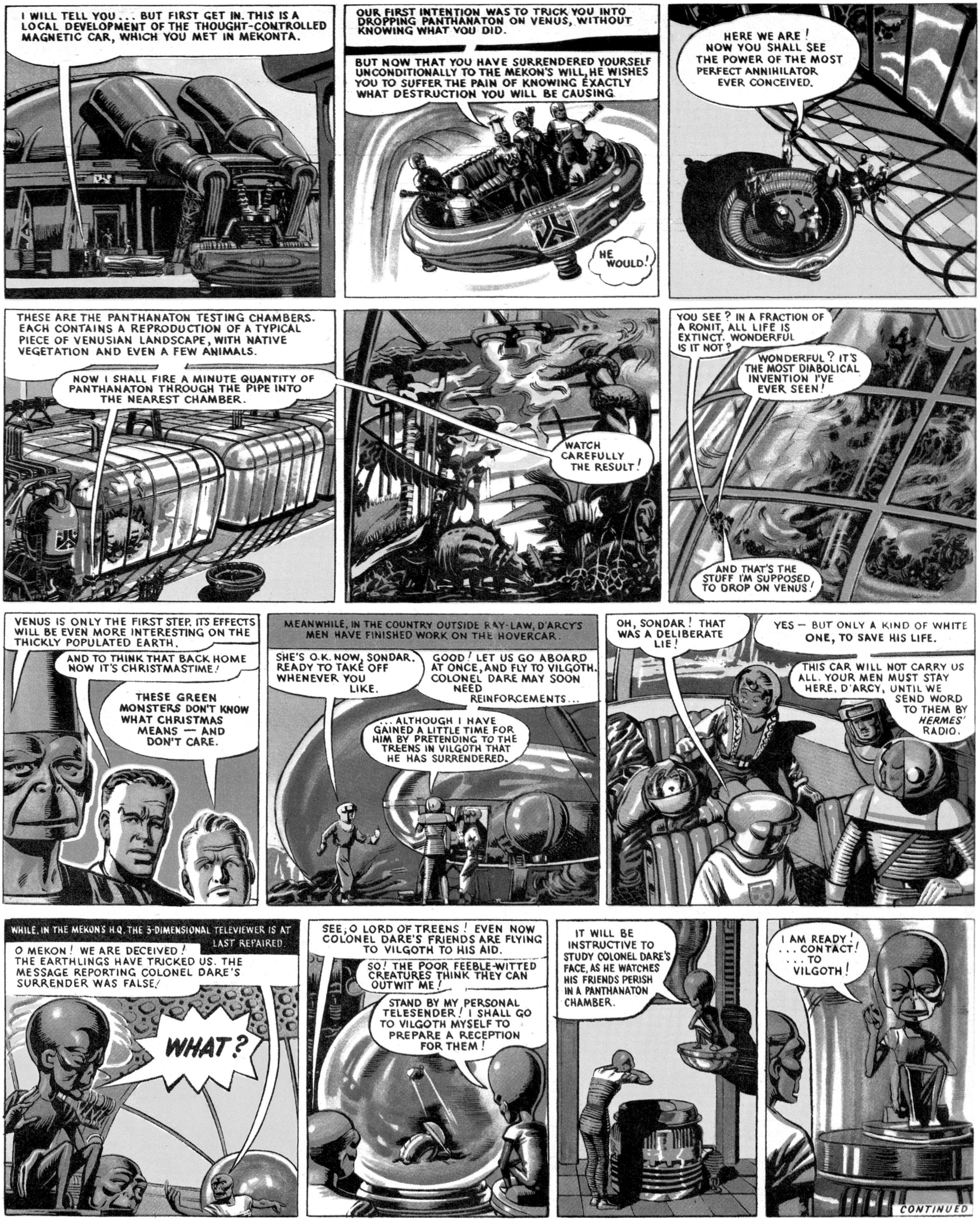
I WILL TELL YOU ... BUT FIRST GET IN. THIS IS A LOCAL DEVELOPMENT OF THE THOUGHT-CONTROLLED MAGNETIC CAR, WHICH YOU MET IN MEKONTA.
OUR FIRST INTENTION WAS TO TRICK YOU INTO DROPPING PANTHANATON ON VENUS, WITHOUT KNOWING WHAT YOU DID.
BUT NOW THAT YOU HAVE SURRENDERED YOURSELF UNCONDITIONALLY TO THE MEKON'S WILL, HE WISHES YOU TO SUFFER THE PAIN OF KNOWING EXACTLY WHAT DESTRUCTION YOU WILL BE CAUSING.
HE WOULD!
HERE WE ARE! NOW YOU SHALL SEE THE POWER OF THE MOST PERFECT ANNIHILATOR EVER CONCEIVED.
THESE ARE THE PANTHANATON TESTING CHAMBERS. EACH CONTAINS A REPRODUCTION OF A TYPICAL PIECE OF VENUSIAN LANDSCAPE, WITH NATIVE VEGETATION AND EVEN A FEW ANIMALS.
NOW I SHALL FIRE A MINUTE QUANTITY OF PANTHANATON THROUGH THE PIPE INTO THE NEAREST CHAMBER.
WATCH CAREFULLY THE RESULT!
YOU SEE? IN A FRACTION OF A RONIT, ALL LIFE IS EXTINCT. WONDERFUL IS IT NOT?
WONDERFUL? IT'S THE MOST DIABOLICAL INVENTION I'VE EVER SEEN!
AND THAT'S THE STUFF I'M SUPPOSED TO DROP ON VENUS!
VENUS IS ONLY THE FIRST STEP. ITS EFFECTS WILL BE EVEN MORE INTERESTING ON THE THICKLY POPULATED EARTH.
AND TO THINK THAT BACK HOME NOW IT'S CHRISTMASTIME!
THESE GREEN MONSTERS DON'T KNOW WHAT CHRISTMAS MEANS — AND DON'T CARE.
MEANWHILE, IN THE COUNTRY OUTSIDE RAY-LAW, D'ARCY'S MEN HAVE FINISHED WORK ON THE HOVERCAR.
SHE'S O.K. NOW, SONDAR, READY TO TAKE OFF WHENEVER YOU LIKE.
GOOD! LET US GO ABOARD AT ONCE, AND FLY TO VILGOTH. COLONEL DARE MAY SOON NEED REINFORCEMENTS ...
... ALTHOUGH I HAVE GAINED A LITTLE TIME FOR HIM BY PRETENDING TO THE TREENS IN VILGOTH THAT HE HAS SURRENDERED.
OH, SONDAR! THAT WAS A DELIBERATE LIE!
YES — BUT ONLY A KIND OF WHITE ONE, TO SAVE HIS LIFE.
THIS CAR WILL NOT CARRY US ALL. YOUR MEN MUST STAY HERE, D'ARCY, UNTIL WE SEND WORD TO THEM BY HERMES' RADIO.
WHILE, IN THE MEKON'S H.Q. THE 3-DIMENSIONAL TELEVIEWER IS AT LAST REPAIRED.
O MEKON! WE ARE DECEIVED! THE EARTHLINGS HAVE TRICKED US. THE MESSAGE REPORTING COLONEL DARE'S SURRENDER WAS FALSE!
WHAT?
SEE, O LORD OF TREENS! EVEN NOW COLONEL DARE'S FRIENDS ARE FLYING TO VILGOTH TO HIS AID.
SO! THE POOR FEEBLE-WITTED CREATURES THINK THEY CAN OUTWIT ME!
STAND BY MY PERSONAL TELESENDER! I SHALL GO TO VILGOTH MYSELF TO PREPARE A RECEPTION FOR THEM!
IT WILL BE INSTRUCTIVE TO STUDY COLONEL DARE'S FACE, AS HE WATCHES HIS FRIENDS PERISH IN A PANTHANATON CHAMBER.
I AM READY! ... CONTACT! ... TO VILGOTH!
CONTINUED

EXCITING NEW SCHOOL SERIAL STARTS TODAY - P. 12.

FOURPENCE-HALFPENNY
EVERY FRIDAY
EAGLE
2 JANUARY 1953 Vol. 3 No. 39
DAN DARE
PILOT OF THE FUTURE
MAROONED ON MERCURY
O TREENS OF VILGOTH, YOU HAVE BEEN DECEIVED! THE REPORT OF THE EARTHLINGS' SURRENDER WAS FALSE.
Deceived by Sondar into believing that Dan has surrendered, Garlok, chief Treen scientist in Vilgoth, proudly displays the deadly stuff called Panthanaton, which Dan is supposed to fly to Venus. Peabody, Sondar, Urb and D'Arcy fly to Vilgoth to join Dan. The Mekon discovers he has been tricked and goes to Vilgoth by telesender.
HOVERCAR TBM/17 IS APPROACHING VILGOTH, WITH COLONEL DARE'S FRIENDS ABOARD.
WARN LANDING CONTROL! THEY WILL BE CONFINED IN THE RECEPTION AIRLOCK, PENDING MY ORDERS.
IMMEDIATELY, O WISEST OF THE WISE!
WHERE IS THE EARTHLING DARE AND HIS PLUMP UNDERLING?
I HAVE THEM IN FOCUS ON THIS TELESCREEN, O MEKON. THEY ARE WITH GARLOK. HE IS SHOWING THEM THE WONDERS OF PANTHANATON.
GOOD! IT IS WELL THAT THE COLONEL SHOULD KNOW JUST WHAT I HAVE IN STORE FOR HIS FRIENDS.
FOLLOW ME AGAIN, O COLONEL, AND I WILL SHOW YOU ANOTHER INTERESTING EXPERIMENT.
HERE IS OUR MERCURIAN GUINEA PIG. NOW, WATCH THE EFFECT WHEN I OPEN THIS VALVE AND LET IN A LITTLE PANTHANATON.
LEAVE THAT ALONE! YOU MURDERING GREEN BRUTE!

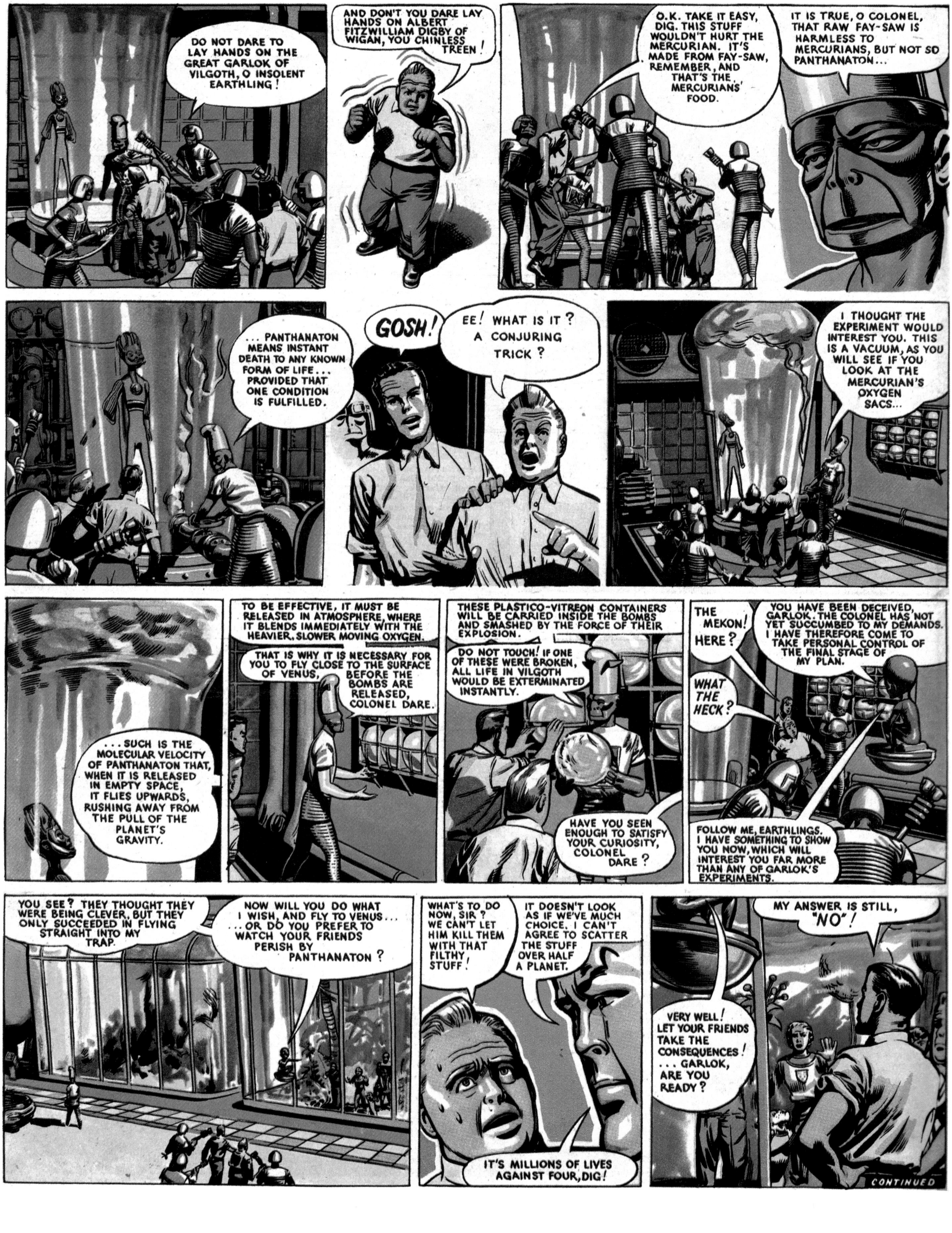
DO NOT DARE TO LAY HANDS ON THE GREAT GARLOK OF VILGOTH, O INSOLENT EARTHLING!
AND DON'T YOU DARE LAY HANDS ON ALBERT FITZWILLIAM DIGBY OF WIGAN, YOU CHINLESS TREEN!
O.K. TAKE IT EASY, DIG. THIS STUFF WOULDN'T HURT THE MERCURIAN. IT'S MADE FROM FAY-SAW, REMEMBER, AND THAT'S THE MERCURIANS' FOOD.
IT IS TRUE, O COLONEL, THAT RAW FAY-SAW IS HARMLESS TO MERCURIANS, BUT NOT SO PANTHANATON...
... PANTHANATON MEANS INSTANT DEATH TO ANY KNOWN FORM OF LIFE... PROVIDED THAT ONE CONDITION IS FULFILLED.
GOSH!
EE! WHAT IS IT? A CONJURING TRICK?
I THOUGHT THE EXPERIMENT WOULD INTEREST YOU. THIS IS A VACUUM, AS YOU WILL SEE IF YOU LOOK AT THE MERCURIAN'S OXYGEN SACS...
... SUCH IS THE MOLECULAR VELOCITY OF PANTHANATON THAT, WHEN IT IS RELEASED IN EMPTY SPACE, IT FLIES UPWARDS, RUSHING AWAY FROM THE PULL OF THE PLANET'S GRAVITY.
TO BE EFFECTIVE, IT MUST BE RELEASED IN ATMOSPHERE, WHERE IT BLENDS IMMEDIATELY WITH THE HEAVIER, SLOWER MOVING OXYGEN.
THAT IS WHY IT IS NECESSARY FOR YOU TO FLY CLOSE TO THE SURFACE OF VENUS, BEFORE THE BOMBS ARE RELEASED, COLONEL DARE.
THESE PLASTICO-VITREON CONTAINERS WILL BE CARRIED INSIDE THE BOMBS AND SMASHED BY THE FORCE OF THEIR EXPLOSION.
DO NOT TOUCH! IF ONE OF THESE WERE BROKEN, ALL LIFE IN VILGOTH WOULD BE EXTERMINATED INSTANTLY.
HAVE YOU SEEN ENOUGH TO SATISFY YOUR CURIOSITY, COLONEL DARE?
THE MEKON! HERE?
YOU HAVE BEEN DECEIVED, GARLOK. THE COLONEL HAS NOT YET SUCCUMBED TO MY DEMANDS. I HAVE THEREFORE COME TO TAKE PERSONAL CONTROL OF THE FINAL STAGE OF MY PLAN.
WHAT THE HECK?
FOLLOW ME, EARTHLINGS. I HAVE SOMETHING TO SHOW YOU NOW, WHICH WILL INTEREST YOU FAR MORE THAN ANY OF GARLOK'S EXPERIMENTS.
YOU SEE? THEY THOUGHT THEY WERE BEING CLEVER, BUT THEY ONLY SUCCEEDED IN FLYING STRAIGHT INTO MY TRAP.
NOW WILL YOU DO WHAT I WISH, AND FLY TO VENUS... ... OR DO YOU PREFER TO WATCH YOUR FRIENDS PERISH BY PANTHANATON?
WHAT'S TO DO NOW, SIR? WE CAN'T LET HIM KILL THEM WITH THAT FILTHY STUFF!
IT DOESN'T LOOK AS IF WE'VE MUCH CHOICE. I CAN'T AGREE TO SCATTER THE STUFF OVER HALF A PLANET.
IT'S MILLIONS OF LIVES AGAINST FOUR, DIG!
MY ANSWER IS STILL, "NO"!
VERY WELL! LET YOUR FRIENDS TAKE THE CONSEQUENCES! ... GARLOK, ARE YOU READY?
CONTINUED

VOTE FOR YOUR FAVOURITE SPORTSMAN – *SEE P. 6*

FOURPENCE-HALFPENNY

EVERY FRIDAY

EAGLE

9 JANUARY 1953 Vol. 3 No. 40

DAN DARE
PILOT OF THE FUTURE
MAROONED ON MERCURY
THINK AGAIN, O COLONEL! THIS IS YOUR VERY LAST CHANCE. ARE YOU SURE YOU HAVE MADE THE RIGHT DECISION?
CERTAIN! I WON'T SACRIFICE MILLIONS OF LIVES TO SAVE THESE FOUR ... EVEN IF THEY ARE MY FRIENDS.
The Mekon discovers that he has been tricked and goes to Vilgoth. Peabody, Urb, Sondar and D'Arcy fly straight into a trap and are shut up in a Pan-thanaton Chamber. The Mekon threatens to kill them unless Dan agrees to fly to Venus to drop the 'poison bombs'. But Dan firmly refuses to do this.

SO BE IT!...... GARLOK! OPEN VALVE TO NUMBER 2 CHAMBER...NORMAL PRESSURE...
STOP!
WAIT, O GARLOK! COLONEL DARE HAS CHANGED HIS MIND AFTER ALL...... WELL, COLONEL?
YES, I HAVE. I'VE DECIDED TO DO.....
THIS!
TAKE CARE OF THE OTHER TWO, DIG!... 10 SECONDS, THAT'S ALL I NEED!
STOP HIM!...... FOOLS, CRETINS, ZANIES, DO NOT LET HIM ESCAPE! ... SURROUND THE BUILDING!
AND, BY GUM, YOU SHALL HAVE IT, TOO!
TAKE THAT, YOU BRUTE!
ALL IS WELL, O MEKON! THAT IS THE ONLY ENTRANCE TO THE BUILDING.
COVER THAT DOORWAY, TREEN!
YOU MIGHT AS WELL COME OUT, COLONEL. THERE IS NO ESCAPE FOR YOU THAT WAY.

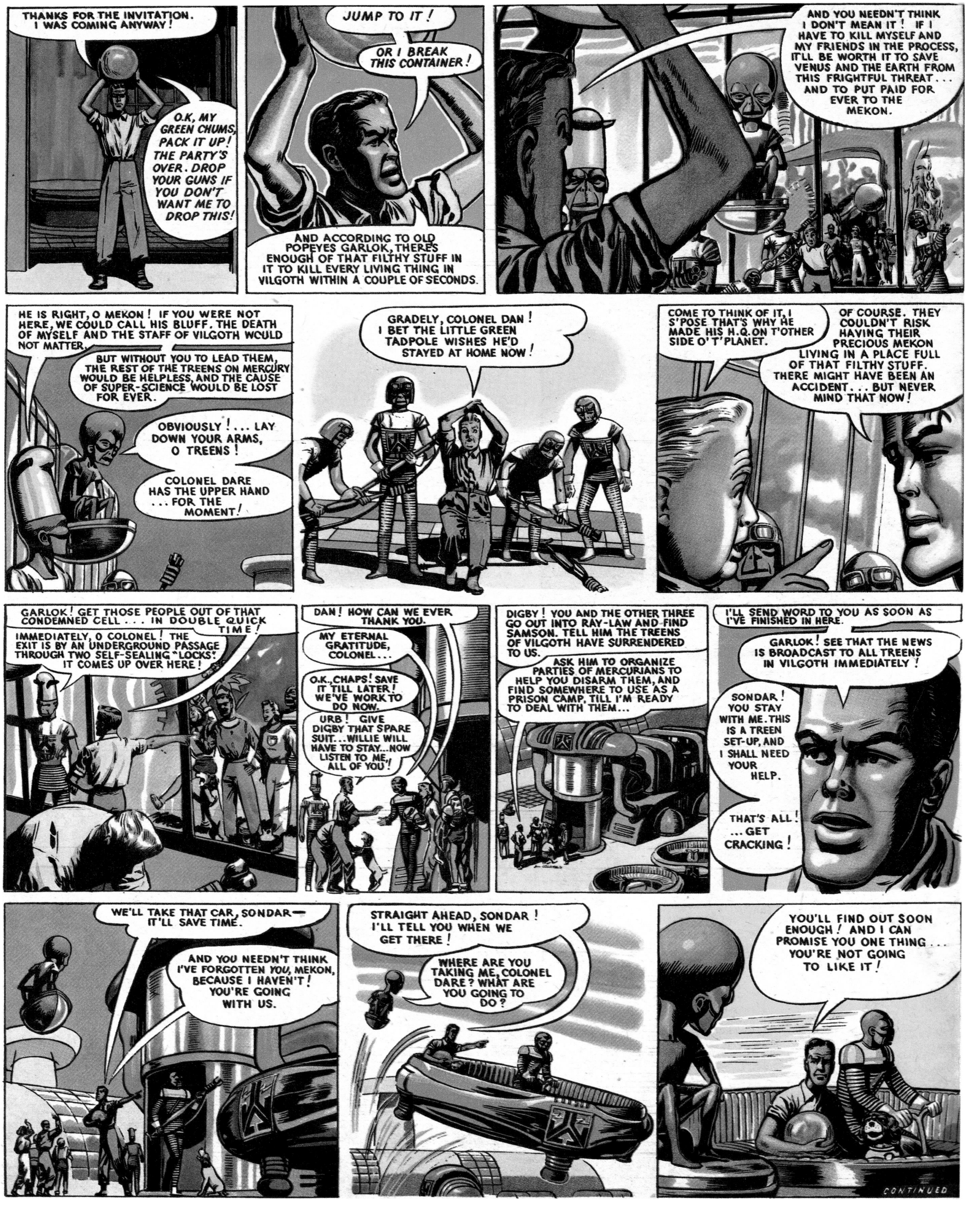
THANKS FOR THE INVITATION. I WAS COMING ANYWAY!
O.K, MY GREEN CHUMS, PACK IT UP! THE PARTY'S OVER. DROP YOUR GUNS IF YOU DON'T WANT ME TO DROP THIS!
JUMP TO IT!
OR I BREAK THIS CONTAINER!
AND ACCORDING TO OLD POPEYES GARLOK, THERE'S ENOUGH OF THAT FILTHY STUFF IN IT TO KILL EVERY LIVING THING IN VILGOTH WITHIN A COUPLE OF SECONDS.
AND YOU NEEDN'T THINK I DON'T MEAN IT! IF I HAVE TO KILL MYSELF AND MY FRIENDS IN THE PROCESS, IT'LL BE WORTH IT TO SAVE VENUS AND THE EARTH FROM THIS FRIGHTFUL THREAT... AND TO PUT PAID FOR EVER TO THE MEKON.
HE IS RIGHT, O MEKON! IF YOU WERE NOT HERE, WE COULD CALL HIS BLUFF. THE DEATH OF MYSELF AND THE STAFF OF VILGOTH WOULD NOT MATTER.
BUT WITHOUT YOU TO LEAD THEM, THE REST OF THE TREENS ON MERCURY WOULD BE HELPLESS, AND THE CAUSE OF SUPER-SCIENCE WOULD BE LOST FOR EVER.
OBVIOUSLY!... LAY DOWN YOUR ARMS, O TREENS!
COLONEL DARE HAS THE UPPER HAND ... FOR THE MOMENT!
GRADELY, COLONEL DAN! I BET THE LITTLE GREEN TADPOLE WISHES HE'D STAYED AT HOME NOW!
COME TO THINK OF IT, I S'POSE THAT'S WHY HE MADE HIS H.Q. ON T'OTHER SIDE O' T' PLANET.
OF COURSE. THEY COULDN'T RISK HAVING THEIR PRECIOUS MEKON LIVING IN A PLACE FULL OF THAT FILTHY STUFF. THERE MIGHT HAVE BEEN AN ACCIDENT... BUT NEVER MIND THAT NOW!
GARLOK! GET THOSE PEOPLE OUT OF THAT CONDEMNED CELL ... IN DOUBLE QUICK TIME!
IMMEDIATELY, O COLONEL! THE EXIT IS BY AN UNDERGROUND PASSAGE THROUGH TWO SELF-SEALING "LOCKS". IT COMES UP OVER HERE!
DAN! HOW CAN WE EVER THANK YOU.
MY ETERNAL GRATITUDE, COLONEL...
O.K., CHAPS! SAVE IT TILL LATER! WE'VE WORK TO DO NOW.
URB! GIVE DIGBY THAT SPARE SUIT... WILLIE WILL HAVE TO STAY... NOW LISTEN TO ME, ALL OF YOU!
DIGBY! YOU AND THE OTHER THREE GO OUT INTO RAY-LAW AND FIND SAMSON. TELL HIM THE TREENS OF VILGOTH HAVE SURRENDERED TO US.
ASK HIM TO ORGANIZE PARTIES OF MERCURIANS TO HELP YOU DISARM THEM, AND FIND SOMEWHERE TO USE AS A PRISON CAMP, TILL I'M READY TO DEAL WITH THEM...
I'LL SEND WORD TO YOU AS SOON AS I'VE FINISHED IN HERE.
GARLOK! SEE THAT THE NEWS IS BROADCAST TO ALL TREENS IN VILGOTH IMMEDIATELY!
SONDAR! YOU STAY WITH ME. THIS IS A TREEN SET-UP, AND I SHALL NEED YOUR HELP.
THAT'S ALL! ... GET CRACKING!
WE'LL TAKE THAT CAR, SONDAR— IT'LL SAVE TIME.
AND YOU NEEDN'T THINK I'VE FORGOTTEN YOU, MEKON, BECAUSE I HAVEN'T! YOU'RE GOING WITH US.
STRAIGHT AHEAD, SONDAR! I'LL TELL YOU WHEN WE GET THERE!
WHERE ARE YOU TAKING ME, COLONEL DARE? WHAT ARE YOU GOING TO DO?
YOU'LL FIND OUT SOON ENOUGH! AND I CAN PROMISE YOU ONE THING... YOU'RE NOT GOING TO LIKE IT!
CONTINUED

EAGLE-BRITAIN'S NATIONAL STRIP CARTOON WEEKLY
FOURPENCE-HALFPENNY
EVERY FRIDAY
EAGLE
16 JANUARY 1953 Vol. 3 No. 41
DAN DARE
PILOT OF THE FUTURE
MAROONED ON MERCURY
THERE YOU ARE, SONDAR! THAT'S THE PLACE I WANT. THE ONE WITH THE RADIO MASTS ON THE ROOF.
By threatening to break a container full of the deadly Panthanaton, Dan forces the Mekon to submit to him. He sends Digby, Peabody, Urb and D'Arcy out to Ray Law to contact Samson and prepare for the surrender of the Treens. Then, with Sondar, he takes the Mekon towards the other end of Vilgoth.
THIS IS THE VILGOTH TELECOMMUNICATIONS CENTRE, COLONEL.
TREENS! YOU WILL OBEY COLONEL DARE'S INSTRUCTIONS . . . UNTIL I GIVE FURTHER ORDERS.
DON'T YOU FOOL YOURSELF, MEKON! YOU WON'T BE GIVING ANY FURTHER ORDERS!
SONDAR, YOU KEEP AN EYE ON THE MEKON WHILE I'M BUSY. YOU'D BETTER TAKE THIS, TOO, BUT FOR HEAVEN'S SAKE DON'T DROP IT UNLESS YOU HAVE TO!
YOU CAN RELY ON ME, COLONEL.
AND, ABOVE ALL, CONCENTRATE ON INTERCEPTING HIS THOUGHTS. I DON'T WANT HIM DOUBLE-CROSSING US AS SOON AS MY BACK'S TURNED, BY FLASHING TELEPATHIC MESSAGES TO HIS PALS.
AHA! THAT'S WHAT I WAS LOOKING FOR. I THOUGHT THERE'D BE A HIGH POWERED TELERADIO SET SOMEWHERE IN THIS SET-UP.
WHAT DO YOU WANT WITH THAT SET? THAT'S A SUPRA-HIGH-FREQUENCY INTERSPACE COMMUNICATOR.
I KNOW...IT'S A NICE JOB, TOO... I'M JUST GOING TO HAVE A WORD WITH SOME PEOPLE WHO'LL BE VERY INTERESTED TO LEARN WHAT'S GOING ON HERE.
MEANWHILE, AT SPACE FLEET H.Q. ON EARTH, A CEREMONY IS TAKING PLACE.
. . . AND I KNOW THE THOUGHTS OF ALL THE WORLD WILL BE WITH ME WHEN I SAY THAT IT IS WITH PRIDE AND GRATITUDE THAT I NOW . . .

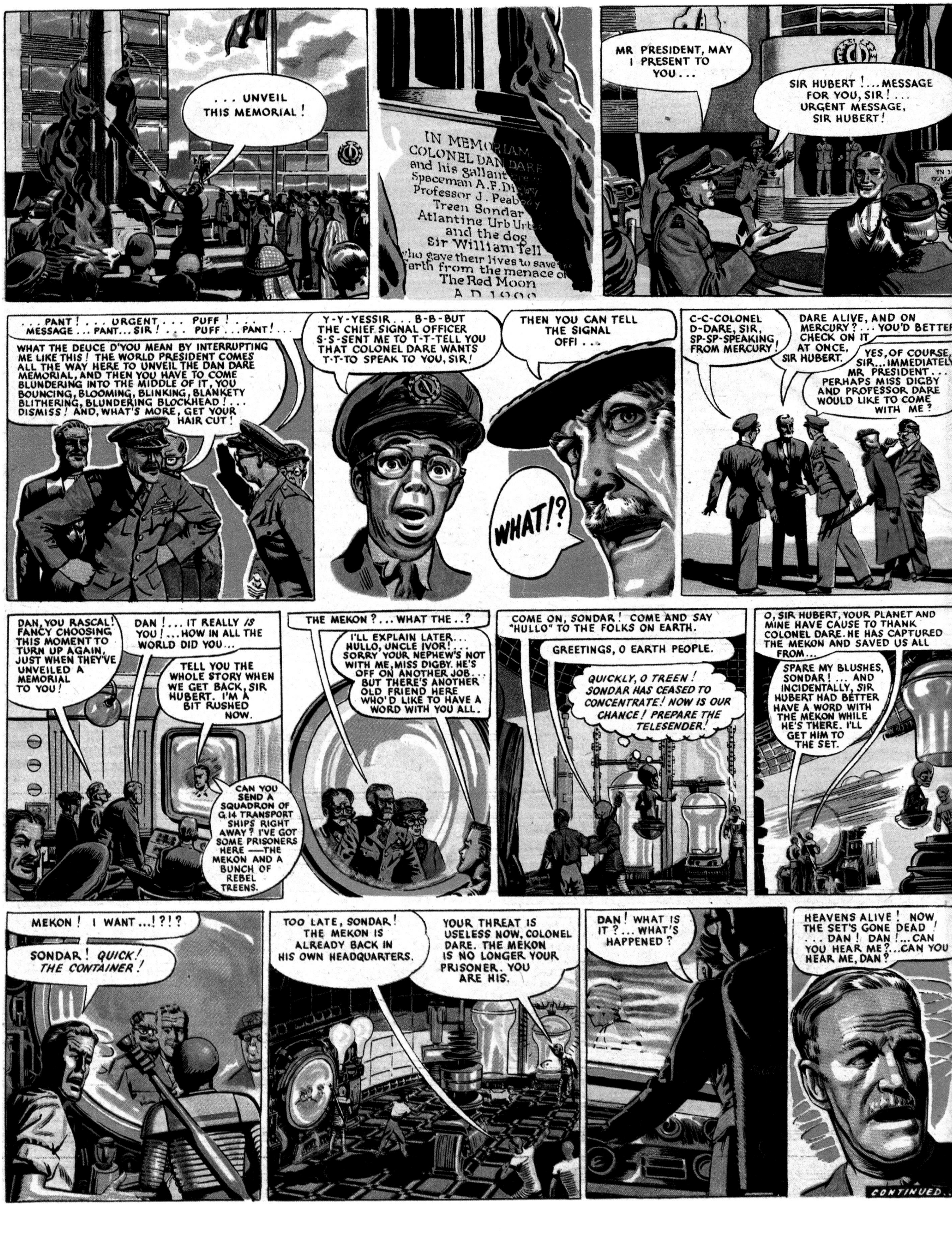
... UNVEIL THIS MEMORIAL!
IN MEMORIAM COLONEL DAN DARE and his gallant crew Spaceman A.F. Digby Professor J. Peabody Treen Sondar Atlantine Urb Urtes and the dog Sir William Tell who gave their lives to save the Earth from the menace of The Red Moon
MR PRESIDENT, MAY I PRESENT TO YOU...
SIR HUBERT!... MESSAGE FOR YOU, SIR!... URGENT MESSAGE, SIR HUBERT!
... PANT!... URGENT... PUFF!... MESSAGE... PANT... SIR!... PUFF... PANT!...
WHAT THE DEUCE D'YOU MEAN BY INTERRUPTING ME LIKE THIS! THE WORLD PRESIDENT COMES ALL THE WAY HERE TO UNVEIL THE DAN DARE MEMORIAL, AND THEN YOU HAVE TO COME BLUNDERING INTO THE MIDDLE OF IT, YOU BOUNCING, BLOOMING, BLINKING, BLANKETY BLITHERING, BLUNDERING BLOCKHEAD!... DISMISS! AND, WHAT'S MORE, GET YOUR HAIR CUT!
Y-Y-YESSIR... B-B-BUT THE CHIEF SIGNAL OFFICER S-S-SENT ME TO T-T-TELL YOU THAT COLONEL DARE WANTS T-T-TO SPEAK TO YOU, SIR!
THEN YOU CAN TELL THE SIGNAL OFFI...
WHAT!?
C-C-COLONEL D-DARE, SIR, SP-SP-SPEAKING FROM MERCURY!
DARE ALIVE, AND ON MERCURY?... YOU'D BETTER CHECK ON IT AT ONCE, SIR HUBERT.
YES, OF COURSE, SIR... IMMEDIATELY, MR PRESIDENT... PERHAPS MISS DIGBY AND PROFESSOR DARE WOULD LIKE TO COME WITH ME?
DAN, YOU RASCAL! FANCY CHOOSING THIS MOMENT TO TURN UP AGAIN, JUST WHEN THEY'VE UNVEILED A MEMORIAL TO YOU!
DAN!... IT REALLY IS YOU!... HOW IN ALL THE WORLD DID YOU...
TELL YOU THE WHOLE STORY WHEN WE GET BACK, SIR HUBERT. I'M A BIT RUSHED NOW.
CAN YOU SEND A SQUADRON OF G.14 TRANSPORT SHIPS RIGHT AWAY? I'VE GOT SOME PRISONERS HERE — THE MEKON AND A BUNCH OF REBEL TREENS.
THE MEKON?... WHAT THE..?
I'LL EXPLAIN LATER... HULLO, UNCLE IVOR!... SORRY YOUR NEPHEW'S NOT WITH ME, MISS DIGBY. HE'S OFF ON ANOTHER JOB... BUT THERE'S ANOTHER OLD FRIEND HERE WHO'D LIKE TO HAVE A WORD WITH YOU ALL.
COME ON, SONDAR! COME AND SAY "HULLO" TO THE FOLKS ON EARTH.
GREETINGS, O EARTH PEOPLE.
QUICKLY, O TREEN! SONDAR HAS CEASED TO CONCENTRATE! NOW IS OUR CHANCE! PREPARE THE TELESENDER!
O, SIR HUBERT, YOUR PLANET AND MINE HAVE CAUSE TO THANK COLONEL DARE. HE HAS CAPTURED THE MEKON AND SAVED US ALL FROM...
SPARE MY BLUSHES, SONDAR!... AND INCIDENTALLY, SIR HUBERT HAD BETTER HAVE A WORD WITH THE MEKON WHILE HE'S THERE. I'LL GET HIM TO THE SET.
MEKON! I WANT...!?!?
SONDAR! QUICK! THE CONTAINER!
TOO LATE, SONDAR! THE MEKON IS ALREADY BACK IN HIS OWN HEADQUARTERS.
YOUR THREAT IS USELESS NOW, COLONEL DARE. THE MEKON IS NO LONGER YOUR PRISONER. YOU ARE HIS.
DAN! WHAT IS IT?... WHAT'S HAPPENED?
HEAVENS ALIVE! NOW THE SET'S GONE DEAD! ... DAN! DAN!... CAN YOU HEAR ME?... CAN YOU HEAR ME, DAN?
CONTINUED...

CATCH UP ON THE THREE 'J's' ADVENTURES ON PAGE 12

FOURPENCE-HALFPENNY

EVERY FRIDAY

EAGLE

23 JANUARY 1953 Vol. 3 No. 42

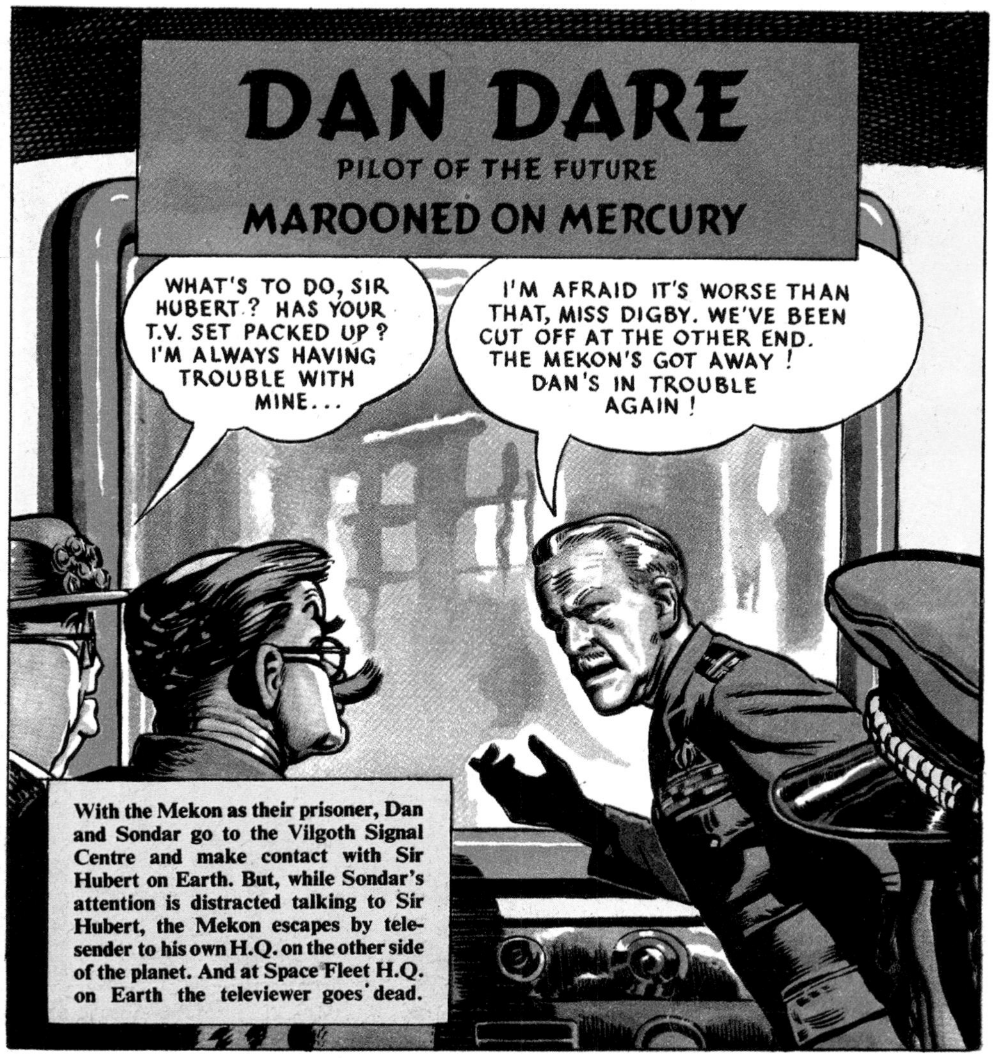
DAN DARE
PILOT OF THE FUTURE
MAROONED ON MERCURY
WHAT'S TO DO, SIR HUBERT? HAS YOUR T.V. SET PACKED UP? I'M ALWAYS HAVING TROUBLE WITH MINE...
I'M AFRAID IT'S WORSE THAN THAT, MISS DIGBY. WE'VE BEEN CUT OFF AT THE OTHER END. THE MEKON'S GOT AWAY! DAN'S IN TROUBLE AGAIN!
With the Mekon as their prisoner, Dan and Sondar go to the Vilgoth Signal Centre and make contact with Sir Hubert on Earth. But, while Sondar's attention is distracted talking to Sir Hubert, the Mekon escapes by telesender to his own H.Q. on the other side of the planet. And at Space Fleet H.Q. on Earth the televiewer goes dead.

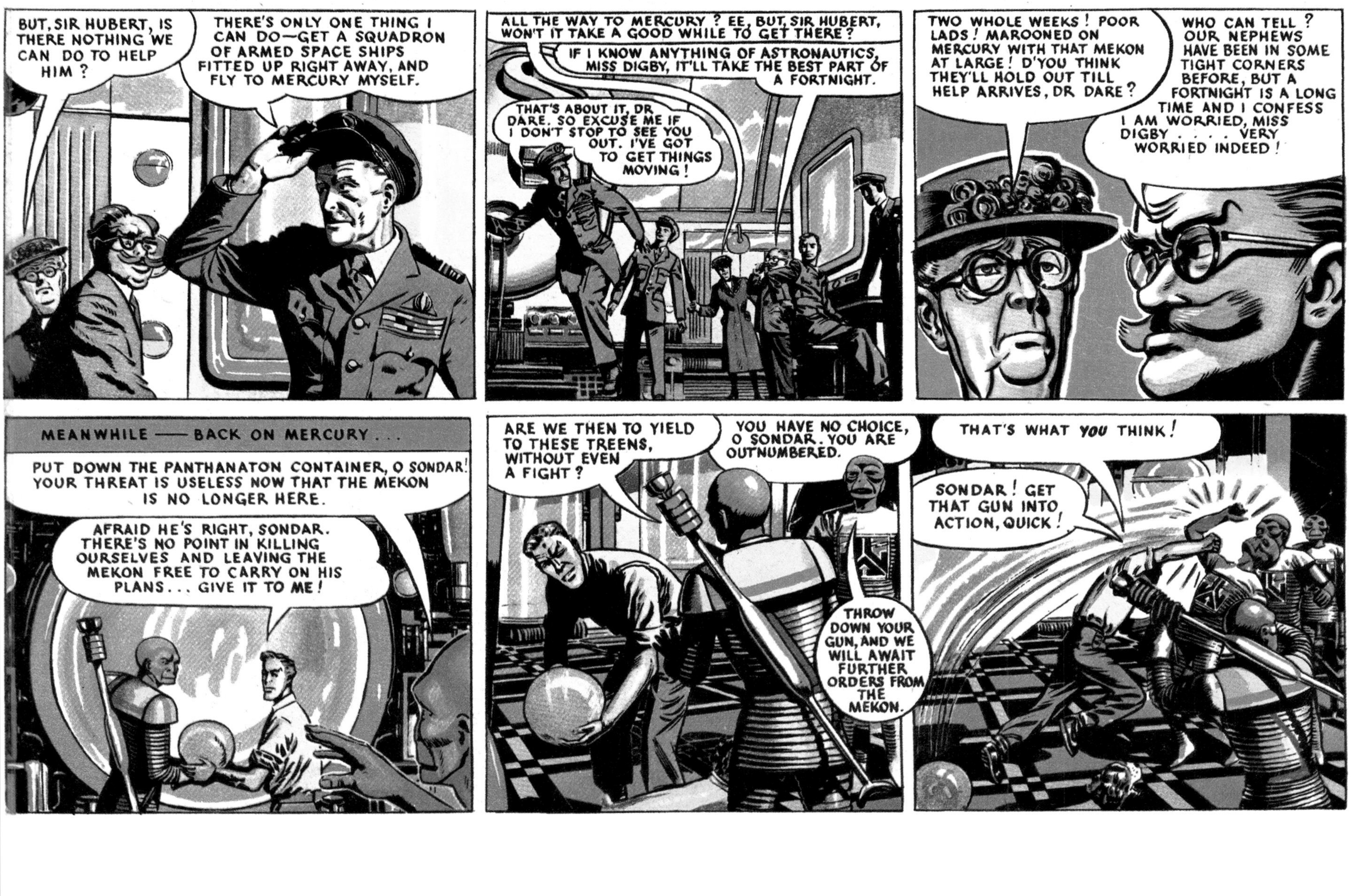
BUT, SIR HUBERT, IS THERE NOTHING WE CAN DO TO HELP HIM?
THERE'S ONLY ONE THING I CAN DO—GET A SQUADRON OF ARMED SPACE SHIPS FITTED UP RIGHT AWAY, AND FLY TO MERCURY MYSELF.
ALL THE WAY TO MERCURY? EE, BUT, SIR HUBERT, WON'T IT TAKE A GOOD WHILE TO GET THERE?
IF I KNOW ANYTHING OF ASTRONAUTICS, MISS DIGBY, IT'LL TAKE THE BEST PART OF A FORTNIGHT.
THAT'S ABOUT IT, DR DARE. SO EXCUSE ME IF I DON'T STOP TO SEE YOU OUT. I'VE GOT TO GET THINGS MOVING!
TWO WHOLE WEEKS! POOR LADS! MAROONED ON MERCURY WITH THAT MEKON AT LARGE! D'YOU THINK THEY'LL HOLD OUT TILL HELP ARRIVES, DR DARE?
WHO CAN TELL? OUR NEPHEWS HAVE BEEN IN SOME TIGHT CORNERS BEFORE, BUT A FORTNIGHT IS A LONG TIME AND I CONFESS I AM WORRIED, MISS DIGBY . . . . VERY WORRIED INDEED!
MEANWHILE —— BACK ON MERCURY . . .
PUT DOWN THE PANTHANATON CONTAINER, O SONDAR! YOUR THREAT IS USELESS NOW THAT THE MEKON IS NO LONGER HERE.
AFRAID HE'S RIGHT, SONDAR. THERE'S NO POINT IN KILLING OURSELVES AND LEAVING THE MEKON FREE TO CARRY ON HIS PLANS... GIVE IT TO ME!
ARE WE THEN TO YIELD TO THESE TREENS, WITHOUT EVEN A FIGHT?
YOU HAVE NO CHOICE, O SONDAR. YOU ARE OUTNUMBERED.
THROW DOWN YOUR GUN, AND WE WILL AWAIT FURTHER ORDERS FROM THE MEKON.
THAT'S WHAT YOU THINK!
SONDAR! GET THAT GUN INTO ACTION, QUICK!

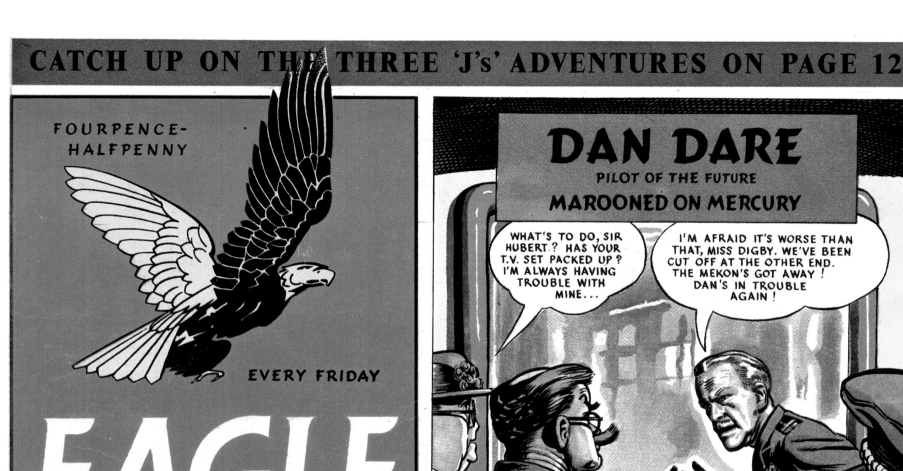

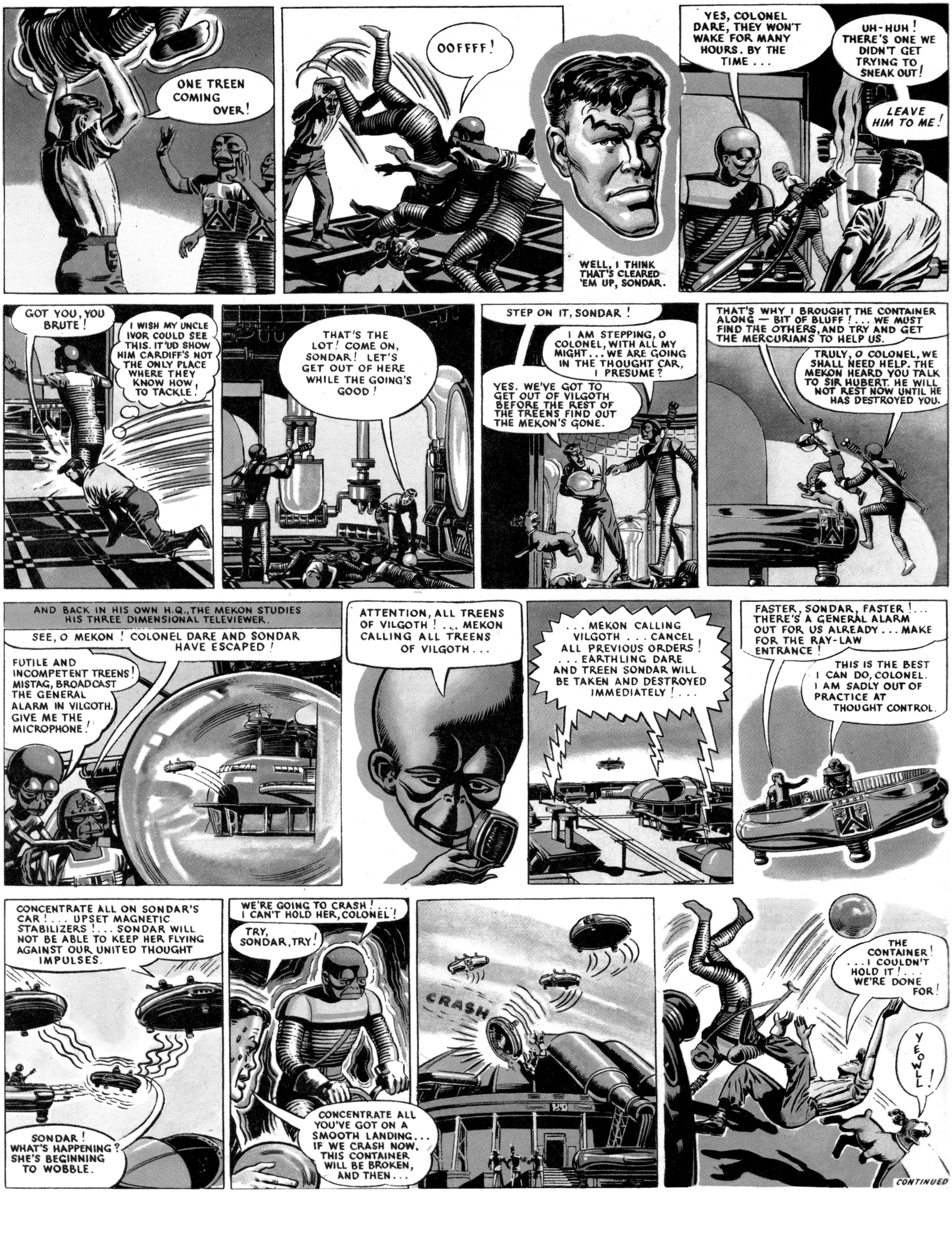
ONE TREEN COMING OVER!
OOFFFF!
WELL, I THINK THAT'S CLEARED 'EM UP, SONDAR.
YES, COLONEL DARE, THEY WON'T WAKE FOR MANY HOURS. BY THE TIME . . .
UH-HUH! THERE'S ONE WE DIDN'T GET TRYING TO SNEAK OUT!
LEAVE HIM TO ME!
GOT YOU, YOU BRUTE!
I WISH MY UNCLE IVOR COULD SEE THIS. IT'UD SHOW HIM CARDIFF'S NOT THE ONLY PLACE WHERE THEY KNOW HOW TO TACKLE!
THAT'S THE LOT! COME ON, SONDAR! LET'S GET OUT OF HERE WHILE THE GOING'S GOOD!
STEP ON IT, SONDAR!
I AM STEPPING, O COLONEL, WITH ALL MY MIGHT . . . WE ARE GOING IN THE THOUGHT CAR, I PRESUME?
YES. WE'VE GOT TO GET OUT OF VILGOTH BEFORE THE REST OF THE TREENS FIND OUT THE MEKON'S GONE.
THAT'S WHY I BROUGHT THE CONTAINER ALONG — BIT OF BLUFF! . . . WE MUST FIND THE OTHERS, AND TRY AND GET THE MERCURIANS TO HELP US.
TRULY, O COLONEL, WE SHALL NEED HELP. THE MEKON HEARD YOU TALK TO SIR HUBERT. HE WILL NOT REST NOW UNTIL HE HAS DESTROYED YOU.
AND BACK IN HIS OWN H.Q., THE MEKON STUDIES HIS THREE DIMENSIONAL TELEVIEWER.
SEE, O MEKON! COLONEL DARE AND SONDAR HAVE ESCAPED!
FUTILE AND INCOMPETENT TREENS! MISTAG, BROADCAST THE GENERAL ALARM IN VILGOTH. GIVE ME THE MICROPHONE!
ATTENTION, ALL TREENS OF VILGOTH! . . . MEKON CALLING ALL TREENS OF VILGOTH . . .
. . . MEKON CALLING VILGOTH . . . CANCEL ALL PREVIOUS ORDERS! . . . EARTHLING DARE AND TREEN SONDAR WILL BE TAKEN AND DESTROYED IMMEDIATELY! . . .
FASTER, SONDAR, FASTER! . . . THERE'S A GENERAL ALARM OUT FOR US ALREADY . . . MAKE FOR THE RAY-LAW ENTRANCE!
THIS IS THE BEST I CAN DO, COLONEL. I AM SADLY OUT OF PRACTICE AT THOUGHT CONTROL.
CONCENTRATE ALL ON SONDAR'S CAR! . . . UPSET MAGNETIC STABILIZERS! . . . SONDAR WILL NOT BE ABLE TO KEEP HER FLYING AGAINST OUR UNITED THOUGHT IMPULSES.
SONDAR! WHAT'S HAPPENING? SHE'S BEGINNING TO WOBBLE.
WE'RE GOING TO CRASH! . . . I CAN'T HOLD HER, COLONEL!
TRY, SONDAR, TRY!
CONCENTRATE ALL YOU'VE GOT ON A SMOOTH LANDING . . . IF WE CRASH NOW, THIS CONTAINER WILL BE BROKEN, AND THEN . . .
CRASH
THE CONTAINER! . . . I COULDN'T HOLD IT! . . . WE'RE DONE FOR!
YEOWLL!
CONTINUED

EAGLE - BRITAIN'S NATIONAL STRIP CARTOON WEEKLY

FOURPENCE-
HALFPENNY
EVERY FRIDAY
EAGLE
30 JANUARY 1953 Vol. 3 No. 43

DAN DARE
PILOT OF THE FUTURE
MAROONED ON MERCURY
FAREWELL, O COLONEL DARE, MY FRIEND! AT LEAST OUR DEATH WILL BE QUICK!
MAGNETS OF MEKONTA! HE HAS LET GO THE CONTAINER! . . . THIS WILL BE A SAD BLOW TO SCIENCE. ALL MY WORK HERE TO BE DONE AGAIN!
Dan and Sondar, still carrying the container of Panthanaton, are trying to rejoin their friends outside Vilgoth. But news of the Mekon's escape arrives, and the Treens concentrate on upsetting the thought-car in which Dan and Sondar are flying. The car crashes into the roof of a building and Dan loses his grip on the container.

WE'RE NOT DEAD YET, SONDAR, AND WHILE THERE'S LIFE . . .
. . . THERE'S HOPE! GOT YOU!
OH, MAGNIFICENT, O COLONEL!
URK! ARRK!

OH! HULLO, GARLOK! JUST THE CHAP I WANTED! HOLD THIS, WILL YOU?

SORRY I CAN'T STOP NOW. GOT A DATE!
WHAT THE . . . TREENS! DO NOT LET THEM ESCAPE! THEY MUST BE DESTROYED AT ALL COSTS.
OVER THE ROOF, SONDAR, QUICK! SEE YOU THE OTHER SIDE!
IT IS THE MEKON'S ORDER!

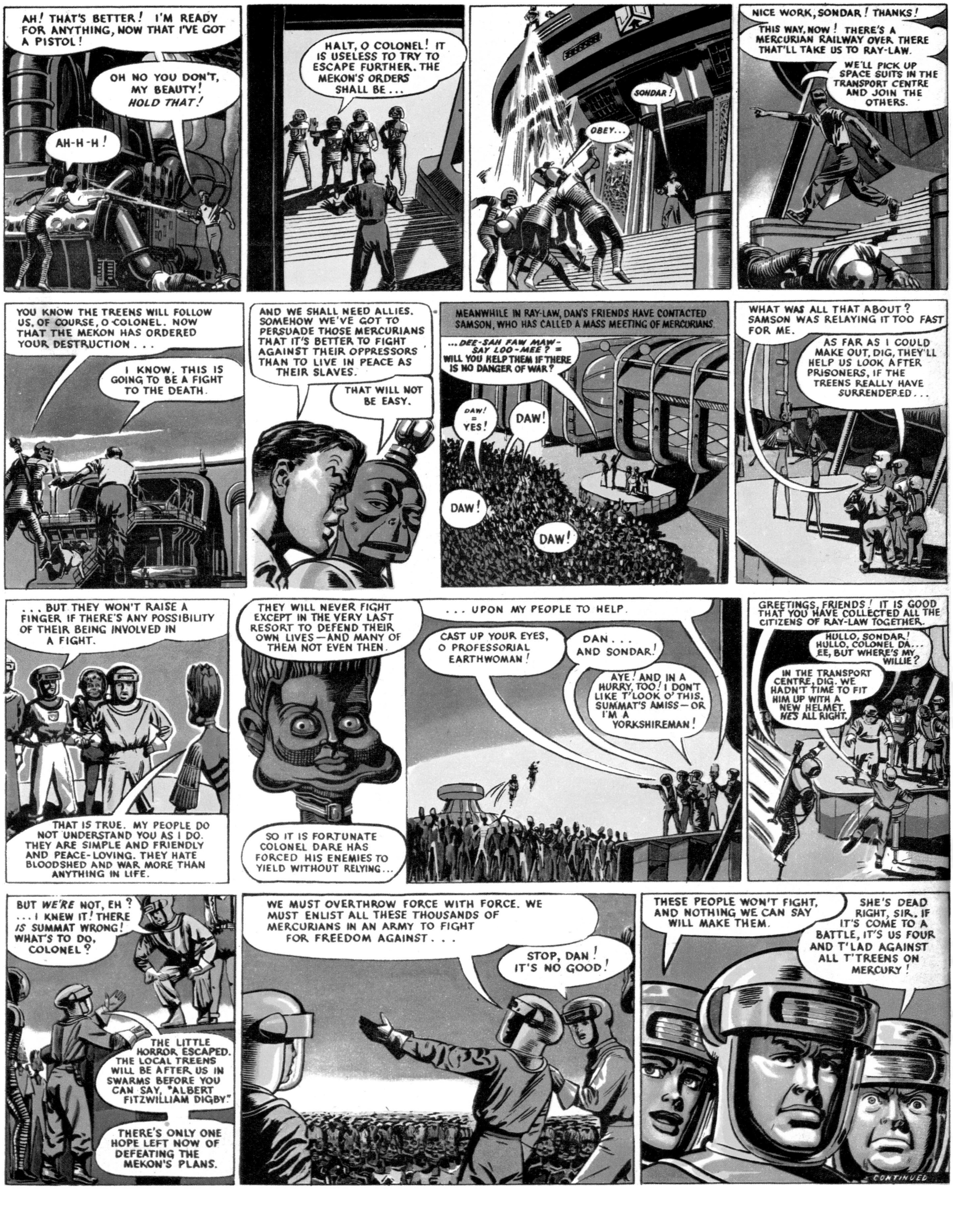
AH! THAT'S BETTER! I'M READY FOR ANYTHING, NOW THAT I'VE GOT A PISTOL!
OH NO YOU DON'T, MY BEAUTY! HOLD THAT!
AH-H-H!
HALT, O COLONEL! IT IS USELESS TO TRY TO ESCAPE FURTHER. THE MEKON'S ORDERS SHALL BE . . .
SONDAR!
OBEY...
NICE WORK, SONDAR! THANKS!
THIS WAY, NOW! THERE'S A MERCURIAN RAILWAY OVER THERE THAT'LL TAKE US TO RAY-LAW.
WE'LL PICK UP SPACE SUITS IN THE TRANSPORT CENTRE AND JOIN THE OTHERS.
YOU KNOW THE TREENS WILL FOLLOW US, OF COURSE, O COLONEL. NOW THAT THE MEKON HAS ORDERED YOUR DESTRUCTION . . .
I KNOW. THIS IS GOING TO BE A FIGHT TO THE DEATH.
AND WE SHALL NEED ALLIES. SOMEHOW WE'VE GOT TO PERSUADE THOSE MERCURIANS THAT IT'S BETTER TO FIGHT AGAINST THEIR OPPRESSORS THAN TO LIVE IN PEACE AS THEIR SLAVES.
THAT WILL NOT BE EASY.
MEANWHILE IN RAY-LAW, DAN'S FRIENDS HAVE CONTACTED SAMSON, WHO HAS CALLED A MASS MEETING OF MERCURIANS.
...DEE-SAH FAW MAW-SAY LOO-MEE? = WILL YOU HELP THEM IF THERE IS NO DANGER OF WAR?
DAW! = YES!
DAW!
DAW!
DAW!
WHAT WAS ALL THAT ABOUT? SAMSON WAS RELAYING IT TOO FAST FOR ME.
AS FAR AS I COULD MAKE OUT, DIG, THEY'LL HELP US LOOK AFTER PRISONERS, IF THE TREENS REALLY HAVE SURRENDERED . . .
. . . BUT THEY WON'T RAISE A FINGER IF THERE'S ANY POSSIBILITY OF THEIR BEING INVOLVED IN A FIGHT.
THAT IS TRUE. MY PEOPLE DO NOT UNDERSTAND YOU AS I DO. THEY ARE SIMPLE AND FRIENDLY AND PEACE-LOVING. THEY HATE BLOODSHED AND WAR MORE THAN ANYTHING IN LIFE.
THEY WILL NEVER FIGHT EXCEPT IN THE VERY LAST RESORT TO DEFEND THEIR OWN LIVES—AND MANY OF THEM NOT EVEN THEN.
SO IT IS FORTUNATE COLONEL DARE HAS FORCED HIS ENEMIES TO YIELD WITHOUT RELYING...
. . . UPON MY PEOPLE TO HELP.
CAST UP YOUR EYES, O PROFESSORIAL EARTHWOMAN!
DAN . . . AND SONDAR!
AYE! AND IN A HURRY, TOO! I DON'T LIKE T'LOOK O' THIS. SUMMAT'S AMISS—OR I'M A YORKSHIREMAN!
GREETINGS, FRIENDS! IT IS GOOD THAT YOU HAVE COLLECTED ALL THE CITIZENS OF RAY-LAW TOGETHER.
HULLO, SONDAR! HULLO, COLONEL DA... EE, BUT WHERE'S MY WILLIE?
IN THE TRANSPORT CENTRE, DIG. WE HADN'T TIME TO FIT HIM UP WITH A NEW HELMET. HE'S ALL RIGHT.
BUT WE'RE NOT, EH? . . . I KNEW IT! THERE IS SUMMAT WRONG! WHAT'S TO DO, COLONEL?
THE LITTLE HORROR ESCAPED. THE LOCAL TREENS WILL BE AFTER US IN SWARMS BEFORE YOU CAN SAY, "ALBERT FITZWILLIAM DIGBY."
THERE'S ONLY ONE HOPE LEFT NOW OF DEFEATING THE MEKON'S PLANS.
WE MUST OVERTHROW FORCE WITH FORCE. WE MUST ENLIST ALL THESE THOUSANDS OF MERCURIANS IN AN ARMY TO FIGHT FOR FREEDOM AGAINST . . .
STOP, DAN! IT'S NO GOOD!
THESE PEOPLE WON'T FIGHT, AND NOTHING WE CAN SAY WILL MAKE THEM.
SHE'S DEAD RIGHT, SIR. IF IT'S COME TO A BATTLE, IT'S US FOUR AND T'LAD AGAINST ALL T'TREENS ON MERCURY!
CONTINUED

EAGLE-BRITAIN'S NATIONAL STRIP CARTOON WEEKLY
FOURPENCE-HALFPENNY
EVERY FRIDAY
EAGLE
6 FEBRUARY 1953 Vol. 3 No. 44
DAN DARE
PILOT OF THE FUTURE
MAROONED ON MERCURY
BUT THEY MUST HELP. THE TREENS ARE THEIR ENEMIES AS MUCH AS OURS. IF THEY DON'T RESIST NOW, SOON IT'LL BE TOO LATE.
I WILL TALK TO THEM MYSELF, SAMSON.
Dan and Sondar escape from Vilgoth and rejoin their friends in Ray-Law, where Samson has called a mass meeting of citizens. Dan wants to enlist all these Mercurians in an army to resist the Treens. But Peabody tells him that the Mercurians hate warfare and will not fight.
NO GOOD, DAN! WE CAN TALK TO EACH OTHER THROUGH THE RADIO SETS IN OUR HELMETS, BUT THEY CAN'T HEAR US AND WE CAN'T HEAR THEM.
GOSH, YES, OF COURSE! I WAS FORGETTING...
THAT'S WHY WE SNITCHED A TREEN "WALKIE-TALKIE" FROM VILGOTH... SO WE COULD KEEP IN TOUCH WITH SAMSON OUT HERE.
ALL RIGHT THEN! SAMSON SHALL SPEAK FOR ME.
I'LL TALK TO YOU, SAMSON; AND YOU PASS IT ON TO THEM. SAY THIS:—
FRIENDS! THE FATE OF EARTH AND VENUS, AS WELL AS YOUR OWN PLANET IS IN YOUR HANDS...
SAW-SAY! LOO-MEE RAH MAY SEE-LAH SAW RAY SEE-LAH...
TIME IS PRESSING. THE MEKON'S PRESENCE HERE IS KNOWN ON EARTH. HE MUST ACT AT ONCE IF HIS PLAN IS TO SUCCEED...
...AND IF HE DOES SUCCEED, FREEDOM WILL VANISH FOR EVER FROM THE INNER PLANETS.
BELIEVE ME, MY FRIENDS, APPEASEMENT NEVER PAYS.
MEANWHILE, ON THE OTHER SIDE OF MERCURY...
O MEKON! O LORD OF TREENS! DISTURBING NEWS FROM VILGOTH!...
...COLONEL DARE HAS ESCAPED! HE IS IN RAY-LAW TRYING TO ROUSE THE MERCURIANS AGAINST US... SEE, O MEKON!
IF THE TREENS HAVE NOT HARMED YOU YET, IT IS ONLY BECAUSE THEY HAVE NEEDED YOUR HELP IN COLLECTING FAY-SAW FOR THEIR HIDEOUS PLAN...
SPLINTERING ATOMS! SOMEONE SHALL PAY FOR THIS!

WHEN THE MEKON NO LONGER NEEDS YOU, HE WILL DESTROY YOU WITHOUT A THOUGHT, AS HE WOULD DESTROY A WORN OUT PIECE OF MACHINERY.
VERY TRUE, COLONEL DARE! BUT, FORTUNATELY THOSE SIMPLE FOOLS OF MERCURIANS WILL NEVER BELIEVE YOU.
MISTAG! PROCEED IMMEDIATELY BY TELESENDER TO VILGOTH...
... AND TAKE COMMAND THERE. PUT INTO OPERATION PLAN QV/13T.
RAY-LAW AND ALL ITS INHABITANTS WILL BE DESTROYED!
TOLZIK! FOLLOW MISTAG TO VILGOTH! LOAD ALL AVAILABLE SPACE-BOMBERS WITH PANTHANATON, AND STAND BY TO TAKE OFF.
VALTOG! WARN ALL LOCAL HANGARS! STAND BY FOR EMERGENCY OPERATION INPLAN!... ALL SPACE SHIPS AT HALF A TAMIT'S NOTICE TO TAKE OFF.
KIMBAR! BROADCAST EMERGENCY OPERATION ORDER TO ALL TREENS...
AND WHILE THE MEKON PRESSES ON WITH HIS PLANS, DAN MAKES HIS LAST APPEAL, THROUGH SAMSON, TO THE MERCURIANS.
IT IS TRUE THAT THEY ARE ARMED, AND YOU ARE NOT, BUT THERE ARE TENS OF THOUSANDS OF YOU, AND ONLY A FEW HUNDRED TREENS IN VILGOTH.
THE BEST FORM OF DEFENCE IS ATTACK! JOIN WITH ME AND MY FRIENDS! STRIKE NOW, BEFORE IT IS TOO LATE!
WELL SPOKEN, DAN!
EE, THAT WERE A REET FINE SPEECH, SIR!
NOBLE AND SPLENDID WORDS, O COLONEL!
BUT HAVE THEY CONVINCED THE MERCURIANS?... THAT'S THE POINT.
SOME ARE CONVINCED; SOME ARE NOT — THEY WILL VOTE.
IT'S TOO LATE FOR VOTING NOW! LOOK!...
TEE DAW? TEE MAW?
MAW-SAY!
DAW-SAY! DAW-SAY!
DOO-MEE MAW-SAY?
DAW-SAY.
... UP THERE! D'YOU SEE?
GOSH! THE MEKON'S MOVED FASTER THAN I THOUGHT HE COULD!
FROM THE HANGARS OF VILGOTH! THIS MAKES THE SITUATION DESPERATE, O COLONEL!
TREEN FIGHTERS! OH, DAN! IT'S GOING TO BE A MASSACRE!
GET DOWN! TAKE COVER!... SAMSON, QUICK! TELL THEM TO SCATTER AND TAKE COVER TILL THE FIRST WAVE'S GONE OVER!... AVOID UNNECESSARY CASUALTIES!...
EE, THAT WAS A CLOSE SHAVE! NEARLY BLEW MY HELMET OFF!
KEEP YOUR HEAD DOWN THEN!
AND WHAT ARE THOSE FOOLS OF MERCURIANS DOING? WHY DON'T THEY TAKE COV...
JUMPING JUPITER! D'YOU SEE WHAT I SEE?
THEIR BLOOD'S UP! THEY'RE HITTING BACK!... THIS IS WHAT I'VE BEEN WAITING FOR!
THEY DON'T WANT TO FIGHT BUT BY JINGO WHEN THEY DO!... EE, WELL DONE, LADS!... LET T'BATTLE COMMENCE!
WHAT JUMPING! I NEVER SAW ANYTHING LIKE IT BEFORE!
TEARING OFF THE DOORS AND OVERPOWERING THE PILOTS!
GOSH, YES! THEY'RE ATTACKING THE TREEN FIGHTERS WITH THEIR BARE HANDS!
NOW WE'VE A 50/50 CHANCE!
CONTINUED

INSTRUCTIONS FOR MAKING MODEL AIRCRAFT - *P. 13*

FOURPENCE-HALFPENNY
EVERY FRIDAY
EAGLE
13 FEBRUARY 1953 Vol. 3 No. 45
DAN DARE
PILOT OF THE FUTURE
MAROONED ON MERCURY
NOW WE'VE A 50/50 CHANCE... IF WE CAN PRODUCE SOME SORT OF TACTICAL ORDER OUT OF THIS CHAOS!
The Mekon presses on with his plans against Venus and Earth. Simultaneously, he orders his fighter squadrons from Vilgoth to destroy Ray-Law and its inhabitants. The Mercurians, who were still hesitating whether to join Dan or not, are roused by this unprovoked Treen attack and, despite their lack of arms, fight back.
GET MOVING, EVERYONE! WE'LL MAKE OUR H.Q. BESIDE THAT BUILDING OVER THERE. IT'LL GIVE A CERTAIN AMOUNT OF COVER.
AYE! AS LONG AS IT STAYS STANDING!
CRUMP
SAMSON! COLLECT A COMPANY OF OUR PALS ON SPRING-BIKES!
PICK UP ANY PISTOLS OR GUNS YOU CAN FIND IN TREEN SHIPS THAT HAVE CRASHED!
ARM THE REST OF THEM WITH BITS OF METAL—STONES—CRYSTAL—ANYTHING YOU CAN LAY HANDS ON...
NOW LISTEN, ALL OF YOU, WE'VE GOT TO THINK AND ACT FAST!
THE TREENS AREN'T GOING TO BE CAUGHT THAT WAY A SECOND TIME. THEY'LL MAKE THEIR NEXT ATTACK FROM HIGH LEVEL.
VERILY THE SPACE COLONEL SPEAKS TRUTHFUL WORDS... SEE! THEY COME AGAIN ALREADY! UP THERE ON HIGH!
GET DOWN THEN, QUICK! BUT KEEP LISTENING!
D'ARCY! AS SOON AS SAMSON GETS BACK, TAKE A SQUAD OF MERCURIANS, GO STRAIGHT TO *HERMES*, PICK UP YOUR CHAPS THERE AND AS MANY WEAPONS AS YOU CAN STRIP FROM THE SHIP, AND REPORT BACK HERE!
DIGBY! YOU AND URB TAKE ANOTHER PARTY, GO TO THE TRANSPORT CENTRE, COLLECT WILLIE AND BLOCK THE RAIL EXIT FROM VILGOTH!
PROF! YOU AND SAMSON STAY HERE AT H.Q. WE'LL KEEP IN TOUCH WITH YOU BY OUR HELMET RADIOS, AND SAMSON CAN PASS ON ORDERS TO THE MERCURIANS.
AH! HERE COMES THE RAY-LAW FLYING SQUAD! GET CRACKING, EVERYONE! TIME IS NOT ON OUR SIDE!
SONDAR! GRAB YOURSELF A SPRINGBIKE AND A DOZEN MERCURIANS AND COME WITH ME!
THAT TREEN THERMITE GUN IS THE KEY TO THE WHOLE OPERATION. IF WE CAN CAPTURE... LOOK OUT! *SWERVE!*

IF WE CAN CAPTURE THAT GUN AND DESTROY THEIR BASE, WE CAN TURN THIS MASSACRE INTO A VICTORY.
YOU KNOW THE PLAN, SONDAR? KEEP THEM BUSY, BUT DON'T TAKE UNNECESSARY RISKS!
ALL READY?
MERCURIANS ATTACKING... LOWER TRAJECTORY!... PREPARE TO FIRE OVER OPEN SIGHTS!
CHARGE!
CRACK
CRACK
NICE WORK, SONDAR!... KEEP THEM BUSY... ANOTHER HALF MINUTE, AND I'LL BE THERE!
O.K., SONDAR! THIS IS IT! COME AND GET 'EM!
GOT YOU, YOU BRUTE!
DON'T LET THEM SPIKE THAT GUN, SONDAR! WE NEED IT.
URGGH!
TREENS! ALERT! WE HAVE BEEN OUTFLANKED!
TRAIN THE GUN ON VILGOTH, SONDAR, QUICK! ... I'M GOING TO WARN THE OTHERS TO KEEP CLEAR...
HULLO, H.Q! HULLO, PEABODY!...
SAMSON! GET ALL YOUR PEOPLE CLEAR OF THE VILGOTH AREA RIGHT AWAY!
HULLO, DIGBY!...HULLO, DIGBY! MESSAGE FROM THE COLONEL! GET CLEAR OF VILGOTH AREA IMMEDIATELY! HE'S GOING TO TRY AND BLOW IT UP!
ALL REPORTED CLEAR NOW, SONDAR!... READY?... ONE SALVO, THERMITE FULL CHARGE... FIRE!
CRASH
CRACK... CRACK
CRACK
GOOD SHOOTING, SONDAR!
NOW FOR IT! WILL THOSE SHELLS PUNCTURE THE PLACE... OR WON'T THEY?
BUT THE THERMITE SHELLS GENERATE A COLOSSAL HEAT AND BURN HOLES IN THE DOME. THE VAST MASS OF PRESSURIZED AIR ESCAPES AND VILGOTH BURSTS OPEN WITH AN EXPLOSION WHICH DESTROYS EVERYTHING IN IT.
THAT'S TORN IT!
WHISTLING WALLABIES! WHAT A WALLOP!
WE MADE IT, SONDAR, WE MADE IT! VILGOTH IS FINISHED!
AND THE PANTHANATON WITH IT! VENUS AND EARTH ARE SAVED!
COME ON, SONDAR! GRAB THAT SPRINGBIKE AND FOLLOW ME! OUR WORK ISN'T DONE YET...
NOW TO DEAL WITH THE MEKON HIMSELF!
To be concluded

EXCITING CORONATION SERIES STARTS TODAY ON PAGE 10

FOURPENCE-HALFPENNY
EVERY FRIDAY
EAGLE
20 FEBRUARY 1953 Vol. 3 No. 46
DAN DARE
PILOT OF THE FUTURE
MAROONED ON MERCURY
THERE CAN BE NO LASTING PEACE FOR THE INNER PLANETS SO LONG AS THE MEKON IS STILL AT LIBERTY. WILL YOUR PEOPLE HELP ME AGAIN, SAMSON?
TO THE LAST DROP OF THEIR BLOOD! YOU HAVE SAVED OUR CIVILIZATION FROM DESTRUCTION. WE WILL DO WHATEVER YOU SAY, AND FOLLOW WHEREVER YOU LEAD.
Dan seizes the Mercurian Thermite Gun and destroys the Treens' base of Vilgoth, together with all their stocks of Panthanaton. Venus and Earth are saved from that awful threat. But the Mekon himself is still at large in his own H.Q. Among the shattered buildings of Ray-Law, Dan confers with Samson and other Mercurian leaders.
GOOD! THEN COLLECT EVERY SINGLE MERCURIAN WHO'LL VOLUNTEER, AND LOAD THEM INTO EVERY AVAILABLE PIECE OF TRANSPORT—SPRING-TRAINS, SPRING-BIKES, CRYSTAL-CARS—ANYTHING THAT'LL TRAVEL AT A DECENT SPEED ACROSS COUNTRY.
REPORT TO ME AGAIN, AS SOON AS YOU'RE READY TO MOVE OFF!
AND A FEW HOURS LATER, A VAST CAVALCADE SETS OUT FROM RAY-LAW.
HOW LONG WILL IT TAKE US TO REACH THE MEKON'S H.Q., DAN?
IT'S THE BEST PART OF 4,000 MILES. BARRING ACCIDENTS, AND IF WE TRAVEL WITHOUT ANY HALTS, WE OUGHT TO MAKE IT IN JUST OVER THREE DAYS.
EE! TAKE A DEKKO AT THAT, URB! MILLIONS OF 'EM—LITERALLY MILLIONS!
AND SAMSON SAYS THERE'LL BE MORE JOINING IN AT EVERY TOWN AND VILLAGE WE GO THROUGH.
THE MORE THE MERRIER! THE MEKON MAY BE CUNNING, AND HIS TREENS MAY BE WELL ARMED, BUT HE'LL NEVER WITHSTAND THE UNITED OPPOSITION OF A WHOLE PLANET!
AND IN THE CONTROL ROOM AT THE MEKON'S H.Q.
FURTHER REPORT FROM NUMBER 4 RECONNAISSANCE SQUADRON, O MEKON . . . COLONEL DARE'S ARMY CONTINUES TO GROW... SHALL I ORDER OUR FIGHTERS TO ATTACK?
NO!
NOT ATTACK ??!!
NO! A WASTE OF MACHINE-TIME AND TREEN-HOURS! WITH VILGOTH GONE AND THE PANTHANATON LOST, WE CANNOT HOPE, FOR THE MOMENT, TO CONQUER A WHOLE PLANET.
ORDER ALL TREENS TO ASSEMBLE IN No. 1 HANGAR IMMEDIATELY! I WILL ISSUE EMERGENCY ORDERS MYSELF.
SO, COLONEL DARE, YOU STUBBORN EARTHLING! FOR THE SECOND TIME YOU THWART ME WITH YOUR SMART TRICKS!

AND, WHILE THE MEKON PREPARES HIS PLANS TO MEET THE EMERGENCY, DAN CONTINUES TO LEAD HIS ARMY ON ITS 4,000 MILE JOURNEY ACROSS MERCURY. UNTIL, THREE DAYS LATER . . . .
I BELIEVE I RECOGNIZE THE COUNTRY, O COLONEL.
YOU'RE RIGHT, SONDAR. SO DO I. WE HAD A SPOT O' BOTHER ROUND HERE WHEN WE FIRST LANDED.
IF I REMEMBER RIGHTLY, THE MEKON'S HIDEOUT SHOULD BE JUST OVER...
SUFFERING SUNSPOTS! LOOK AT THAT!
TREEN SPACESHIPS! DOZENS OF THEM!
OH, DAN! IT'S THE MEKON — IT MUST BE —! MAKING A GETAWAY!
I'VE BEEN AFRAID OF THIS, EVER SINCE I REALIZED HE WASN'T GOING TO ATTACK US ON THE LINE OF MARCH.
IF ONLY WE HAD ONE SPACE-WORTHY SHIP, WE COULD GO AFTER HIM . . . BUT WE HAVEN'T!
SO WHAT'S TO DO NOW, SKIPPER?
PUSH ON FAST TO THE MEKON'S H.Q. HE MAY HAVE LEFT A SERVICEABLE RADIO BEHIND... IF SO WE CAN CONTACT THE SHIPS THAT ARE ON THE WAY FROM EARTH, AND . . .
TOO LATE, DAN! THE MEKON DOESN'T LEAVE THINGS TO CHANCE!
THERE GOES THE LAST TRACE OF TREEN CIVILIZATION ON MERCURY.
HALT . . . SAMSON, TELL THEM TO STOP . . . DON'T LET THEM GO ANY FURTHER, OR THEY'LL RUN INTO A RADIO-ACTIVE ZONE.
EE, BY GUM! THAT'S A PROPER SELL, THAT IS! . . . LOOKS LIKE WE'VE TAKEN THE WHOLE POPULATION OF MERCURY ON A CONDUCTED TOUR OF THEIR OWN PLANET ALL FOR NOTHING!
NO, DIG! NOT FOR NOTHING! IF THE MERCURIANS HADN'T RISEN AGAINST HIM, THE MEKON WOULD STILL BE MASTER HERE.
AS IT IS, WE'VE SENT HIM SCUTTLING OUT INTO SPACE, FLYING FOR HIS LIFE . . . AND THIS TIME THERE'S NOWHERE LEFT FOR HIM TO TOUCH DOWN!
THEIR WORK ON MERCURY SUCCESSFULLY COMPLETED, DAN AND HIS FRIENDS RETURN TO RAY-LAW AND HELP WITH SALVAGE AND REPAIR WORK TO THE DAMAGED CITY. THEN, A WEEK LATER, THE SPACE-EXPRESS GRASSHOPPER, FIRST OF THE RELIEF SHIPS FROM EARTH, TOUCHES DOWN AMONG THE WRECKAGE OF WHAT WAS ONCE VILGOTH, AND DAN AND CO GO ABOARD.
RETURN AND VISIT US AGAIN, MY FRIENDS.
GOOD-BYE, SAMSON. THERE'LL BE OTHER SHIPS HERE SOON. THE CREWS WILL GIVE YOU ALL THE HELP THEY CAN.
AND WHEN WE GET BACK, WE'LL SEND MACHINES AND MEN TO WORK THEM. YOU'LL HAVE RAY-LAW REBUILT IN NO TIME.
DAW-MEE FOO-MEE. SAW-SAY! GOOD WISHES, FRIENDS!
SO THE MEKON GOT AWAY AGAIN, DAN?
YES. I'LL TELL YOU THE WHOLE STORY . . . BUT FIRST, WHAT ABOUT SOME REAL SOLID EARTHLY FOOD?
HEAR THAT, WILLIE? GRUB UP!
AND A FORTNIGHT LATER THE GRASSHOPPER TOUCHES DOWN AGAIN AT SPACE FLEET H. Q. ON EARTH —
HURRAY!
WELCOME HOME!
WATCH HOW YOU GO, DIGBY! DON'T FORGET THAT GRAVITY HERE IS . . .
HURRAH!
. . . FOUR TIMES WHAT IT WAS ON MERCURY . . . OH! I SEE I SPOKE TOO LATE.
OO! . . . OUCH! . . . WHAT A WELCOME FOR MOTHER EARTH TO GIVE HER WANDERING BOY!
EE, BUT I DON'T MIND. GOOD OLD MOTHER EARTH! YOUR GRAVITY MAY BE A BIT FIERCER THAN SOME PLACES I'VE BEEN TO, BUT YOU'RE HOME SWEET HOME TO ME! . . .
HA-HA!
HA-HA!
. . . AND I RECKON I COULD DO WITH A NICE LONG TOUR O'DUTY NOW, RIGHT HERE ON MY OWN PLANET . . . ANY CHANCE OF THAT, COLONEL DAN?
YOUR GUESS IS AS GOOD AS MINE, DIG. WE'LL HAVE TO WAIT AND SEE . . . UNTIL . . .
THE END

SPECIAL BONUS!
DAN DARE
8 PAGE ADVENTURE
REPRINTED FROM THE
EAGLE
ANNUAL
CHRISTMAS 1952

DAN DARE
PILOT OF THE FUTURE
MARS 1988
SOME YEARS BEFORE DAN DARE'S GREAT JOURNEY TO VENUS, CONSTRUCTION ON THE SPACE STATION ON MARS HAS BEEN BROUGHT TO A STOP BY MYSTERIOUS CRASHES TO FREIGHT-CARRYING ROCKETS, BRINGING SUPPLIES AND EQUIPMENT TO MARS. UNLESS A REMEDY CAN BE FOUND, THE SPACE STATION THERE MAY HAVE TO BE ABANDONED.
IN THE CONTROL TOWER
FREIGHT ROCKET XJ3 ON THE VIEWER SIR. SHE'S ASKING FOR LANDING INSTRUCTIONS
XJ3? THIS IS IT CHAPS! THE CONTROLLER SAYS THAT IF WE CAN'T GET THIS ONE DOWN SAFELY WE MAY AS WELL PACK UP AND GO HOME. SO KEEP YOUR FINGERS CROSSED!
RIGHT, WILKINS, GIVE IT TO ME! I'LL BRING HER IN.
HELLO XJ3! MARS LANDING CONTROL CALLING — TIME COUNT STARTING.
AT ZERO. CUT PROPULSION UNITS AND SWITCH ON IMPULSE REACTOR JETS 17-16-15-14-
SHE'S ALRIGHT SO FAR
XJ3? THAT'S OLD TIGGY'S SHIP
GOOD OLD TIGGY! HE'LL GET HER DOWN IF ANYBODY CAN.
4-3-2-1
ZERO
PREPARE TO-
HELLO!
HELLO, XJ3!
HELLO!
IT'S NO GOOD, SHE'S GONE JUST LIKE THE OTHERS. LOOK AT THE SCREEN! AND THE RADIO'S AS DEAD AS MUTTON.
MEANWHILE —
I'VE LOST TOUCH WITH LANDING CONTROL-
IMPULSE REACTORS HAVE CUT SIR
WE'RE GAINING SPEED!
SWITCH ON EMERGENCY REACTOR ROCKETS!
EXTEND WINGS!
LOWER LANDING WHEELS!
ALL HANDS STAND BY FOR CRASH LANDING!

THERE SHE IS!
SHE'S GOING TOO FAST.
SHE'S OUT OF CONTROL!
LOOK OUT! IT'S COMING STRAIGHT AT US!
PHEW! — THAT WAS CLOSE
THOUGHT WE'D HAD IT THAT TIME!
I THINK HE'S GOING TO MAKE IT ALRIGHT
NO! NO! HE'S GOING TO HIT THE RUNWAY SIDE ON
CRUNCH
CRUMP
WOOMPH
ON EARTH
"LATE FINAL" READ ALL ABOUT IT! ANOTHER 'ORRIBLE CRASH.
WEDNESDAY JUNE 14
98,062
MARS DISAST
Third crash in one week
SURVIVOR'S GRAPHIC ACCOUNT
MARS - TUESDAY 1300hrs
IT WAS OFFICIALLY DISCLOSED THAT YESTERDAY'S CRASH ON MARS WAS THE SEVENTH MAJOR DISASTER SINCE WORK ON THE SPACE STATION THERE BEGAN.
Lieutenant Holmes, one of the survivors, considers that failure of the impulse reactor jets caused the crash.
He says that they were making a normal run in to when suddenly the

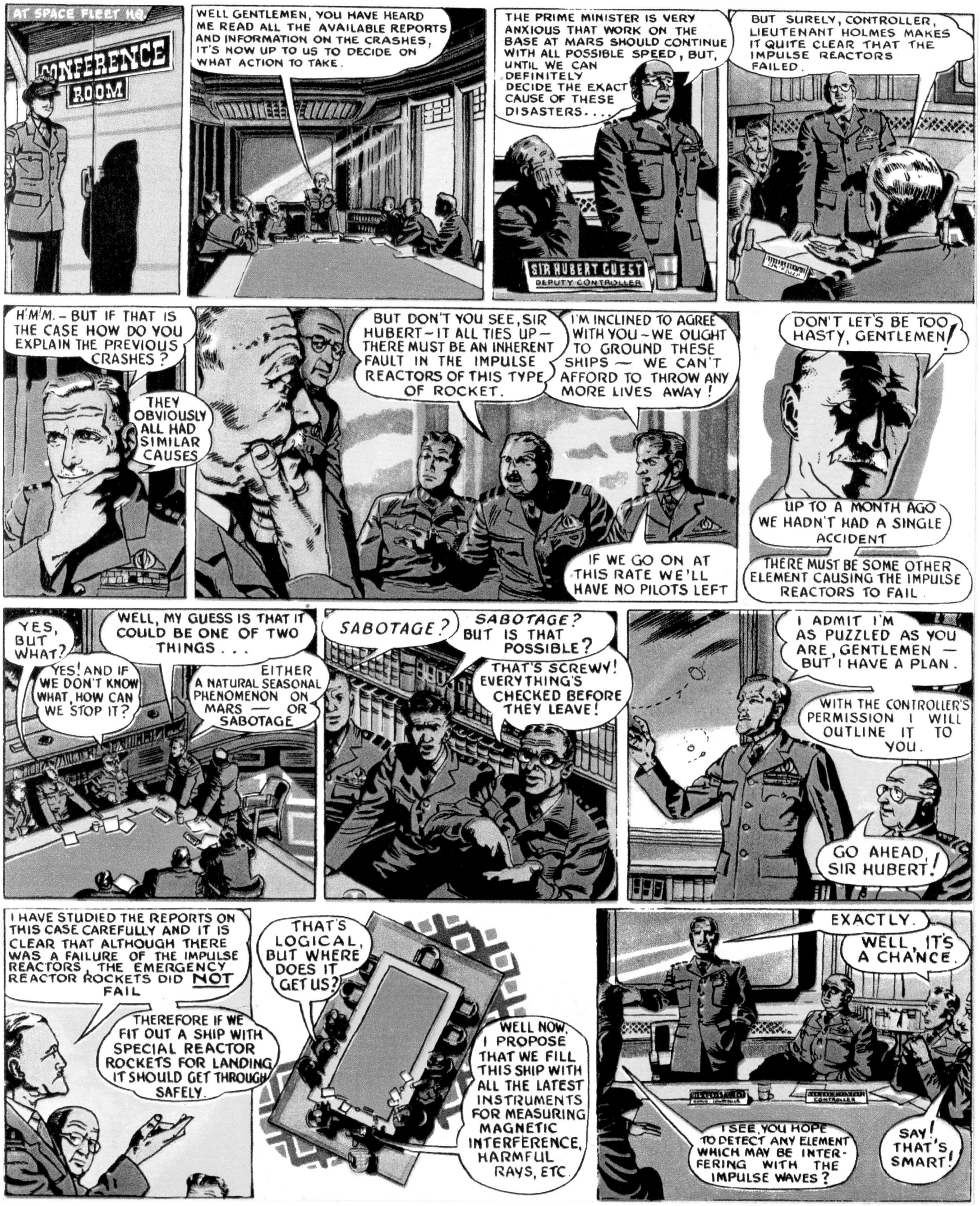
AT SPACE FLEET H.Q.
CONFERENCE ROOM
WELL GENTLEMEN, YOU HAVE HEARD ME READ ALL THE AVAILABLE REPORTS AND INFORMATION ON THE CRASHES, IT'S NOW UP TO US TO DECIDE ON WHAT ACTION TO TAKE.
THE PRIME MINISTER IS VERY ANXIOUS THAT WORK ON THE BASE AT MARS SHOULD CONTINUE WITH ALL POSSIBLE SPEED, BUT, UNTIL WE CAN DEFINITELY DECIDE THE EXACT CAUSE OF THESE DISASTERS....
SIR HUBERT GUEST
DEPUTY CONTROLLER
BUT SURELY, CONTROLLER, LIEUTENANT HOLMES MAKES IT QUITE CLEAR THAT THE IMPULSE REACTORS FAILED.
H'M'M.- BUT IF THAT IS THE CASE HOW DO YOU EXPLAIN THE PREVIOUS CRASHES?
THEY OBVIOUSLY ALL HAD SIMILAR CAUSES
BUT DON'T YOU SEE, SIR HUBERT - IT ALL TIES UP - THERE MUST BE AN INHERENT FAULT IN THE IMPULSE REACTORS OF THIS TYPE OF ROCKET.
I'M INCLINED TO AGREE WITH YOU - WE OUGHT TO GROUND THESE SHIPS — WE CAN'T AFFORD TO THROW ANY MORE LIVES AWAY!
IF WE GO ON AT THIS RATE WE'LL HAVE NO PILOTS LEFT
DON'T LET'S BE TOO HASTY, GENTLEMEN!
UP TO A MONTH AGO WE HADN'T HAD A SINGLE ACCIDENT
THERE MUST BE SOME OTHER ELEMENT CAUSING THE IMPULSE REACTORS TO FAIL.
YES, BUT WHAT?
WELL, MY GUESS IS THAT IT COULD BE ONE OF TWO THINGS...
YES! AND IF WE DON'T KNOW WHAT, HOW CAN WE STOP IT?
EITHER A NATURAL SEASONAL PHENOMENON ON MARS — OR SABOTAGE
SABOTAGE?
SABOTAGE? BUT IS THAT POSSIBLE?
THAT'S SCREWY! EVERYTHING'S CHECKED BEFORE THEY LEAVE!
I ADMIT I'M AS PUZZLED AS YOU ARE, GENTLEMEN — BUT I HAVE A PLAN.
WITH THE CONTROLLER'S PERMISSION I WILL OUTLINE IT TO YOU.
GO AHEAD, SIR HUBERT!
I HAVE STUDIED THE REPORTS ON THIS CASE CAREFULLY AND IT IS CLEAR THAT ALTHOUGH THERE WAS A FAILURE OF THE IMPULSE REACTORS, THE EMERGENCY REACTOR ROCKETS DID NOT FAIL
THEREFORE IF WE FIT OUT A SHIP WITH SPECIAL REACTOR ROCKETS FOR LANDING, IT SHOULD GET THROUGH SAFELY.
THAT'S LOGICAL, BUT WHERE DOES IT GET US?
WELL NOW, I PROPOSE THAT WE FILL THIS SHIP WITH ALL THE LATEST INSTRUMENTS FOR MEASURING MAGNETIC INTERFERENCE, HARMFUL RAYS, ETC.
EXACTLY.
WELL, IT'S A CHANCE.
I SEE, YOU HOPE TO DETECT ANY ELEMENT WHICH MAY BE INTERFERING WITH THE IMPULSE WAVES?
SAY! THAT'S SMART!

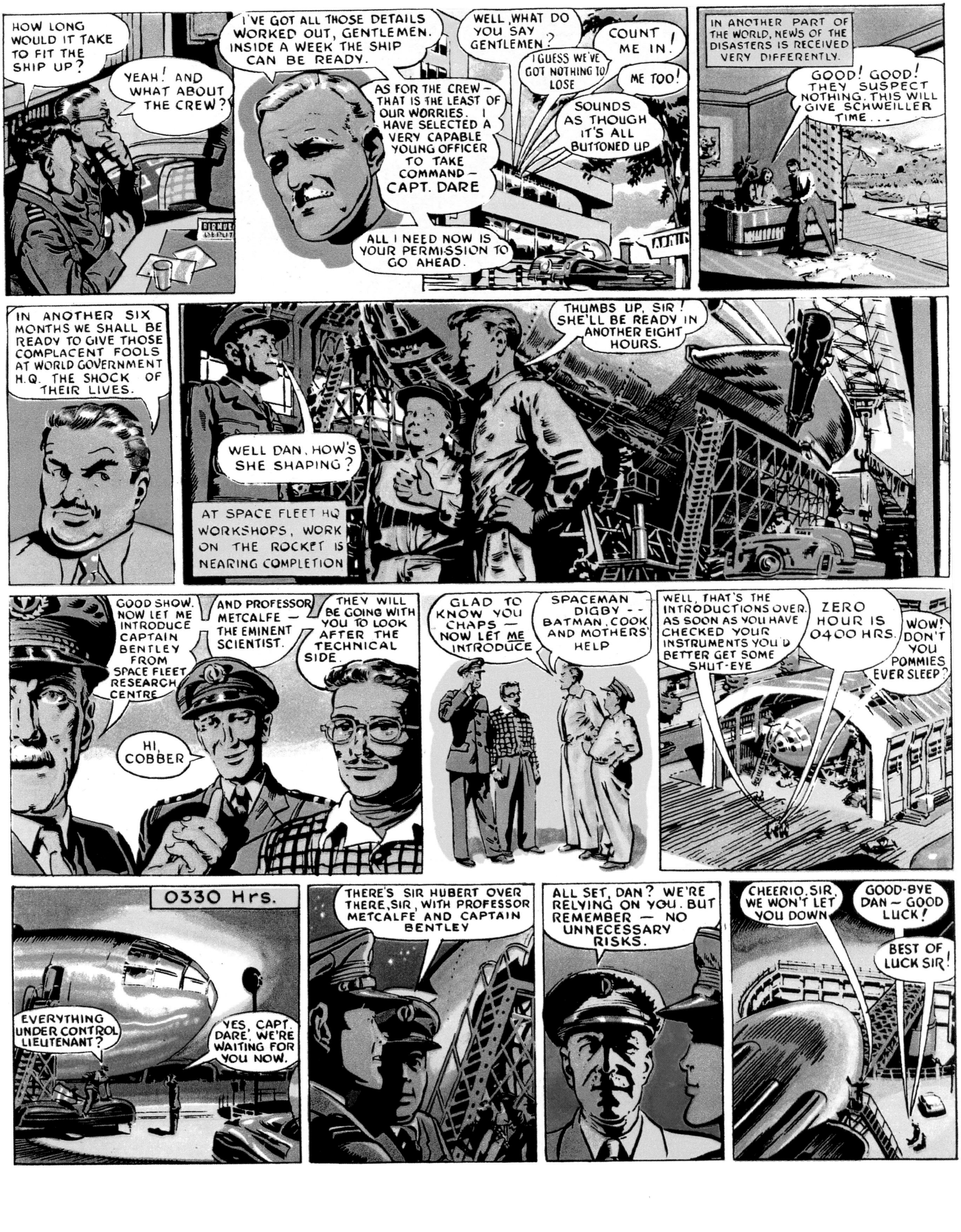

HOW LONG WOULD IT TAKE TO FIT THE SHIP UP?
YEAH! AND WHAT ABOUT THE CREW?
I'VE GOT ALL THOSE DETAILS WORKED OUT, GENTLEMEN. INSIDE A WEEK THE SHIP CAN BE READY.
AS FOR THE CREW — THAT IS THE LEAST OF OUR WORRIES. I HAVE SELECTED A VERY CAPABLE YOUNG OFFICER TO TAKE COMMAND — CAPT. DARE
ALL I NEED NOW IS YOUR PERMISSION TO GO AHEAD.
WELL, WHAT DO YOU SAY GENTLEMEN?
COUNT ME IN!
I GUESS WE'VE GOT NOTHING TO LOSE
ME TOO!
SOUNDS AS THOUGH IT'S ALL BUTTONED UP
IN ANOTHER PART OF THE WORLD, NEWS OF THE DISASTERS IS RECEIVED VERY DIFFERENTLY.
GOOD! GOOD! THEY SUSPECT NOTHING. THIS WILL GIVE SCHWEILLER TIME...
IN ANOTHER SIX MONTHS WE SHALL BE READY TO GIVE THOSE COMPLACENT FOOLS AT WORLD GOVERNMENT H.Q. THE SHOCK OF THEIR LIVES.
AT SPACE FLEET HQ WORKSHOPS, WORK ON THE ROCKET IS NEARING COMPLETION
WELL DAN, HOW'S SHE SHAPING?
THUMBS UP, SIR! SHE'LL BE READY IN ANOTHER EIGHT HOURS.
GOOD SHOW. NOW LET ME INTRODUCE CAPTAIN BENTLEY FROM SPACE FLEET RESEARCH CENTRE
AND PROFESSOR METCALFE — THE EMINENT SCIENTIST.
THEY WILL BE GOING WITH YOU TO LOOK AFTER THE TECHNICAL SIDE.
HI, COBBER
GLAD TO KNOW YOU CHAPS — NOW LET ME INTRODUCE
SPACEMAN DIGBY -- BATMAN, COOK AND MOTHERS' HELP
WELL, THAT'S THE INTRODUCTIONS OVER. AS SOON AS YOU HAVE CHECKED YOUR INSTRUMENTS YOU'D BETTER GET SOME SHUT-EYE
ZERO HOUR IS 0400 HRS.
WOW! DON'T YOU POMMIES EVER SLEEP?
0330 Hrs.
EVERYTHING UNDER CONTROL LIEUTENANT?
YES, CAPT. DARE, WE'RE WAITING FOR YOU NOW.
THERE'S SIR HUBERT OVER THERE, SIR, WITH PROFESSOR METCALFE AND CAPTAIN BENTLEY
ALL SET, DAN? WE'RE RELYING ON YOU. BUT REMEMBER — NO UNNECESSARY RISKS.
CHEERIO, SIR, WE WON'T LET YOU DOWN
GOOD-BYE DAN — GOOD LUCK!
BEST OF LUCK SIR!

LET HER GO, DANNY BOY!
EE, WHY DID I HAVE THAT BACON?
I'M READY CAPTAIN
AS DAN GIVES THE ALL CLEAR THE ROCKET GLIDES SMOOTHLY FORWARD INTO POSITION.
TIME COUNT STARTING. CLEAR THE LAUNCHING AREA!
AND THE MIGHTY LAUNCHING RAMP RISES AND POINTS TOWARDS THE LIGHTENING MORNING SKY
6-5-4-3-2-1
ZERO!
OOOPS! THIS IS WORSE THAN THE BIG DIPPER AT BLACKPOOL
A WEEK LATER
YOU TAKE OVER, DIG! I WANT A WORD WITH THE "BACK ROOM" BOYS.
ANYTHING DOING CHAPS?
NOPE! EVERYTHING'S RUNNING SMOOTHLY, DAN
NO REACTION WHATEVER
SIR! MARS LANDING CONTROL CALLING
RIGHT, DIG.
HULLO, MARS CONTROL! SPACE SHIP XJ 14 CALLING, AM COMING IN INDEPENDENTLY! STAND BY — OFF!
SWITCH ON IMPULSE REACTORS AND SPECIAL REACTOR ROCKETS, DIG!
RIGHT, SIR
THE IMPULSE REACTORS HAVE CUT OUT, SIR!
STRONG REACTION ON THE RAY DETECTOR!
BONZER! WE'VE GOT SOMETHING HERE, DAN
METRONIC RAYS!

GET THIS, BILL! BEARING 98° 21' ANGLE OF INCIDENCE 28° 43' STRENGTH - - - - - -
RIGHT! CHECK!
O.K. COBBER, THAT'S FIXED IT! HEY, DAN, WE'VE GOT ALL THE DOPE ON IT, NOW!
GREAT SHOW, CHAPS!
NOW KEEP YOUR FINGERS CROSSED. WE'RE COMING IN TO LAND!
AND AMIDST TREMENDOUS EXCITEMENT, DAN BRINGS THE ROCKET SAFELY DOWN.
WIZARD PRANG OLD BOY – YOU MADE IT, EH?
MY NAME'S FOSTER-STATION COMMANDER HERE YOU KNOW AND ALL THAT
HOW DO YOU DO, MAJOR? MY NAME'S DARE.
HE'S A JOLLY
JOLLY GOOD FELL
WELL DARE OLD FELLAH, THIS CALLS FOR A NOGGIN, WHAT!
'FRAID NOT, MAJOR. BUSINESS BEFORE PLEASURE YOU KNOW. WE'VE GOT A LITTLE JOB TO DO.
YOU SEE, WE KNOW NOW WHAT HAS BEEN CAUSING ALL THESE CRACK-UPS! "METRONIC RAYS"!
WE'VE GOT THREE SEPARATE BEARINGS ON THEIR SOURCE – ALL WE WANT NOW IS A MAP.
ONCE THOSE BOYS CAN PLOT THEIR SOURCE, WE MAY GET SOME IDEA OF WHAT IS CAUSING THEM.
RIGHT, CAPTAIN DARE, WE'VE FIXED THE POSITION ON THE MAP.
EVERY BEARING LANDS UP IN THAT AREA. THAT'S WHERE THE RAYS ARE COMING FROM.
BY JOVE! WHAT A COINCIDENCE – SLAP BANG IN THE MIDDLE OF OLD SCHWEILLER'S RESEARCH CAMP!
RESEARCH CAMP?
YES! I'LL GIVE THE OLD BOY A RING HE'LL BE TICKLED TO DEATH TO...
NOT SO FAST, MAJOR! THIS MAY NOT BE SUCH A COINCIDENCE AS YOU THINK. EVER HEARD OF SABOTAGE?
SABOTAGE? OLD SCHWEILLER? ARE YOU SERIOUS, OLD BOY?
WHY, HE'S AS HARMLESS AS A... A... A...
A RATTLESNAKE SIR?
ALRIGHT, DIG!
SERIOUSLY THOUGH WE CAN'T AFFORD TO TAKE ANY RISKS. WE MUST PAY A SURPRISE CALL ON OUR FRIEND SCHWEILLER
AT THE RESEARCH CAMP
TWO PLANES ARE APPROACHING, PROFESSOR KARL TOLD ME TO WARN YOU.
ACH!

IN THE LABORATORY
THAT'S THE ALARM!
GET THE STUFF OUT OF SIGHT!
AH, MAJOR, TO WHAT DO I OWE THE PLEASURE OF THIS VISIT?
NONE OF MY DOING PROFESSOR. CAPT. DARE WILL EXPLAIN
PROFESSOR SCHWEILLER, IN THE NAME OF THE WORLD GOVERNMENT, I HAVE AUTHORITY TO SEARCH YOUR CAMP!
BUT WHY, CAPTAIN? WHAT HAVE I DONE?
THAT IS JUST WHAT WE INTEND TO FIND OUT, PROFESSOR
ACH! BUT I CANNOT..
I MUST WARN YOU, PROFESSOR, I WILL STAND NO NONSENSE. I HAVE TWENTY ARMED MEN WITH ME, AND I WILL NOT HESITATE TO USE THEM.
BY GAD! THAT'S A BIT STRONG, DARE OLD FELLOW. JUST A ROUTINE CHECK, YOU UNDERSTAND, PROFESSOR!
ZO! IT SEEMS I HAVE NO CHOICE — BUT WHAT MATTER — I HAVE NOTHING TO HIDE.
SEVERAL HOURS LATER
YOU ZATISFY NOW, NO? YOU SEARCH MY DIGGINGS, MY WORKSHOPS, MY LABORATORIES — AND WHAT YOU FIND? NOTHING! NOTHING!
JUST A MINUTE PROFESSOR LET ME THINK!
HE'S HIDING SOMETHING, I'M SURE OF IT
BUT WHERE? HE'S SHOWN US EVERYTHING! THERE'S NO MACHINE HERE CAPABLE OF GENERATING THE POWER TO TRANSMIT THOSE RAYS -- WAIT A MINUTE, THOUGH! THE ROCKETS!
WE HAVEN'T EXAMINED THEM YET. JIMINY, YES! THAT ONE'S POINTING STRAIGHT TOWARDS THE SPACE STATION
WITH A GENERATOR IN THAT THEY COULD CREATE A POWERFUL RAYFIELD OVER THE SPACE STATION. THAT WOULD EXPLAIN EVERYTHING!
ROCKETS FROM EARTH HAVE TO PASS THROUGH RAY FIELD
RAY FIELD
RESEARCH CAMP
SPACE STATION
NO, PROFESSOR — I AM NOT SATISFIED YET. THERE IS STILL SOMETHING YOU HAVEN'T SHOWN US!
I WANT TO SEE WHAT YOU HAVE GOT INSIDE THAT ROCKET — COULD IT BE A RAY TRANSMITTER?
ZO! IT IS TIME TO STOP BLUFFING — PUT YOUR HANDS UP, MY FRIENDS AND DO NOT COME A STEP CLOSER!
I WAS RIGHT THEN! — IT WAS YOU, SCHWEILLER!
YES, CAPTAIN "CLEVER" DARE — YOU HAVE WRECKED OUR PLANS — BUT YOU HAVEN'T GOT US YET. WARM UP THE MOTORS KARL, I WILL HOLD THEM BACK.
YES, PROFESSOR

COME ON! WE CAN'T LET THEM GET AWAY SIR.
KEEP BACK – OR I FIRE!
DIG!
YOU MEDDLESOME FOOL – I WARNED YOU – TAKE THAT!
YOU CALLOUS HOUND! IF YOU'VE KILLED DIG, I'LL KNOCK THE LIVING DAYLIGHTS OUT OF YOU!
NO! HE'S ALRIGHT, DAN. JUST A GRAZE.
THANK GOODNESS FOR THAT!
NOW TO DEAL WITH "FRIEND" KARL.
NO NEED FOR THAT, DAN. HE'S RUN INTO PLENTY OF TROUBLE – OUR BOYS HAVE GOT HIM.
LATER – IN THE ROCKET
YOU WERE RIGHT, DAN. THIS ROCKET IS NOTHING BUT A HUGE GENERATING PLANT, DIRECTING DEADLY RAYS OVER THE SPACE STATION.
BUT WHY? WHAT WAS THE REASON FOR IT?
HEY, YOU TWO! I'VE JUST HAD A LOOK-SEE INSIDE THOSE ROCKETS. THEY'RE STACKED TIGHT WITH PLUTONIUM
SO THAT'S IT! THEY WERE MINING PLUTONIUM HERE!
AND SHIPPING IT BACK TO EARTH
BY CRIPPLING THE AIRFIELD, I SUPPOSE THEY HOPED TO KEEP US BUSY AND STOP US FROM GETTING TOO INQUISITIVE.
INSIDE SIX MONTHS, THEY COULD HAVE SHIPPED ENOUGH PLUTONIUM TO HAVE THE REST OF THE WORLD AT THEIR MERCY.
WE CAN COUNT OURSELVES VERY LUCKY TO HAVE COME OUT TOP AGAINST SUCH UNSCRUPULOUS MEN WITHOUT SUFFERING ANY CASUALTIES--
AHEM!
OH! I WAS FORGETTING YOU DIG. HOW'S THE HEAD NOW, OLD CHAP?
IT'S NOBBUT A SCRATCH, SIR! NOTHING THAT A GOOD CUP OF TEA WON'T PUT RIGHT!
THE END

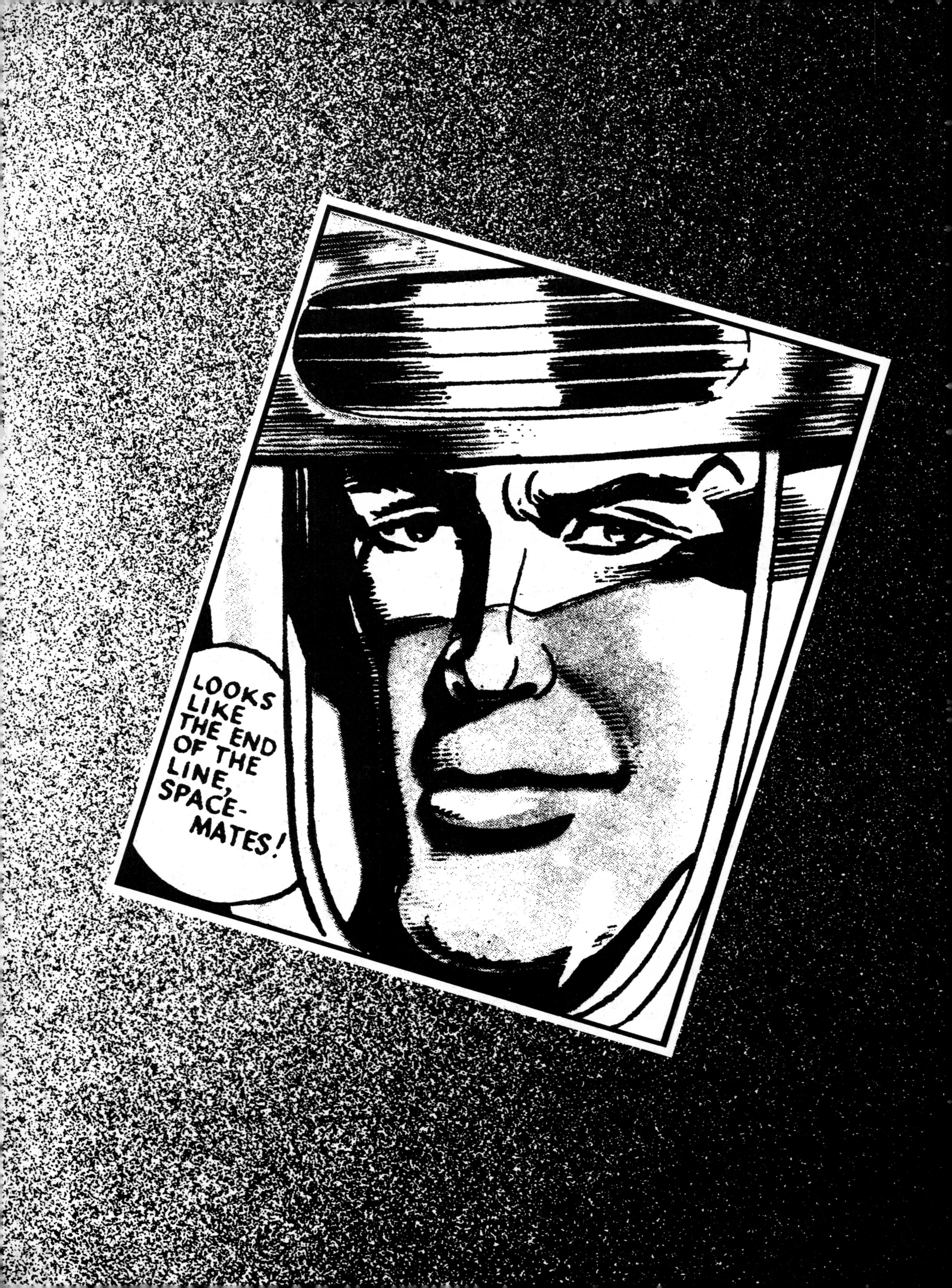
LOOKS LIKE THE END OF THE LINE, SPACE-MATES!